a consumer's dictionary of food additives

a consumer's dictionary of food additives

ruth winter

Crown Publishers, Inc., New York

Acknowledgments

The author gratefully acknowledges the following sources used in compiling this book:

Bowes, Helen N., and Church, Charles F. *Food Values of Portions Commonly Used.* 11th ed., rev. Philadelphia: J. B. Lippincott Co., 1970.

Chemicals Used in Food Processing. Washington, D.C.: National Academy of Sciences Publication 1274, 1965.

Food Chemicals Codex. 1st ed. Washington, D.C.: National Academy of Sciences Publication 1406, 1966.

Gleason, Marion N.; Gosselin, Robert E.; Hodge, Harold C.; and Smith, Roger P. *Clinical Toxicology of Commercial Products.* Baltimore: The Williams & Wilkins Co., 1969. Permission granted.

Miall, L. Mackenzie, and Sharp, D. W. A. *A New Dictionary of Chemistry.* 4th ed. New York: John Wiley & Sons, Inc., 1968.

Martin, Eric W.; Alexander, Stewart F.; Hassan, William E., Jr.; and Farage, Donald J. *Hazards of Medication.* Philadelphia: J. B. Lippincott Co., 1971. Permission granted.

The Merck Index. 8th ed. Edited by Paul G. Stecher. Rahway, N.J.: Merck and Company, 1968. Permission granted.

The Merck Manual. 11th ed. Edited by Charles E. Lyght. Rahway, N.J.: Merck, Sharp and Dohme Research Laboratories, 1966.

Recommended Dietary Allowances. 7th ed. Washington, D.C.: National Academy of Sciences Publication 1694, 1968.

Stedman's Medical Dictionary. 21st ed. Baltimore: The Williams & Wilkins Co., 1966.

White, John Henry. *A Reference Book of Chemistry.* 3rd ed. New York: Philosophical Library, 1965.

Printed in the United States of America
Published simultaneously in Canada by General Publishing Company Limited

Designed by Wesley Barry

Second Printing, October, 1972

Introduction

THIS book tells you about the additives in your food, where they come from, how they are used, and how they affect your health.

A food additive is a substance or mixture of substances, other than basic foodstuffs, present in food as a result of any aspect of production, processing, storage, or packaging. The term does not include chance contaminants.

Food processors have in their armamentaria an estimated 10,000 chemicals they can add to what we eat. Some are poisonous, some are harmless, and some are beneficial.

Every one of these chemicals used in food processing must serve one or more of the following purposes: *

- Improve nutritional value.
- Enhance quality or consumer acceptability.
- Improve the keeping quality.
- Make the food more readily available.
- Facilitate its preparation.

The majority of food additives have nothing to do with *nutritional value,* as anyone can see from the contents of this Dictionary.

Most of the chemicals added to enhance *consumer acceptability* are to feed our illusions. We want enhanced food because all our lives we have been subjected to the beautiful pictures of foods in our magazines and on television. We have come to expect an advertiser's concept of perfection in color and texture, even though Mother Nature may not turn out all her products that way. As a result, the skin of the oranges we eat are dyed bright orange to match our mental image of an ideal orange. Our poultry is fed a chemical to turn the meat yellower and more appetizing and our fruits and vegetables are kept unblemished by fungicides, pesticides, herbicides, and other antispoilants.

To improve the *keeping quality* of some products, processors embalm them. Bread has sixteen chemicals to keep it feeling "fresh." One type of bread, balloon bread, undergoes *rigor mortis* thanks to its additive plaster of Paris.

Making foods *more readily available* is a worthwhile objective but

* According to the Food Protection Committee of the National Academy of Sciences, which rules on the safety of additives.

is it always necessary? One third of the country's late summer crops of onions, celery, and iceberg lettuce is grown in Orange County, New York, less than an hour from New York City. Yet New Yorkers must get their lettuce, onions, and celery from California—a two-week trip—because the New York produce distribution center prefers to handle refrigerated rail cars rather than trucks carrying fresh produce.

When processors make foods *easier to prepare*, they are merely pandering to the demands of the public. These products pass through many hands to be mashed, mushed, and mangled and loaded with chemicals so that consumers can have cake mixes, and peeled and sliced potatoes, and instant everything.

Technology has so far advanced, or retreated, depending upon one's view, that some foods are almost pure ersatz. One well-known "natural" orange-flavored drink consists of sugar, citric acid, natural flavor, gum arabic, monosodium phosphate, potassium citrate, calcium phosphate, Vitamin C, cellulose gum, hydrogenated coconut oil, artificial flavor, artificial coloring, Vitamin A, and butylated hydroxyanisole. No orange could live in that environment. One whipped topping consists of sodium caseinate, dextrose, corn sugar, polysorbate 60, sorbitan monostearate, carrageenan, and guar gum. All these ingredients are listed on the labels.

By law, the label must identify the product in a language the consumer can understand. It must indicate the manufacturer, the packer or distributor, and declare the quantity of contents either in net weight or volume, and the ingredients must be declared on the label in order of their predominance. The label must be accurate in any statement about the product. Also, if a vignette, or picture, of the product is placed on the label, it must be truly representative of the container's contents. A few years ago, the FDA stopped macaroni manufacturers from using on the box a window with yellow cellophane to give the impression that the macaroni was more egg-yellow than it was.

However, for over 200 "standard" foods—including ice cream, catsup, and mayonnaise—no ingredients need be listed. For standard foods, processors follow the standard chemical recipes written out by the government. The manufacturer has been given the option to choose among many alternative standard chemicals, and only if he substitutes or adds a nonstandard chemical must he indicate the fact on the label. Ice cream, for example, which can have some 30 additives, need indicate no ingredients on the label. In still other products such as canned fruit and gelatin desserts, instead of indicating the specific artificial coloring or flavoring, the processor need only state "artificial coloring" or "artificial flavoring." Nor does the law require that chemicals added in small amounts during processing, such as calcium bromate (a maturing agent for dough), be stated on the label.

Food companies ostensibly test additives for acute toxicity. Additives are fed to animals in large amounts at one time. Although most companies do not use control groups—for comparison, animals not fed any additive—or perform autopsies to determine any effects on tissues, they observe the animals for symptoms of ill effects. They also usually determine the lethal dose (if in fact the additive can be determined to be lethal) based on what kills 50 percent of the animals (L_{50}). In subacute (*see*) studies, which have also been done for a number of food additives, the food chemical is fed to groups of animals in varying amounts nearly to the point of death. These tests usually last a minimum of three months and are made on at least two species of animals, most often rats and dogs. The data collected during the study includes appetite, thirst, growth rate, weight, blood and urine analyses, and behavior patterns. At the end of the study, all surviving animals are autopsied. These tests are expensive and time consuming.

A large percentage of the food additives have not been tested longterm, one of the great problems in determining chemical safety. Cancer, for instance, may take 20 years to develop in humans, and often more than two years in animals. Long-term safety is determined from rats, which live from 18 to 24 months. However, researchers point out that laboratory animals are in a nonnatural, sterile environment and that in two years, 70 to 90 percent of them would be dead anyway and only two to three would be left for evaluation. Therefore, longterm tests may have invalid assurances of safety.

Although officially the FDA claims to know what additives are being used in food, FDA researchers report that it is impossible to check small manufacturers. Furthermore, members of the Drug Law Institute, a liaison between the Food and Drug Administration and the food industry, addressing Washington officials late in February 1971, branded the FDA's claim a myth. One example of how the FDA obtains its data was a questionnaire sent to food processors in October 1971 asking how much of the various generally-recognized-as-safe ingredients the processors used. Answering the questionnaire was voluntary.

Contrary to public belief, food additives are not a modern innovation. Adding chemicals to food began in the dawn of civilization when man first discovered that by adding salt to meat, the meat would last longer.

The father of modern food additives laws was Dr. Harvey W. Wiley, who in the early 1900s led the fight against chemical preservatives such as boric acid, formaldehyde, and salicylic acid. He dramatized the problem by his famous "Poison Squad" comprised of young men willing to be guinea pigs, which meant eating measured amounts of these chemicals to determine toxicity.

As a result of Dr. Wiley's pioneering work, the first Federal Food and Drug Act was passed in 1906.

However, as can be determined from the contents of this Dictionary, not all questions concerning food additive safety have been answered. In fact, you can see that boric acid, formaldehyde, and salicylic acid are still being added to our food.

In the mid-1950s when Food and Drug Administration scientists pushed for further laws, the FDA could not stop the use of a chemical simply because it was questionable or had not been adequately tested. It was necessary to be able to prove in court that the chemical was poisonous or deleterious. But on September 6, 1958, the Food Additives Amendment law was passed. Food and chemical manufacturers, as of that date, were required to run extensive tests on additives before they were marketed. Results of these tests had to be submitted to the FDA.

The famous, or infamous, again depending on one's view, Delaney Amendment was part of the 1958 law. Written by Congressman James Delaney, the law specifically states that no additive may be permitted in any amount if the tests show that it produces cancer when fed to man or animals or by other appropriate tests.

This part of the law has been severely attacked by food and chemical manufacturers and even by the Nutrition Council of the American Medical Association. The AMA Council on Nutrition urged either repeal or revision of certain clauses in the Food Additives Amendments and in the subsequent 1960 Color Additives Amendments. The clauses prohibit the setting of tolerances for the use of cancer-causing agents in food.

The opposition claimed that these clauses could prohibit the addition of certain essential nutrients to foods if "any amount" of the substance was shown to cause cancer. Technically, they said, these clauses contributed nothing to the safe use of food additives since any hazardous use of an additive was already prohibited in the general provision of the food additives amendment. However, according to the National Academy of Sciences' Food Protection Committee: "The possibility exists that doses at 'no effect' levels do in fact exert carcinogenic effects but that the effects are too weak to detect with the numbers of animals feasible for routine testing. Such a possible effect, though extremely weak, might become evident in a large population such as, for example, the population potentially exposed to food additives in our culture. There is also the possibility of synergistic effects among substances present in the diet and of an individual susceptibility to carcinogens, although little is known about these factors."

The FDA has thus far withstood attacks on the "no cancer" clause but there is a renewed effort by food chemical manufacturers to void the Delaney Amendment.

Generally Recognized as Safe (GRAS) list

The GRAS list was established in 1958 by Congress. Those substances that were being added to food over a long time, which, under conditions of their intended use, were generally recognized as safe by qualified scientists, would be exempt from premarket clearance. Congress had acted on a very marginal response—on the basis of returns from those scientists sent questionnaires. Approximately 355 out of 900 responded, and only about 100 of those responses had substantive comments. Three items were removed from the originally published list.

INTRODUCTION

Since then, in recent years, developments in the scientific fields and in consumer awareness brought to light the inadequacies of the testing of food additives and, ironically, the complete lack of testing of the generally recognized as safe list.

As a result, President Nixon has directed the FDA to reevaluate all the items on the GRAS list. The in-depth investigation is in progress at the FDA's new testing laboratories at Pine Bluff, Arkansas, a facility once used by the armed services to develop chemical warfare materials.

The FDA claims that only 100 of the chemicals can be tested initially because of the limitation of space, funds, and manpower. Chemicals being given top priority for this testing are designated in the text of this Dictionary, as are all items on the GRAS list therein included.

Alan T. Spiner, Jr., project manager of the GRAS list review, said that it will be 1974 or 1975 before the results of chronic toxicity testing are in for suspected GRAS additives. Considering the FDA's own scientists' warning about the cancer-causing potential of the artificial sweetener cyclamate in 1958 and the sweetener's removal in 1969, it may be a decade beyond 1975 before we reap the benefits of such toxicity tests.

In the meantime, the over 31 million Americans who are allergic even to the tiniest amount of some chemicals in foods (with allergic reactions ranging from a mild skin rash to death) can't wait.

Apologists for the food processing industry and government regulating agencies perform a poor service when they try to convince us that additives are put into foods in carefully controlled amounts during processing and that the amounts necessary to achieve the desired effect are usually very small—one government source even giving an example of "less than 4 grams of synthetic color per person per year are used for coloring our foods." The "low" figure is because color units have powerful coloring effect. Besides, fatalities have followed ingestion of doses of eucalyptol (a synthetic mint flavoring for beverages, ice cream, ices, candy, baked goods, and chewing gum) even as small as 3 milliliters (1 milliliter is equivalent to 1 gram)! And what of the fact that our bodies are playing host to thousands of different potentially toxic chemicals at any given moment?

INTRODUCTION

The purpose of this Dictionary is to enable you to look up any additive under its alphabetical listing, to determine the feasibility of continuing with the product because it is beneficial or rejecting it in favor of its betters.

The Dictionary includes most of the food additives in common use. For the sake of clarity and ease of use, their nearly 50 functions are grouped under the following broad categories:

Preservatives

These "antispoilants" are used to help prevent microbiological spoilage and chemical deterioration. They are of many different types, of which about 100 are in common use.

Preservatives for fatty products are called antioxidants, which prevent the production of off-flavors and off-odors. These include benzoic acid used in margarine, butylated hydroxyanisole (BHA) used in lard, shortenings, crackers, soup bases, and potato chips.

In bread, preservatives are "mold" and "rope" inhibitors. They include sodium and calcium propionate, sodium diacetate, and such acetic substances as acetic acid and lactic acid. Sorbic acid and sodium and potassium salts are preservatives used in cheeses, syrups, and pie fillings. Preservatives used to prevent mold and fungus growth on citrus fruits are called "fungicides." Sequestering agents, still another type of preservative, prevent physical or chemical changes that affect color, flavor, texture, or appearance. Ethylenediaminetetracetic acid (EDTA) and its salts, for instance, are used to prevent the adverse effects of the presence of metals in such products as soft drinks where metal ions can cause clouding. Sequestrants used in dairy products to keep them "fresh and sweet" include sodium, calcium, and potassium salts of citric, tartaric, and pyrophosphoric acids. Other common multipurpose preservatives are the gas sulfur dioxide, propyl gallate, and, of course, sugar, salt, and vinegar.

Acids, Alkalies, Buffers, Neutralizers

The degree of acidity or alkalinity is important in many processed foods. An acid such as potassium acid tartrate, sodium aluminum phosphate, or tartaric acid acts on the leavening agent in baked goods and releases the gas which causes the desired "rising." The flavor of many soft drinks, other than cola types, is modified by the use of an acid such as citric acid from citrus fruits, malic acid from apples, or tartaric acid, a component of grapes. Phosphoric acid is used to give colas that "tangy" taste. The same acids that are used in soft drinks are also used in churning cream to help preserve the flavor and keeping quality of butter. Alkalies such as ammonium hydroxide in cocoa products and ammonium carbonate in candy, cookies, and crackers are employed to make the products more alkaline. Buffers and neutralizing agents are chemicals added to foods to control acidity or alkalinity, just as acids and alkalies are added directly. Some common chemicals in this class are ammonium bicarbonate, calcium carbonate, potassium acid tartrate, sodium aluminum phosphate, and tartaric acid.

Moisture Content Controls

Humectants are necessary in the production of some types of confections and candy to prevent drying out. Without a humectant, shredded coconut, for example, would not remain soft and pliable. Substances used for this purpose include glycerine, which retains the soft, moist texture in marshmallows, propylene glycol, and sorbitol. On the other hand, calcium silicate is used to prevent table salt from caking due to moisture absorption from the air.

Coloring Agents

Food colors of both natural and synthetic origin are extensively used in processed foods, and they play a major role in increasing the acceptability and attractiveness of these products. However, the indiscriminate use of color can conceal damage or inferiority, or make the product appear better than it actually is. The World Health Organization in delineating some 140 different kinds of colorants found many to be unsafe. Coal-tar colors were subject to a special provision in a 1938 law that required every coal-tar color used in food to be listed with the government as "harmless and suitable for use" and every batch of the color intended for use in food had to be certified by a government agency as "safe." Some of the colors originally listed as "harmless" were found to produce injury when fed to animals and were removed from the list. In 1960, the federal government required manufacturers to retest all artificial colors to determine safety. At present, six are permanently listed as safe. The other chemical colorings are still "temporarily listed." Violet I, Blue I, and Green 3 cause tumors at the site of injection in animals but the FDA does not consider this significant because the colors in the experiment were injected by needle and not ingested in food.

Among the natural colors used in foods are alkanet, annatto, carotene, chlorophyll, cochineal, saffron, and turmeric. Foods that are frequently colored include candies, baked goods, soft drinks, and some dairy products such as butter, cheese, and ice cream.

Flavorings

A wide variety of spices, natural extractives, oleoresins, and essential oils are used in processed foods. In addition, the modern flavor chemist has produced many synthetic flavors. Both types of products are used extensively in soft drinks, baked goods, ice cream, and confectionery. Flavoring agents are the most numerous additive, with over 2,000 in use. Of these, some 500 are natural and the balance synthetic. They are usually employed in amounts ranging from a few to 300 parts per million. Amyl acetate, benzaldehyde, carvone, ethyl acetate, ethyl butyrate, and methyl salicylate are typical compounds employed in the preparation of flavoring materials. However, many of the compounds used in synthetic flavorings are also found in natural products or derive from natural acids. Essential oils, such as oil of lemon and oil of orange, are natural flavors made by extraction of the fruit rind. There are also flavor enhancers, the commonest being monosodium glutamate (MSG) and maltol.

Physiologic Activity Controls

The chemicals in this group are added to fresh foods to serve as ripeners or antimetabolic agents. For instance, ethylene gas is used to hasten the ripening of bananas and maleic hydrazide is used to prevent potatoes from sprouting. Coming into increasing use are enzymes which are of natural origin and generally believed to be nontoxic. Of all the food enzyme additives, amylases which act on starch have the most numerous applications. Various amylases from plant, animal, fungal, and bacterial sources have been used to break down the components of starch to make it more digestible. Enzymes are also used in the fermentation of sugar to make candy, in the brewing industry, and in the manufacture of artificial honey, bread, and frozen milk concentrates.

Bleaching and Maturing Agents/Bread Improvers

Fresh ground flour is pale yellow. Upon storage, it slowly becomes white and undergoes an aging process that improves its baking qualities. For more than 50 years, processors have added oxidizing agents to the flour to accelerate this process, thus reducing storage costs, spoilage, and the opportunity for insect infestation. Compounds such as benzoyl peroxide bleach the flour without effect on baking qualities. Other compounds, such as oxides of nitrogen, chlorine dioxide, nitrosyl chloride, and chlorine have both a bleaching and maturing, or "improving," ability. Bread improvers used by the baking industry contain oxidizing substances such as potassium bromate, potassium iodate, and calcium peroxide. They also contain inorganic salts such as ammonium or calcium sulfate and ammonium phosphates which serve as yeast foods and dough conditioners. Quantities used are relatively small since these can easily result in an inferior product. Bleaching agents may also be used in other foods such as cheese to improve the appearance of the finished product.

Processing Aids

Many chemicals fall into this category. Sanitizing agents, for instance, to clean bacteria and debris from products, are considered such aids. So are clarifying agents which remove extraneous materials. Tannin, for instance, is used for clarifying liquids in the wine and brewing industries. Gelatin and albumen remove small particles and minute traces of copper and iron in the production of vinegar and some beverages. Emulsifiers and emulsion stabilizers help to maintain a mixture and assure a consistency. They affect characteristics such as volume, uniformity, and fineness of grain (bakery products have a softer "crumb" and slower "firming" rate). They influence ease of mixing and smoothness, such as the whipping property of frozen desserts and the smoothness of cake mixes. They help maintain homogeneity and keeping quality in such products as mayonnaise, candy, and salad dressing. Some common emulsifiers are lecithin, the monoglycerides and diglycerides, and propylene glycol alginate. Sorbitan derivatives are used to retard "bloom," the whitish deposits of high-melting components of cocoa butter that occasionally appear on the surface of chocolate candy. Food chemists sometimes call emulsifiers "surfacants" or "surface-active agents."

Texturizers or stabilizers are added to products to give them "body" and maintain a desired texture. For instance, calcium chloride or some other calcium salt is added to canned tomatoes and canned potatoes to keep them from falling apart. Sodium nitrate and sodium nitrite are used in curing meats to develop and stabilize the pink color. Nitrogen, carbon dioxide, and nitrous oxide are employed in pressure-packed containers of certain foods to act as whipping agents or as propellants. The texture of ice cream and other frozen desserts is dependent on the size of the ice crystals in the product. By the addition of agar-agar, gelatin, cellulose gum, or some other gum, the size of the ice crystals are stabilized. Texturizer gums are also used in chocolate milk to increase the viscosity of the product and to prevent the settling of cocoa particles to the bottom of the container. Gelatin, pectin, and starch are used in confectionery products to give a desired texture. Artificially sweetened beverages also need bodying agents because they do not contain the "thickness" normally contributed by sugar. The thickeners employed include such natural gums as sodium alginate and pectins. The foaming properties of brewed beer can also be improved by the addition of texturizers.

Nutrition Supplements

Enrichment of food means that the natural nutrients have been removed during processing and then replaced. Enrichment of cereal foods, much touted by the big producers, according to them is supposed to provide 12 to 23 percent of the daily supply of thiamine, niacin, and iron, and 10 percent of the riboflavin recommended for human consumption.

INTRODUCTION

Fortification of food means that additional nutrients are added to the product to make it more nutritious than it was before. For instance, Vitamin C is added to orange drinks and Vitamin A to margarine. Vitamin D is used to fortify milk to prevent rickets and potassium iodide is added to iodized salt to prevent goiter, a thyroid tumor caused by iodine deficiency.

Amino acids may become commonly used as additives. The major use of amino acids in the food industry today is monosodium glutamate, which enhances flavor. Actually the human body needs certain amino acids not manufactured in the body in sufficient amounts. Proposals to add these acids as nutrients await FDA testing along with items on the GRAS list at the Pine Bluff facility.

A number of additional substances are employed for various purposes. Certain sugar substitutes are used in foods for persons who must restrict their intake of ordinary sweets. Saccharin and sorbitol are commonly used for this purpose. Glazes and polishes such as waxes and gum benzoin are used on coated confections to give luster to an otherwise dull surface. Magnesium carbonate and tricalcium phosphate are employed as anticaking agents in table salt, and calcium stearate is used for a similar purpose in garlic salt.

While unique in content, this Dictionary follows the format of most standard dictionaries. The following are sample entries with any explanatory notes that may be necessary:

MARJORAM, POT. *Sweet Marjoram.* The natural extract of the flowers and leaves of two varieties of the fragrant marjoram plant. The *oleoresin* (*see*) is used in sausage and spice flavorings for condiments and meats. The *seed* is used in sausage and spice flavorings for meats (3,500 ppm) and condiments. Sweet marjoram is used in sausage and spice flavorings for beverages, baked goods (2,000 ppm), condiments, meats, and soups. The *sweet oil* is used in vermouth, wine, and spice flavorings for beverages, ice cream, ices, candy, baked goods, and condiments. No known toxicity. GRAS.

We have learned that pot marjoram is a natural flavoring extract, that there are pot and sweet marjoram, that they are utilized as an oleoresin, a seed, and as sweet oil. By looking up "oleoresin" we learn that it means "a thick, sticky product obtained when a substance is extracted from a plant by a solvent and the solvent is then removed." The "ppm" figures stand for "parts per million," that is, 3,500 parts of marjoram is added to a million parts of meat. However, because ppm amounts (they do not appear on labels) represent maximum rather than actual usage, they are not reliable estimates of consumption, and are included here only to show how amounts can be relatively quite large or small. "No known toxicity" is not an assurance that an additive is absolutely harmless but rather that no deleterious effects have been recorded in the literature. GRAS means, of course, that the item is on the government's generally recognized as safe list, without having undergone thorough laboratory testing. ("GRAS in packaging" means that even though substances from the containers may migrate into the food, they are assumed not harmful.)

WORMWOOD. Absinthium. A European woody herb with a bitter taste, used in bitters and liquor flavorings for beverages and liquors. The *extract* is used in bitters, liquor, and vermouth flavorings for beverages, ice cream, candy, and liquors, and in making absinthe. The *oil* is a dark green to brown and a narcotic substance. Used in bitters, apple, vermouth, and wine flavorings for beverages, ice cream, ices, candy, baked goods, and liquors. In large doses or frequently repeated doses, it is a narcotic poison, causing headache, trembling, and convulsions. Ingestion of the volatile oil or of the liqueur (absinthe) may cause gastrointestinal symptoms, nervousness, stupor, convulsions, and death.

"Absinthium," of course, is another name for wormwood and is cross-referenced in the Dictionary. Source material for the comments on toxicity is indicated in the Notes at the end of the Dictionary. A similar example is the entry for lye.

SODIUM SESQUICARBONATE. Lye. Produced on a large scale from sodium carbonate and a slight excess of sodium bicarbonate (*see both*). Used as a neutralizer for butter, cream, fluid milk, ice cream, in the processing of olives before canning, cacao products, and canned peas. Chiefly used in laundering in conjunction with soap. Irritating to skin and mucous membrane. GRAS.

Under the entry *Acacia. Gum Arabic. Catechu,* the first two terms are used interchangeably. *Catechu* (from the Latin *Acacia catechu*) is less commonly used. Under the entry *Acetaldehyde. Ethanal,* the term ethanal is used interchangeably with acetaldehyde.

Some chemicals that are derived from a natural source are considered synthetic because they represent only a portion of the original compound or because other chemicals have been added. For instance:

NONANAL. Pelargonic Aldehyde. A synthetic flavoring that occurs naturally in lemon oil, rose, sweet orange oil, mandarin, lime, orris, and ginger. Used in lemon and fruit flavorings for beverages, ice cream, ices, candy, baked goods, gelatin desserts, and chewing gum. No known toxicity.

Terminology generally has been kept to a middle road between technician and average-interested-citizen, while at the same time avoiding oversimplification of data. If in doubt, look up any term, listed alphabetically, such as *isolate* (used in its chemical context), or *extract,* or *anhydride,* or *oleoresin,* or *demulcent, emollient, mutogenic, teratogenic, subacute,* and so on.

With *A Consumer's Dictionary of Food Additives* you will be able to work with the current labels to determine the purpose and the desirability or toxicity of the additives listed. You will be able to assert your right to wholesome food along with a wholesome environment. By having options in the marketplace, by rejecting those products that are needlessly costly or unsafe or unpalatable in favor of "clean" food, you strike back at greed and ignorance as practiced by too many in the food industry. And you reward those manufacturers who deserve your purchases.

Presently many legislators are fighting for more pervasive and informed labeling. Consequently, more chemical identities, included in the Dictionary, may be expected to appear on food labels.

Consumer groups are demanding that all foods, including standard foods, carry labeling showing all ingredients. The FDA has published a proposed regulation requiring manufacturers to list sources of fats in processed foods to allow consumers to avoid certain fats, such as polyunsaturated fats, in dietary foods, and requiring labels on baby food to state the protein content. Consumer action groups want more. They want nutritional labeling on all foods, including calories, protein content, mineral elements, vitamins, and fat levels. Hopefully, they will succeed.

In the meantime, this book takes some of the guesswork out of the chemicals you eat.

A

ABIES ALBA MILL. See Pine Needle Oil.

ABIETIC ACID. A widely available natural acid prepared from pine rosin, usually yellow, and comprised of either glassy or crystalline particles. Used in the manufacture of soaps, vinyls, lacquers, and plastics. Employed to carry nutrients that are added to enriched rice in amounts up to .0026 percent of the weight of the nutrient mixture. Little is known about abietic acid toxicity; it is harmless when injected into mice but causes paralysis in frogs and is slightly irritating to human skin and mucous membranes.

ABSINTHIUM. Extract or Oil. See Wormwood.

ABSOLUTE. The term refers to a plant-extracted material that has been concentrated but which remains essentially unchanged in its original taste and odor. For example, see Rose, Absolute.

ACACIA. Gum Arabic. Acacia is the odorless, colorless, tasteless dried gummy exudate from the stem of the acacia tree grown in Africa, the Near East, India, and the southern United States. Its most distinguishing quality among the natural gums is its ability to dissolve rapidly in water. The use of acacia dates back 4,000 years when the Egyptians employed it in paints. Its principal use in the confectionery industry is to retard sugar crystallization and as a thickener for candies, jellies, glazes, and chewing gum. As a stabilizer, it prevents chemical breakdown in food mixtures. Gum acacia is a foam stabilizer in soft drink and brewing industries. Other uses are for mucilage, and the gum gives form and shape to tablets. Medically, it is used as a demulcent to soothe irritations, particularly of the mucous membranes. Oral toxicity is low but it can cause allergic reactions such as skin rash and asthmatic attacks. It is one of the additives given priority by the FDA for study of its mutagenic, teratogenic, subacute, and reproductive effects. See Catechu Extract.

ACER SPICATUM LAM. See Mountain Maple.

ACETAL. A synthetic flavoring agent made from acetaldehyde (*see*) and alcohol. Acetal goes into beverages, ice cream, ices, candy, and baked goods as apple, apricot, peach, banana, and whiskey flavorings. A volatile liquid, it is employed as a solvent in synthetic perfumes such as jasmine. Medically, acetal is administered as a hypnotic —as a central nervous system depressant, similar in action to paralde-

ACETALDEHYDE

hyde, but more toxic. Paraldehyde is a hypnotic and sedative whose side effects are respiratory depression, cardiovascular collapse, and possible hypersensitive reactions.

ACETALDEHYDE. Ethanal. A flammable, colorless liquid with a distinct odor. It boils at 21 degrees C. and must be stored at below 15 degrees. It occurs naturally in apples, broccoli, cheese, coffee, grapefruit, grape juice (Concord), grapes, onions, lemon, milk (skimmed and heated), oranges, peaches, pears, pineapples, raspberries, strawberries, peppermint oil, anise, cooked beef, and cooked chicken. Acetaldehyde is a synthetic berry, butter, chocolate, apple, apricot, banana, grape, peach, black walnut, rum and wine flavoring agent for beverages, ice cream, ices, candy, baked goods, gelatin desserts, and chewing gum. Used in the commercial manufacture of acetic acid, perfumes, aniline dyes, synthetic rubber, plastics, drugs, and for silvering mirrors. It is irritating to the mucous membranes, narcotic, and in large doses may cause death by respiratory paralysis. Its ability to depress the central nervous system is greater than that of formaldehyde (see), and ingestion produces symptoms of "drunkenness." Acetaldehyde is thought to be a factor in the toxic effect caused by drinking alcohol after taking the antialcohol drug antabuse.

ACETALDEHYDE PHENETHYL PROPYL ACETAL PEPITAL. A synthetic fruit flavoring agent for beverages, ice cream, ices, candy, and baked goods. See Acetaldehyde for toxicity.

ACETANISOLE. A synthetic flavoring agent, colorless to pale yellow, solid, with an odor of hawthorne or hay, moderately soluble in alcohol and most fixed oils. Acetanisole is used in butter, caramel, chocolate, fruit, nut, and vanilla flavorings, which go into beverages, ice cream, ices, candy, baked goods, and chewing gum. No known toxicity.

ACETATE PA. See Allyl Phenoxyacetate.

ACETIC ACID. Utilized as a synthetic flavoring agent, it is one of the earliest known food additives. Occurs naturally in apples, cheese, cocoa, coffee, grapes, grape juice (Concord), milk (skimmed and irradiated), oranges, parsley, peaches, pineapples, raspberries, strawberries, bay and bay-leaf extract. (Vinegar is about 4 to 6 percent acetic acid; essence of vinegar is about 14 percent.) A colorless liquid, it is used in raspberry, strawberry, butter, butterscotch, chocolate, grape, rum, wine, spice tobacco, cheese, and vinegar flavorings for beverages, ice cream, ices, baked goods, condiments (5,900 ppm), gelatin desserts, and chewing gum. Acetic acid is used as an acidulant (*see*) in syrup, sherbets, ice cream, ices, beverages, baked goods, confections, pickles, catsup, canned artichokes, cottage cheese, pasteurized processed cheese, and cheese spreads. In its glacial form, (less than 1 per cent water), in use as a solvent for oils and resins, acetic acid is highly corrosive, and the vapors are capable of producing bronchial obstruction. GRAS when used only in packaging.

ACETIC ANHYDRIDE. A dehydrating agent and food starch modifier. A strong acetic odor, it produces irritation and necrosis of tissues in vapor state and carries a warning against contact with skin and eyes. The FDA believes that further study of modified starch (*see*) is necessary.

ACETIC ETHER. A synthetic agent, transparent, colorless, liquid, with a fragrant, refreshing odor, used in butter, butterscotch, fruit, nut, and spice flavorings for beverages, ice cream, ices, candy, baked goods (1,000 ppm.) and chewing gum (4,000 ppm.). Acts as a mild local irritant and a central nervous depressant. It readily vaporizes and is highly flammable.

(tri-) ACETIN. A synthetic flavoring agent, colorless, oily liquid, with a fatty odor and bitter taste. Used in butter, butterscotch, fruit, nut, and spice flavorings for beverages, ice cream, ices, candy, baked goods (1,000) ppm), and chewing gum (4,100 ppm). Also a coating for vegetables and fruits and a fixative for perfumes. Laboratory rats have tolerated diets of 50 percent triacetin.

ACETOACETIC ESTER. See Ethyl Acetoacetate.

ACETOIN. Acetyl Methyl Carbinol. A flavoring agent that occurs naturally in broccoli, grapes, pears, cultured dairy products, cooked beef, and cooked chicken. As a product of fermentation and of cream ripened for churning, it is a colorless or pale yellow liquid or a white powder, it has a characteristic buttery odor and must be stored in a light-resistant container. It is used in raspberry, strawberry, butter, butterscotch, caramel, coconut, coffee, fruit, liquor, rum, nut, walnut, vanilla, cream soda, and cheese flavorings for beverages, ice cream, ices, candy, baked goods, margarine, gelatin desserts, cottage cheese, and shortenings. No known toxicity. GRAS.

2′ACETONAPHTHONE. See Methyl β-Naphthyl Ketone.

ACETONE. A solvent, obtained by fermentation, for fats, oils, and waxes. A tolerance of 30 ppm is allowed for a residue of acetone in spice extracts. It is also used in the manufacture of airplane dopes, nail-polish remover, rayon, and photographic films. Continued use may irritate the skin. Inhalation may irritate the lungs, and in large amounts has a narcotic effect, causing symptoms such as "drunkenness."

ACETONE PEROXIDE. Acetone (see) to which an oxygen-containing compound has been added. A maturing agent for bleaching flour and dough. It has a sharp, acrid odor similar to hydrogen peroxide. A strong oxidizing agent, it can be damaging to the skin and eyes. The FDA is pursuing testing for short and long-term effects of mutagenic, teratogenic, subacute, and reproductive effects of this widely used additive.

ACETOPHENONE. A synthetic agent derived from coal tar, with an odor of bitter almonds, used in strawberry, floral, fruit, cherry, almond, walnut, tobacco, vanilla, and tonka bean flavorings for beverages, ice cream, ices, candy, baked goods, gelatin desserts, and chewing gum. It occurs naturally in strawberries and tea and may cause allergic reactions. It has been used as a hypnotic.

p-ACETYL-ANISOLE. See Acetanisole.

ACETYL BENZENE. See Acetophenone.

ACETYL BUTYRYL. See 2, 3-Hexanedione.

ACETYL-o-CRESOL. See o-Tolyl Acetate.

ACETYL-p-CRESOL. See p-Tolyl Acetate.

ACETYL EUGENOL. See Eugenyl Acetate.

ACETYL FORMALDEHYDE. See Pyruvaldehyde.

ACETYL FORMIC ACID. See Pyruvic Acid.

ACETYL METHYL CARBINOL. See Acetoin.

ACTYL NONYRYL. See 2, 3-Undecadione.

ACETYL PELARGONYL. See 2, 3-Undecadione.

ACETYL PENTANOYL. See 2, 3-Heptanedione.

ACETYL PROPIONYL. See 2, 3-Pentanedione.

p-ACETYL TOLUENE. See 4'-Methyl Acetophenone.

ACETYL VALERYL. See 2, 3-Heptanedione.

ACETYL VANILLIN. See Vanillin Acetate.

ACETYLATED. Any organic compound heated with acetic anhydride or acetyl chloride (see Acetic Acid), usually in the presence of an inert solvent such as benzene or acetic acid. Used to coat candy and other foods to hold in moisture.

ACHILLEIC ACID. See Aconitic Acid.

ACID POTASSIUM SULFITE. See Sulfites, Potassium.

ACIDULANTS. *Acids.* An acid is a substance capable of turning blue litmus paper red and of forming hydrogen ions when dissolved in water. An acid aqueous solution is one with a pH less than 7 see pH). Acidulants are acids that make a substance more acid and function as flavoring agents to intensify taste, to blend unrelated flavoring characteristics, and to mask any undesirable after-taste. Acidulants are used also as preservatives to prevent germ and spore growths that spoil food. Acidulants control the acid-alkali (pH) balance and are used in meat curings to enhance color and flavor, and as a preservative. Among the most common acids added to foods are acetic, propionic, and sorbic (*see all*).

ACONITIC ACID. Citridic Acid. A flavoring agent found in beetroot and cane sugar. Most of the commercial aconitic acids however, are manufactured by sulfuric acid dehydration of citric acid. It is used in fruit, brandy, and rum flavorings for beverages, ice cream, ices, candy, baked goods, liquors, and chewing gum. Also used in the manufacture of plastics and buna rubber. No known toxicity. GRAS.

ACRYLAMIDE RESIN. Acrylic Acid. A clarifying agent in beet sugar and cane sugar juice. The acid is used in the synthesis of this acrylic resin. No known toxicity.

ACTIVATED 7-DEHYDROCHOLESTEROL. See Vitamin D_3.

ADIPIC ACID. Occurs naturally in beets. Used in synthetic fruit flavorings for beverages and gelatin desserts (5000 ppm) to impart a smooth tart taste. Also used as a buffer and neutralizing agent in confections, but limited to 3 percent of contents, and in the manufacture of plastics and nylons, and as a substitute for tartaric acid (*see*) in baking powders because it is impervious to humidity. Nontoxic. GRAS.

ADIPIC ANHYDRIDE. A starch-modifying agent, not to exceed .12 percent of the starch compound. No known toxicity. See Modified Starch.

AGAR-AGAR. Japanese Isinglass. A stabilizer and thickener, it is transparent, odorless, and tasteless, and obtained from various seaweeds found in the Pacific and Indian oceans and the sea of Japan. Agar was the first seaweed to be extracted, purified, and dried. Discovered by a Japanese innkeeper around 1658 and introduced in Europe and the United States by visitors from China in the 1800s as a substitute for gelatin. It goes into beverages, ice cream, ices, frozen custard, sherbert, meringue, baked goods, jelly, frozen candied sweet potatoes, icings, confections, artificially sweetened jellies and preserves, and serves as a substitute for gelatin and is used for thickening milk and cream. It is also a bulk laxative, and, aside from causing an occasional allergic reaction, is nontoxic. GRAS

AGROPYRUN. See Dog Grass Extract.

ALANINE. L and DL forms. Amino acids (*see*) obtained from most proteins but believed to be nonessential. The general amino acid groups are the building blocks of proteins. While these two forms are considered supplementary nutrients, the FDA has asked industry for additional information. Nontoxic. GRAS

ALCOHOL C-7. See Heptyl Alcohol.

ALCOHOL C-9. See Nonyl Alcohol.

ALDEHYDE C-7. See Heptanal.

ALDEHYDE C-9. See Nonanal.

ALDEHYDE C-10. See Decanal.

ALDEHYDE C-11 UNDECYLENIC. See 9-Undecenal.

ALDEHYDE C-12 MNA. See 2-Methylundecanal.

ALFALFA. Herb and Seed. A natural cola, liquor, and maple flavoring agent for beverages and cordials. Alfalfa is widely cultivated for forage and is a commercial source of chlorophyll. Also called lucerne. No known toxicity.

ALGAE, BROWN. Kelp. Ground, dried seaweed used to carry natural spices, seasonings, and flavorings. A source of alginic acid (*see*). Also used in chewing-gum base. All derivatives of alginic acid are designated "algin." The food industry is one of the major users of alginates (*see*) along with pharmaceutical, cosmetic, rubber, and paper industries. The United States is the largest producer of alginates. Nontoxic. GRAS

ALGAE, RED. A natural extract of seaweed used to carry natural spices, seasonings, and flavorings. See Alginates. Nontoxic. GRAS

ALGINATES. Ammonium, Calcium, Potassium, and Sodium. A gelatinous substance obtained from certain seaweeds used as stabilizers and water retainers in beverages, ice cream, ices, frozen custard, emulsions, desserts, baked goods, and confectionery ingredients. A clarifying agent for wine, chocolate milk, meat, toppings, cheeses, cheese spreads, cheese snacks, salad dressings, and artificially sweetened jelly and jam ingredients. Alginates are used also as stabilizers in gassed cream (pressure-dispensed whipped cream). The alginates assure a creamy texture and prevent formation of ice crystals in ice creams. Alginates have been used in the making of ice pops to impart smoothness of texture by ensuring that the fruit flavors are uniformly distributed throughout the ice crystals during freezing, helping the pops to retain flavor and color, and to stop dripping. The FDA is pursuing tests on sodium alginate (largest use in ice cream) for short-term mutagenic birth-deforming, reproduction, and subacute effects. No known toxicity. GRAS

ALGINIC ACID. Obtained from seaweeds. It is odorless and tasteless and is used as a stabilizer in ice cream, frozen custard, ice milk, fruit sherbet, water ices, beverages, icings, cheeses, cheese spreads, cheese snacks, French dressing, and salad dressing. It is also used as a defoaming agent in processed foods. Capable of absorbing 200 to 300 times its weight of water and salts. Also used in sizing paper and textiles; as binder for briquettes; in manufacture of artificial horn, ivory, celluloid; and for emulsifying mineral oils and in mucilage. No known toxicity. GRAS

ALKALI. The term originally covered the caustic and mild forms of potash and soda. A substance such as potash, soda, or "animosia" that neutralizes acids. An alkaline aqueous solution is one with a pH (*see*) greater than 7. Sodium bicarbonate is an example of an alkali that is used to neutralize excess acidity in foods.

ALKANET ROOT. The extraction of the tree root grown in Asia Minor and the Mediterranean. Used as a colorant in wines, cosmetics, confections, sausage casings, oleomargarine, shortening, and inks. Used in berry, fruit, and meat flavorings for beverages, ice cream, ices, candy, baked goods, icings, and meats. Formerly used as an astringent. Alkanet may be mixed with approved synthetic dyes or harmless inert material such as common salt and sugar. Nontoxic.

ALLOMALEIC ACID. See Fumaric Acid.

ALLSPICE. A natural flavoring from the dried berries of the allspice tree. Allspice is used in liquor, meat, and spice flavorings for beverages, ice cream, ices, candy, baked goods (1,400 ppm), chewing gum, condiments (1,000 ppm), and meats. Allspice *oleoresin* (a natural mixture of oil and resin) is used in sausage flavoring for baked goods, meat, and condiments. Allspice *oil* is used in sausage, berry, cola, peach, rum, nut, allspice, cinnamon, ginger, nutmeg, and eggnog flavorings for beverages, ice cream, ices, candy, baked goods, chewing gum (1,700 ppm), condiments, pickles, meats, liquors, and soups. Nontoxic. GRAS

ALLYL ANTHRANILATE. A synthetic citrus fruit and grape flavoring agent for beverages, ice cream, ices, candy, baked goods, and gelatin desserts. No known toxicity.

ALLYL BUTYRATE. A synthetic butter, fruit, and pineapple flavoring agent for beverages, ice cream, ices, candy, baked goods, and gelatin desserts. No known toxicity.

ALLYL CINNAMATE. A synthetic fruit flavoring agent for beverages, ice cream, ices, candy, and baked goods. No known toxicity.

ALLYL CYCLOHEXANE ACETATE. A synthetic pineapple flavoring agent for beverages, ice cream, ices, candy, and baked goods. No known toxicity.

ALLYL CYCLOHEXANE BUTYRATE. A synthetic pineapple flavoring agent for beverages, ice cream, ices, candy, and baked goods. No known toxicity.

ALLYL CYCLOHEXANE HEXANOATE. A synthetic fruit flavoring agent for beverages, ice cream, ices, candy, and baked goods. No known toxicity.

ALLYL CYCLOHEXANE PROPIONATE. A synthetic agent, liquid and colorless, with a pineapplelike odor, used in pineapple flavorings for beverages, ice cream, ices, candy, baked goods, gelatin desserts, puddings, chewing gum, and icings. No known toxicity.

ALLYL CYCLOHEXANE VALERATE. A synthetic pineapple flavoring agent for beverages, ice cream, ices, candy, and baked goods. No known toxicity.

ALLYL DISULFIDE. Found naturally in garlic and leeks, but considered a synthetic flavoring. It is used in garlic, onion, and spice flavorings for meats and condiments. No known toxicity.

ALLYL ENANTHATE. See Allyl Heptanoate.

ALLYL 2-ETHYLBUTYRATE. A synthetic fruit flavoring agent for butter, candy, gelatin desserts, and pudding. No known toxicity. GRAS

ALLYL 2-FUROATE. A synthetic coffee and pineapple flavoring agent for beverages, ice cream, ices, candy, baked goods, and gelatin desserts. No known toxicity. GRAS

ALLYL HEPTANOATE. A synthetic berry, fruit, and brandy flavoring agent for beverages, ice cream, ices, candy, baked goods, gelatin desserts, and chewing gum. No known toxicity. GRAS

ALLYL HEXANOATE. A synthetic orange, strawberry, apple, apricot, peach, pineapple, and tutti-frutti flavoring agent for beverages, ice cream, ices, candy, baked goods, gelatin desserts, and chewing gum. No known toxicity.

ALLYL α-IONONE. Cetone V. A synthetic agent, yellow, with a strong, fruity, pineapplelike odor, used in fruit flavoring for beverages, ice cream, ices, candy, baked goods, gelatin desserts, and toppings. No known toxicity. GRAS

ALLYL ISOTHIOCYANATE. A naturally occurring agent in mustard, horseradish, and onion used in meat and spice flavorings for beverages, ice cream, ices, candy, condiments, meat, and pickles. Colorless or pale yellow with a very pungent irritating odor and acrid taste. It is used also in the manufacture of war gas. Can cause blisters. Toxic.

ALLYL MERCAPTAN. A synthetic spice flavoring agent for beverages, ice cream, ices, candy, baked goods, condiments, and meats. No known toxicity.

4-ALLYL-2-METHOXPHENOL. See Eugenol.

ALLYL NONANOATE. A synthetic fruit and wine flavoring agent for beverages, ice cream, ices, candy, baked goods, and meats. No known toxicity.

ALLYL OCTANOATE. A synthetic pineapple flavoring agent for beverages, ice cream, ices, candy, baked goods, and gelatin desserts. No known toxicity.

ALLYL PHENOXYACETATE. Acetate PA. A synthetic fruit flavoring agent for beverages, ice cream, ices, candy, baked goods, and gelatin desserts. No known toxicity.

ALLYL PHENYLACETATE. A synthetic pineapple and honey flavoring agent for beverages, ice cream, ices, candy, and baked goods. No known toxicity.

ALLYL PROPIONATE. A synthetic pineapple flavoring agent for beverages, ice cream, ices, candy, and baked goods. No known toxicity.

ALLYL SORBATE. A synthetic fruit flavoring agent for beverages, ice cream, ices, candy, baked goods, and gelatin desserts. No known toxicity.

ALLYL SULFHYDRATE. See Allyl Mercaptan.

ALLYL SULFIDE. A synthetic fruit and garlic flavoring agent for beverages, ice cream, ices, baked goods, candy, condiments, and meats. Occurs naturally in garlic and horseradish. Produces irritation of the eyes and respiratory tract. Readily absorbed through the skin. Acute exposure can cause unconsciousness. Long-term exposure can cause liver and kidney damage.

ALLYL UNDECYLENATE. See Allyl 10-Undecenoate.

ALLYL TIGLATE. A synthetic fruit flavoring agent for beverages, ice cream, ices, candy, and baked goods. No known toxicity.

ALLYL 10-UNDECENOATE. A synthetic fruit flavoring agent for beverages, ice cream, candy, and baked goods. No known toxicity.

p-ALLYLANISOLE. See Estragole.

ALLYLTHIOL. See Allyl Mercaptan.

4-ALLYLVERATROLE. See Eugenyl Methyl Ether.

ALMOND. Bitter Oil. A flavoring agent from the ripe seed of a small tree grown in Italy, Spain, and France. Colorless or slightly yellow, strong almond odor, and mild taste. Used in cherry and almond flavorings for beverages, ice cream, ices, candy, baked goods, gelatin desserts, chewing gum, and Maraschino cherries. Used also in the manufacture of liqueurs and perfumes. It is distilled to remove hydrocyanic acid (Prussic acid), which is very toxic. Nontoxic without the hydrocyanic acid. GRAS

ALOE EXTRACT. From the leaves of various plants grown in Curacao, Dutch West Indies, and South Africa. Used in bitters, vermouth, and spice flavorings for beverages (2,000 ppm) and alcoholic drinks. It has been used as a cathartic but was found to cause severe intestinal cramps and sometimes kidney damage.

ALTHEA ROOT. Marshmallow Root. A natural flavoring substance from a plant grown in Europe, Asia, and the U.S. The dried root is used in strawberry, cherry, and root beer flavorings for beverages. The boiled root is used as a demulcent to smoothe mucous membranes; the roots, leaves, and flowers are used externally as a poultice. Nontoxic.

ALUM. A colorless, odorless, crystalline, water-soluble solid used in packaging. It is also called aluminum potassium sulfate, common alum, potash alum, and potassium alum. A double sulfate of aluminum and ammonium potassium, it is also employed to harden gelatin, size paper, or waterproof fabrics; in medicine, an astringent and styptic. It has a low toxicity in experimental animals, but ingestion of 30 grams (one ounce) has killed adult humans. Concentrated solutions have caused breakdown of gum tissues, kidney damage, and fatal intestinal bleeding. Liquid alum has been found by Penn State researchers capable of removing over 99 percent of phosphates from waste water effluent. GRAS when used in packaging only.

ALUMINUM AMMONIUM SULFATE. Odorless, colorless crystals with a strong astringent taste. Used in purifying drinking water; in baking powders; as a buffer and neutralizing agent in milling; and in the cereal industries. Used also for fireproofing and in the manufacture of vegetable glue and artificial gems. In medicine, it is an astringent and styptic (stops bleeding). Ingestion of large amounts may cause burning in mouth and pharnyx, vomiting, and diarrhea. GRAS

ALUMINUM CALCIUM SILICATE. Anticaking agent used so that it is 2 percent of table salt. Used also in vanilla powder to prevent caking. Essentially harmless when given orally. GRAS

ALUMINUM HYDROXIDE. An alkali used as a leavening agent in the production of baked goods. It is also used in antiperspirants and dentifrices and as a gastric antacid but it can cause constipation. GRAS when used in packaging only.

ALUMINUM NICOTINATE. Used as a source of niacin in special diet foods, also as a medication to dilate blood vessels and to combat fat. Tablets of 625 mg. are a complex of aluminum nicotinate, nicotinic acid, and aluminum hydroxide. Side effects are flushing, rash, and gastrointestinal distress when taken in large doses.

ALUMINUM OLEATE. A yellow, thick, acidic mass practically insoluble in water. Used in packaging, as lacquer for metals, in waterproofing, and for thickening lubricating oils. Low toxicity. GRAS when used in packaging only.

ALUMINUM PALMITATE. A whitish, yellow mass or powder, practically insoluble in water or alcohol, used in packaging. Also used to thicken petroleum, in waterproofing, and for glazing paper and leather. No known toxicity. GRAS when used in packaging only.

ALUMINUM PHOSPHIDE. Used to fumigate processed foods, the

FDA requires that processors aerate the finished food for 48 hours before it is offered to the consumer. It further warns that under no condition should the formulation containing aluminum phosphide be used so that it or its unreacted residues will come in contact with any processed food. Reacts with moist air to produce the highly toxic phosphine. Residues of phosphine in or on processed food may not exceed .01 parts per million, according to the FDA. Phosphine may cause pain in the region of the diaphragm, a feeling of coldness, weakness, vertigo, shortness of breath, bronchitis, edema, lung damage, convulsions, coma, and death.

ALUMINUM POTASSIUM SULFATE. Colorless, odorless, hard, transparent crystals or powder with a sweet, antiseptic taste used for clarifying sugar, and as a firming agent and carrier for bleaching agents. It is used in the production of sweet and dill pickles, cereal flours, bleached flours, and cheese. Ingestion of large quantities may cause burning in the mouth and throat and stomach distress. GRAS

ALUMINUM SODIUM SULFATE. Firming agent and carrier for bleaching agents. For other uses see Aluminum Potassium Sulfate. No known toxicity. GRAS

ALUMINUM STEARATE. Hard, plasticlike material used in waterproofing fabrics, thickening lubricating oils, and as a chewing gum base component and a defoamer component used in processing beet sugar and yeast. No known toxicity.

ALUMINUM SULFATE. Cake Alum. Patent Alum. Firming agent that occurs as a white powder or crystals in the earth. Odorless, with a sweet, mildly astringent taste. Used in producing sweet and dill pickles and as a modifier for food starch. Also used in tanning leather, sizing paper, waterproofing, for antiperspirants, agricultural pesticides, antiseptics, and detergents. Low in toxicity.

AMARANTH. See FD and C Red No. 2.

AMBERGRIS. Concretion from the intestinal tract of the sperm whale found floating in tropical seas or on shores. A waxy grayish mass, it is about 80 percent cholesterol and is used as a fixative for delicate odors in perfumery. In food, used in berry, fruit, rum, spice, and vanilla flavorings for beverages, ice cream, ices, candy, and baked goods. No known toxicity. GRAS

AMBRETTE. A natural flavoring agent from the seed of the Hibiscus plant, clear yellow to amber as a liquid, with a musky odor.

Seed used in berry and floral flavorings for beverages, ice cream, ices, candy, and baked goods. The *tincture* is used in black walnut and vanilla flavorings for the same products, and in cordials. The *seed oil* is used in fruit flavoring for beverages, ice cream, candy, and baked goods. No known toxicity. GRAS

AMBRETTOLIDE. See ω-6-Hexadecenlactone.

AMINO ACIDS. The body's building blocks, from which proteins are constructed. Of the 22 known amino acids, eight cannot be manufactured by the body in sufficient quantities. These eight are called "essential" because they are necessary to maintain good health. A ninth, histidine, is thought to be necessary for growth in childhood.

AMMONIUM ALGINATE. A stabilizer and water retainer. See Alginates. GRAS

AMMONIUM BICARBONATE. An alkali used as a leavening agent in the production of baked goods, confections, and cacao products. The shiny, hard crystals or mass, with a faint odor of ammonia, do not combine with acids. Used also in soothing baths, in compost heaps to accelerate decomposition, as an expectorant, and to relieve flatulence. Nontoxic. GRAS

AMMONIUM CARBONATE. See Ammonium Bicarbonate. GRAS

AMMONIUM CHLORIDE. Colorless, odorless crystals or white powder used as a yeast food and dough conditioner in bread, rolls, buns, and so on. Saline in taste, and incompatible with alkalies. Industrially employed in freezing mixtures, batteries, dyes, safety explosives, and in medicine as an expectorant, urinary acidifier, and diuretic; keeps snow from melting on ski slopes. Can cause nausea, vomiting, and acidosis in doses of 0.5 to 1 gram. GRAS for packaging only.

AMMONIUM HYDROXIDE. An alkali and cacao product. See uses for Ammonium Bicarbonate. GRAS when used in packaging.

AMMONIUM ISOVALERATE. A synthetic butter, nut, and cheese flavoring agent for baked goods and syrups. No known toxicity.

AMMONIUM PHOSPHATE. Monobasic and Dibasic. White, odorless, salty crystals or powders, used as acidic constituents of baking powder. They are used as buffers, leavening agents, and bread, roll, and bun improvers up to 10 percent of product. Used in brewing industry. Also used in fireproofing, purifying sugar, in yeast cultures, dentifrices, and fertilizers. Monobasic is used as baking powder with sodium bicarbonate. Medically used for their saline action. They have a diuretic effect (reducing body water) and they make urine more acid. Nontoxic. GRAS

AMMONIUM SULFATE. A yeast food, dough conditioner, and buffer in bakery products. Colorless, odorless, white crystals or powder. Industrial uses in freezing mixtures, fireproofing fabrics, tanning, and fertilizers. Used also in the production of caramel. Medically it has been employed to prolong analgesia. No known toxicity. GRAS. See use for Ammonium Phosphate.

AMMONIUM SULFIDE. A synthetic spice flavoring agent for baked goods and condiments. Also used to apply patina to bronze and in film developers. May evolve into toxic hydrogen sulfide and a fatality has been reported from use of ammonium sulfide "permanent wave" lotion.

AMYL ACETATE. See Isoamyl Acetate.

AMYL ALCOHOL. A synthetic berry, chocolate, apple, banana, pineapple, liquor, and rum flavoring agent for beverages, ice cream, ices, candy, baked goods, gelatin desserts, and chewing gum. Occurs naturally in cocoa and oranges. Highly toxic and narcotic. Ingestion of 30 mil. has killed humans. Smells like camphor. Inhalation causes violent coughing.

AMYL ALDEHYDE. See Valeraldehyde.

AMYL BUTYRATE. A synthetic flavoring agent, colorless, with a strong apricot odor. Occurs naturally in cocoa. Used in raspberry, strawberry, butter, butterscotch, fruit, apple, apricot, banana, cherry, grape, peach, pineapple, and vanilla flavorings for beverages, ice cream, ices, candy, baked goods, gelatin desserts, puddings, chewing gum, and cherry syrup. Also used in perfume compositions. No known toxicity.

AMYL CAPRATE. See Cognac Oil.

AMYL FORMATE. Formic Acid. A synthetic flavoring agent, colorless, with a plumlike odor. Used in strawberry, apple, apricot, banana, cherry, peach, plum, nut and walnut flavorings for beverages, ice cream, ices, candy, baked goods, and chewing gum. Occurs naturally in apples. See Formic Acid for toxicity.

AMYL 2-FUROATE. A synthetic rum and maple flavoring agent for beverages, candy, baked goods, and condiments. No known toxicity.

AMYL HEPTANOATE. A synthetic lemon, coconut, fruit, and nut flavoring agent for beverages, ice cream, ices, candy, baked goods, gelatin desserts, puddings, and chewing gum. No known toxicity.

AMYL HEXANOATE. A synthetic citrus, chocolate, apple, grape, pineapple, honey, and liquor flavoring agent for beverages, ice cream, ices, candy, baked goods, gelatin desserts, puddings, and chewing gum. No known toxicity.

2-AMYL-5 (OR 6)-KETO-1, 4-DIOXAME. A synthetic fruit flavoring agent for beverages, ice cream, ices, candy, baked goods, and shortening. No known toxicity.

AMYL OCTANOATE. Occurs naturally in apples. A synthetic chocolate, fruit, and liquor flavoring agent for beverages, ice cream, ices, candy, baked goods, and gelatin desserts. No known toxicity.

α-AMYL β-PHENYLACROLEIN BUXINE. See α-Amylcinnamaldehyde.

AMYL VINYL CARBINOL. See 1-Octen-3-ol.

α-AMYLASE. An enzyme prepared from hog pancreas used in flour to break down starch into smaller sugar molecules. Then, in turn, the enzymes produced by yeast in the dough again split these sugar molecules to form carbon dioxide gas, which causes the dough to rise. Used medically to combat inflammation. Nontoxic.

α-AMYLCINNAMYL ACETATE. A synthetic chocolate, fruit, and honey flavoring agent for beverages, ice cream, ices, candy, baked goods, and chewing gum. No known toxicity.

α-AMYLCINNAMYL ALCOHOL. A synthetic chocolate, fruit, and honey flavoring agent for beverages, ice cream, ices, candy, baked goods, and chewing gum. No known toxicity.

α-AMYLCINNAMYL FORMATE. A synthetic chocolate, fruit, maple, and nut flavoring agent for beverages, ice cream, ices, candy, baked goods, and chewing gum. No known toxicity.

α-AMYLCINNAMYL ISOVALERATE. A synthetic chocolate, fruit, grape, and nut flavoring agent for beverages, candy, ice cream, ices, baked goods, and chewing gum. No known toxicity.

α-AMYLCINNAMALDEHYDE. A synthetic agent, yellow, with a strong floral odor of jasmine, used in strawberry, apple, apricot, peach, and walnut flavorings for beverages, ice cream, ices, candy, baked goods, gelatin desserts, and chewing gum. Very susceptible to oxidation by air. No known toxicity.

α-AMYLCINNAMALDEHYDE DIMETHYL ACETAL. A synthetic fruit flavoring agent for beverages, ice cream, candy, and baked goods. No known toxicity.

AMYRIS OIL. Sandalwood Oil. The volatile oil obtained from a gummy wood and used as a flavoring agent in chewing gum and candy. It is a clear, pale yellow viscous liquid with a distinct odor of sandalwood. No known toxicity.

ANCHUSIN EXTRACT. See Alkanet Root.

ANETHOLE. Occurs naturally in anise, fennel, and star anise, with a strong smell and sweet taste. Chief constituent of star anise. Used in fruit, honey, licorice, anise, liquor, nut, root beer, sarsaparilla, spice, vanilla, wintergreen, and birch beer flavorings for beverages, ice cream, ices, candy, baked goods, chewing gum (1,500 ppm) and liquors (1,400 ppm). Intestinal stimulant in colic, also an expectorant, and used in perfumes, soaps, dentifrices. Applied to the skin it causes blisters and scaling. Inflammation of the mouth after use of a denture cream containing anethole was reported. GRAS

ANETHUM GRAVEOLENS L. See Dill.

ANGELICA. Grown in Europe and Asia, the aromatic seeds, leaves, stems, and roots have been used a medicine for flatus (gas), to increase sweating, and to reduce body water. The *root oil* is used in fruit, gin, and rum flavorings for beverages, ice cream, ices, candy, baked goods, gelatin desserts, chewing gum, and liquors. The *root extract* is used in berry, liquor, wine, maple, nut, walnut, and root beer flavorings for the same foods, up to baked goods, plus syrups. The *seed extract* is used in berry, fruit, maple, walnut, and spice flaxorings for beverages, candy, baked goods, syrups, and condiments. The *seed oil* is used for fruit and gin flavoring for beverages, ice cream, ices, candy, baked goods, gelatin desserts, and liquors. The *stem oil* is used for fruit flavoring for the same foods as is seed oil, excepting liquors. Angelica can induce sensitivity to light. GRAS

ANGOSTURA. Flavoring agent from the bark of trees, grown in Venezuela and Brazil. Unpleasant musty odor and bitter aromatic taste. The light yellow liquid extract is used in bitters, liquor, root beer, and spice flavorings for beverages and liquors (1,700 ppm). Formerly used to lessen fever. No known toxicity. GRAS

ANHYDRIDE. A residue resulting from water being removed from a compound, for example, acetic anhydride (*see*). Anhydrous describes a substance that contains no water.

ANISE. Anise Seed. Dried ripe fruit of Asia, Europe, and the U.S. Used in licorice, anise, pepperoni, sausage, spice, and vanilla flavorings for beverages, ice cream, ices, candy, baked goods, condiments (5,000 ppm), and meats (1,200 ppm). The *oil* is used for butter, caramel, licorice, anise, rum, sausage, nut, root beer, sarsaparilla, spice, vanilla, wintergreen, and birch beer flavorings for the same foods as above excepting condiments but including chewing gum (3,200 ppm) and liquors. Sometimes used to break up intestinal gas Nontoxic. See Star Anise. GRAS

ANISIC ALCOHOL. See Anisyl Alcohol.

ANISOLE. A synthetic agent with a pleasant odor used in licorice, root beer, sarsaparilla, wintergreen, and birch beer flavorings for beverages, ice cream, ices, candy, and baked goods. Used also in perfumes. No known toxicity.

ANISYL ACETATE. A synthetic berry, chocolate, cocoa, fruit, and vanilla flavoring agent for beverages, ice cream, ices, candy, baked goods, gelatin desserts, and chewing gum. No known toxicity.

ANISYL ALCOHOL. A synthetic chocolate, cocoa, fruit, licorice, and vanilla flavoring agent for beverages, ice cream, ices, candy, baked goods, and gelatin desserts. Found naturally in vanilla. No known toxicity.

ANISYL BUTYRATE. A synthetic fruit and licorice flavoring agent for beverages, ice cream, ices, candy, and baked goods. No known toxicity.

ANISYL FORMATE. Formic Acid. A synthetic raspberry, fruit, licorice, and vanilla flavoring agent for beverages, ice cream, ices, baked goods, and gelatin desserts. Found naturally in currant and vanilla. See Formic Acid for toxicity.

ANISYL METHYL KETONE. See 1-(*p*-Methoxyphenyl)-2-Propanone.

ANISYL PHENYLACETATE. A synthetic honey flavoring agent for beverages, ice cream, ices, candy, and baked goods. No known toxicity.

ANISYL PROPIONATE. Occurs naturally in quince, apple, banana, cherry, peach, and pineapple. A raspberry, cherry, and licorice flavoring agent for beverages, ice cream, ices, candy, baked goods, and gelatin deserts. No known toxicity.

ANNATTO. Extract and Seed. A vegetable dye from the pulp surrounding the seeds of the tropical annatto tree. Its yellow to peach coloring goes into such dairy products as butter, cheese, cottage cheese, and buttermilk in addition to margarine, beverages, ice cream, ices, baked goods, cake mixes, and breakfast cereals. It is used also to color such meat-product casings as bologna and frankfurters. A A spice flavoring for beverages, ice cream, baked goods (2,000 ppm), margarine, breakfast cereals, (2,000 ppm) and baked goods. No known toxicity.

APPLE ACID. See Malic Acid.

APRICOT KERNEL. Persic Oil. A natural cherry flavoring agent for beverages, ice cream, ices, candy, baked goods, and soups. No known toxicity. GRAS

ARABINOGALACTAN. A polysaccharide extracted with water from larch wood. Used in the minimum quantity required to be effective as an emulsifier, stabilizer, binder, or bodying agent in essential oils, nonnutritive sweeteners, nonstandard dressings, flavors, and puddings. On the FDA priority list of additives to be studied for mutagenic, teratogenic, subacute, and reproductive effects.

ARAMANTH. See FD and C Red No. 2.

ARGININE. L and DL Forms. An essential amino acid (*see*), strongly alkaline given for liver deficiency. The FDA wants further information on the nutrient, which plays an important role in the production of urea in excretion. GRAS

ARHEOL. See Sandalwood Oil, yellow.

ARNOTTA EXTRACT. See Annatto Extract.

ARNOTTA SEED. See Annatto Seed.

ARTIFICIAL. In foods, the term follows the standard meaning: a substance not duplicated in nature. A flavoring, for instance, may have all natural ingredients but it must be called artificial if it has no counterpart in nature.

ASAFETIDA. Devil's Dung. A natural flavoring extracted from the roots of several plants grown in Iran, Turkestan, and Afghanistan. The *fluid extract* is used in sausage, onion, and spice flavorings for beverages, ice cream, ices, candy, baked goods, meat, condiments, and soups. The *gum* is used in onion and spice flavorings for beverages, ice cream, ices, candy, baked goods, and seasonings. The *oil* is used for spice flavoring in candy, baked goods, and condiments. Asafetida has a bitter taste, an offensive charcoal odor, and is particularly used in India and Iran as a condiment. It has been used medically as an expectorant and to break up intestinal gas. No known toxicity. GRAS

ASCORBATE. Calcium and Sodium. Antioxidants used in concentrated milk produces, cooked, cured, or pulverized meat food products, and in the pickle in which pork and beef products are cured or packed. Nontoxic.

ASCORBIC ACID. Vitamin C. A preservative and antioxidant used in frozen fruit, particularly sliced peaches, frozen fish dip, dry milk, beer and ale, flavoring oils, apple juice, soft drinks, fluid milk, candy, artificially sweetened jellies and preserves, canned mushrooms, cooked, cured, pulverized meat food products, pickle in which beef or pork is cured or packed (75 ounces of Vitamin C per 100 gallons). It is an antiscurvy vitamin used in fruit juices, frozen concentrated drinks, grape juice, orangeade, and carbonated drinks. The commercial available vitamin is produced by synthesis. Vitamin C is essential for normal teeth, bones, and blood vessels. The recommended daily requirements are 60 mg (2 ozs) to 100 mgs for adults, 35 for infants, and 40 for children. The white or slightly yellow powder darkens when exposed to air. Reasonably stable when it remains dry in air but deteriorates rapidly when exposed to air in solution. Nobel Laureate Linus Pauling caused a run on Vitamin C in 1970 by endorsing it as a cold preventative. In 1971, Dr. Ralph Mumma (Pennsylvania State University) reported that ascorbic acid flushes cholesterol from arteries and organs of the body. Too much cholesterol is believed to be a precursor to hardening of the arteries and heart disease. Vitamin C is known to affect the excretion of medications such as barbiturates and to make them more toxic. Pharmaceutically incompatible with sodium salicylate, sodium nitrate, theobromine sodium salicylate, and methenamine.

ASCORBYL PALMITATE. A derivative of ascorbic acid (*see*) used as a preservative and antioxidant for candy. Like ascorbic acid, prevents rancidity, browning of cut apples and other fruit, used in meat curing. Nontoxic.

ASH BARK. Prickly Extract. A natural cola, maple, and root beer flavoring agent for beverages, candy, and baked goods. No known toxicity.

ASPARTIC ACID. DL and L forms. A nonessential amino acid (*see*) occurring in animals and plants, especially young sugar cane and sugar beet molasses, but synthesized for commercial use as a supplement. The FDA is seeking further information. GRAS

ASPERGILLUS. A genus of fungi. It contains many species of molds, some of which are very toxic. *Aspergillus Flavus* is a form with yellow spores, which produces the antibiotic aspergillic acid. An *Aspergillus Flavus-Oryzae Group* of mold has been cleared by the U.S. Department of Agriculture's Meat Inspection Division to soften tissues of beef cuts, to wit: "Solutions containing water, salt, mono-sodium glutamate, and approved proteolytic enzymes applied or injected into cuts of beef shall not result in a gain of more than 3 percent above the weight of the untreated product." It is also used in bakery products such as bread, rolls, and buns. Toxicity is unknown but because of the use of the fungi-antibiotic and mono-sodium glutamate, allergic reactions would certainly be possible.

ATTAR OF ROSES. See Rose Bulgarian.

AUBEPINE LIQUID. See *p*-Methoxybenzaldehyde.

AZODICARBONAMIDE. A bleaching and maturing agent for flour, yellow to orange red, a crystalline powder, practically insoluble in water. Used in amounts up to 45 ppm. The FDA wants further study of this chemical for both short-term and long-term effects.

B

BACTERIAL CATALASE. A catalase is an enzyme in plant and animal tissues. It exerts a chemical reaction that converts hydrogen peroxide into water and oxygen. Derived from bacteria by a pure culture fermentation process, bacterial catalase may be used safely, according to the FDA, in destroying and removing hydrogen peroxide that has been used in the manufacture of cheese—providing "the organism *Micrococcus Lysodeikticus* from which the bacterial catalase is to be derived, is demonstrated to be nontoxic and non-pathogenic." The organism is removed from the bacterial catalase prior to the use of the catalase, the catalase to be used in an amount not in excess of the minimum required to produce its intended effect. No known toxicity.

BAKING POWDER. In baking, any powders used as a substitute for yeast, usually a mixture of sodium bicarbonate, starch, as a filler, and a harmless acid such as tartaric. Cream of tartar is often used as the necessary acid. Nontoxic.

BAKING SODA. A common name for sodium bicarbonate (*see*).

BALM OIL. A natural fruit and liquor flavoring agent for beverages, ice cream, ices, candy, and baked goods. The balm leaves extract also is used in fruit flavors for beverages. Nontoxic. GRAS

BALSAM, PERU. Peruvian balsam, a natural liquid extracted from a variety of evergreens. Used in strawberry, chocolate, cherry, grape, brandy, rum, maple, walnut, coconut, spice, and vanilla flavoring for beverages, ice cream, ices, candy, baked goods, gelatin desserts, chewing gum, and syrups. Dark brown, with a pleasant aromatic odor and a bitter, persistent aftertaste. Used also in the manufacture of chocolate. Applied to the skin as a stimulant for wounds and ulcers, and to remove scabs. Peruvian balsam *oil* is used in berry, coconut, fruit, rum, maple, and vanilla flavoring for beverages, ice cream, ices, candy, and baked goods. Balsam *fir oil* is a natural pineapple, lime, and spice flavoring for beverages, ice cream, ices, candy, baked goods, and gelatin desserts. Balsam *fir oleoresin* is a natural fruit and spice flavoring for beverages, ice cream, ices, candy, and baked goods. Fir balsam is yellowish green, thick, transparently liquid, with a pine-like smell, and a bitter aftertaste. It is used in the manufacture of fine lacquers. Balsam is mildly antiseptic and may be slightly irritating to the skin. Practically nontoxic upon ingestion.

BASIL. Sweet Basil. An herb having spikes of small white flowers and aromatic leaves used as seasoning. A natural flavoring distilled from the flowering tops of the plant. Slightly yellow, liquid, with a spicy odor. Used in sausage and spice flavorings for beverages, candy, ice cream, baked goods, condiments, and meats. The *oleoresin* is used in spice flavorings for baked goods and condiments. The *oil* is used in loganberry, strawberry, orange, rose, violet, cherry, honey, licorice, basil, muscatel, meat, and root beer flavorings for beverages, ice cream, ices, candy, baked goods. No known toxicity. GRAS

BAY, SWEET. A natural flavoring native to a Mediterranean plant with stiff, glossy, fragrant leaves. Used in vermouth, sausage, and spice flavorings for beverages, ice cream, ices, candy, baked goods, condiments, and meats. The oil, from the laurel, is used in fruit and spice flavorings for beverages, ice cream, ices, candy, baked goods, chewing gum, and condiments. No known toxicity.

BAY LEAVES. The West Indian extract is a natural flavoring used in vermouth and spice flavorings for beverages, ice cream, ices, candy, baked goods, meats, and soups. The *oil* is used in fruit,

37

liquor, and bay flavorings for beverages, ice cream, ices, candy, baked goods, condiments, and meats. The *oleoresin* (*see*) is used in sausage flavoring for meats and soups. No known toxicity.

BEEF TALLOW. See Tallow Flakes. GRAS for packaging.

BEESWAX. Yellow Wax. From the honeycomb of the bee. Used as a candy glaze and polish. Yellowish, soft to brittle, with a honey-like odor. Practically insoluble in water, it is used also in the manufacture of wax paper, candles, artificial fruit, and shoe polish. Formerly employed in the treatment of diarrhea, it has been utilized as a repository for slow-release medicines. See Bleached Beeswax. Non-toxic. GRAS

BEESWAX, BLEACHED. White Wax. Yellow wax bleached and purified, from the honeycomb of the bee. Remains yellowish white, is solid, somewhat translucent and fairly insoluble in water. Differs slightly in taste from yellow beeswax. Used in fruit and honey flavorings for beverages, ice cream, ices, baked goods, and honey. See yellow beeswax for medical uses. Nontoxic. GRAS

BEET. Juice and Powder. Vegetable dye used to color dairy products. Listed for food use in 1967. No known toxicity.

BENTONITE. A clarifying agent derived from clays from the Midwest and Canada. It forms a highly viscous suspension or gel. Used in wine, and it has been prescribed as a bulk laxative and base for many dermatologic formulas. The FDA intends to give it further study. GRAS

BENZALDEHYDE. Artificial essential oil of almond with an almondlike odor used in berry, butter, coconut, apricot, cherry, peach, liquor, brandy, rum, almond, pecan, pistachio, spice, and vanilla flavoring. Occurs naturally in cherries, raspberries, tea, almonds, bitter oil, cajeput oil, cassia bark. Used in beverages, ice cream, ices, candy, baked goods, chewing gum, and cordials. Narcotic in high concentrations and may cause skin rash. Produces central nervous system depression and convulsions. Fatal dose is estimated to be 2 ounces. GRAS

BENZALDEHYDE DIMETHYL ACETAL. A synthetic agent used in fruit, cherry, nut, and almond flavorings for beverages, ice cream, ices, candy, baked goods, gelatin, puddings, and alcoholic beverages. See Benzaldehyde for toxicity.

BENZALDEHYDE GLYCERYL ACETAL. A synthetic agent used in fruit, cherry, nut, and almond flavorings for beverages, ice cream, ices, candy, baked goods, and chewing gum. See Benzaldehyde for toxicity.

BENZALDEHYDE PROPYLENE GLYCOL ACETAL. A synthetic agent used in fruit, cherry, nut, and almond flavorings for beverages, ice cream, ices, candy, baked goods, gelatin, and puddings. See Benzaldehyde for toxicity.

BENZENECARBONAL. See Benzaldehyde.

BENZENECARBOXYLIC ACID. See Benzoic Acid.

BENZENEMETHYLAL. See Benzaldehyde.

BENZILIDENE ACETONE. See 4-Phenyl-3-Buten-2-one.

BENZOATE OF SODA. See Sodium Benzoate.

1,2-BENZODIHYDROPYRONE. See Dihydrocoumarin.

BENZOE. See Benzoin.

BENZOIC ACID. A preservative that occurs in nature in cherry bark, raspberries, tea, anise, and cassia bark. First described in 1608 when it was found in gum benzoin. Used in chocolate, lemon, orange, cherry, fruit, nut, and tobacco flavorings for beverages, ice cream, ices, candy, baked goods, icings, and chewing gum. Also used in margarine. Also an antifungal agent. Used as a chemical preservative and as a dietary supplement up to .1 percent. Mild irritant to skin and eyes and mucous membranes, and the FDA is requiring further study. GRAS

BENZOIC ALDEHYDE. See Benzaldehyde.

BENZOIN. Any of several resins containing benzoic acid (*see*), obtained as a gum from various trees. Also called "gum benjamin" and "gum benzoin." Used as a preserving ointment for fumigating, in perfumes and cosmetics, as a compound tincture of benzoin, as a skin protective and respiratory inhalant. The resin is used as a natural agent in chocolate, cherry, rum, spice, and vanilla flavorings for beverages, ice cream, ices, candy, baked goods, gelatin desserts, and chewing gum. Benzoin also is a natural flavoring agent for butterscotch, butter, fruit liquor, and rum. Nontoxic.

BENZOPHENONE. A synthetic agent used in berry, butter, fruit, apricot, peach, nut, and vanilla flavorings in beverages, ice cream, ices, candy, and baked goods. Its persistent roselike odor makes a good fixative for heavy perfumes, especially when used in soaps. Used also in the manufacture of pesticides, antihistamines, and hypnotics. No known toxicity.

2,3-BENZOPYRROLE. See Indole.

BENZOYL EUGENOL. See Eugenyl Benzoate.

BENZOYLBENZENE. See Benzophenone.

BENZOYL PEROXIDE. A bleaching agent for flours, blue cheese, Gorgonzola, and milk. A catalyst for hardening certain fiberglass resins. May explode when heated. Reported to be a skin allergen. Has been used topically for burns and poison ivy (as paste).

BENZYL ACETATE. Acetic Acid. A synthetic raspberry, strawberry, butter, violet, apple, cherry, banana, and plum flavoring agent for beverages, ice cream, ices, candy, baked goods, chewing gum, and gelatin desserts. Colorless liquid, with a floral odor. If ingested, can cause gastrointestinal irritation, vomiting, diarrhea. Irritating to skin, eyes, and respiratory tract.

BENZYL ACETOACETATE. A synthetic berry and fruit flavoring agent for beverages, ice cream, ices, candy, baked goods, gelatin desserts, and chewing gum. See Benzyl Acetate for toxicity.

BENZYL ACETYL ACETATE. See Benzyl Acetoacetate.

BENZYL ALCOHOL. A flavoring that is a constituent of jasmine, hyacinth, and other plants. Faint, sweet odor, and burning taste. Occurs naturally in raspberries and tea. Used in synthetic blueberry, loganberry, raspberry, orange, floral, rose, violet, fruit, cherry, grape, honey, liquor, muscatel, nut, walnut, root beer, and vanilla flavorings for beverages, ice cream, ices, candy, baked goods, gelatin desserts, and chewing gum. Ingestion of large doses can cause vomiting, diarrhea, and central nervous system depression. Irritating and corrosive to the skin and mucous membranes. Used as a solvent in perfumes, as a local anesthetic, and topical antiseptic.

BENZYL BUTYL ETHER. Synthetic fruit flavoring agent for beverages, ice cream, ices, candy, baked goods, gelatin desserts, and puddings. No known toxicity.

BENZYL BUTYRATE. Butyric Acid. A synthetic flavoring agent, colorless, liquid, with a plumlike odor. Used in loganberry, raspberry, strawberry, butter, apricot, peach, pear, liquor, muscatel, cheese, and nut flavorings for beverages, ice cream, ices, candy, baked goods, gelatin desserts, and chewing gum. No known toxicity.

BENZYL CARBINOL. See Phenethyl Alcohol.

BENZYL CINNAMATE. A synthetic flavoring agent, white to pale yellow, solid, with a sweet, balsamic odor. Used in raspberry, chocolate, apricot, cherry, peach, pineapple, plum, prune, honey, liquor, and rum flavorings for beverages, ice cream, ices, candy, baked goods, gelatin desserts, and chewing gum. Employed in perfumes. No known toxicity.

BENZYL DIMETHYL CARBINYL ACETATE. See a,a-Dimethylphenethyl Acetate.

BENZYL DIMETHYL CARBINYL BUTYRATE. See a,a-Dimethylphenethyl Butyrate.

BENZYL DIMETHYL CARBINYL FORMATE. See a,a-Dimethylphenethyl Formate.

BENZYL 2,3-DIMETHYLCROTONATE. A synthetic fruit and spice flavoring agent for beverages, ice cream, ices, candy, and baked goods.

BENZYL DIPROPYL KETONE. See 3-Benzyl-4-Heptanone.

BENZYL DISULFIDE. A synthetic coffee and caramel flavoring agent for baked goods, beverages, ice cream, ices, and candy. No know toxicity.

BENZYL ETHYL ETHER. A synthetic fruit flavoring agent for beverages, ice cream, ices, candy, and baked goods. Aromatic odor. No known toxicity. Probably narcotic in high concentrations.

BENZYL FORMATE. *Formic Acid.* A synthetic chocolate, apricot, cherry, peach, pineapple, plum, prune, honey, and liquor flavoring agent for beverages, ice cream, ices, candy, baked goods, and chewing gum. Pleasant, fruity odor. Most esters of this type are narcotic in high concentrations. See Formic Acid for toxicity.

3-BENZYL-4-HEPTANONE. Synthetic fruit flavoring agent for beverages, ice cream, ices, candy, and baked goods. No known toxicity.

BENZYL o-HYDROXYBENZOATE. See Benzyl Salicylate.

BENZYL ISOAMYL ALCOHOL. See a-Isobutylphenyl Alcohol.

BENZYL ISOBUTYL CARBINOL. See a-Isobutylphenethyl Alcohol.

BENZYL ISOBUTYRATE. A synthetic strawberry and fruit flavoring agent for beverages, ice cream, ices, candy, and baked goods. No known toxicity.

BENZYL ISOEUGENOL. A synthetic spice and banana flavoring agent for beverages, ice cream, ices, candy, and baked goods. No known toxicity.

BENZYL ISOVALERATE. A synthetic raspberry, apple, apricot, banana, cherry, pineapple, walnut, and cheese flavoring agent for beverages, ice cream, ices, candy, baked goods, gelatin desserts, and chewing gum. No known toxicity.

BENZYL MERCAPTAN. Synthetic coffee flavoring agent for beverages, ice cream, ices, candy, and baked goods. No known toxicity.

BENZYL METHOXYETHYL ACETAL. Synthetic fruit and cherry flavoring agent for beverages, ice cream, ices, candy, and baked goods. No known toxicity.

BENZYL METHYL TIGLATE. See Benzyl 2,3-Dimethylcrotonate.

BENZYL PHENYLACETATE. A synthetic butter, caramel, fruit, and honey flavoring agent for beverages, ice cream, ices, candy, baked goods, and toppings. A colorless liquid with a sweet, floral odor, it occurs naturally in honey. No known toxicity.

BENZYL β-PHENYLACRYLATE. See Benzyl Cinnamate.

BENZYL PROPIONATE. A synthetic flavoring substance, colorless, liquid, with a sweet fruity odor. Used in berry, apple, banana, grape, pear, and pineapple flavorings for beverages, ice cream, ices, candy, baked goods, chewing gum, and icings. No known toxicity.

BENZYL SALICYLATE. Salicylic Acid. An almost colorless liquid with a faint, sweet odor, used in floral and peach flavorings for beverages, ice cream, ices, candy, and baked goods. Also used as a fixer in perfumes and sun-screen lotions. As with other salicylates it may interact adversely with such medications as antidepressants and anticoagulants, and may cause allergic reactions.

BENZYLACETIC ACID. See 3-Phenylpropionic Acid.

BENZYLACETONE. See 4-Phenyl-3-Buten-2-one.

BENZYLETHYL ALCOHOL. See 3-Phenyl-1-Propanol.

1-BENZYLOXY (β-METHOXY) ETHOXY ETHANE. See Benzyl Methoxyethyl Acetal.

BENZYLPROPYL ACETATE. See a,a-Dimethylphenethyl Acetate.

BENZYLPROPYL ALCOHOL. See a,a-Dimethylphenethyl Alcohol.

BENZYLPROPYL CARBINOL. See a-Propylphenethyl Alcohol.

BENZYLTHIOL. See Benzyl Mercaptan.

BERGAMOL. See Linalyl Acetate.

BERGAMOT. Bergamot Orange. A natural flavoring extracted from the rind of the fruit of a small, spiny tree. Used in strawberry, lemon, orange, tangerine, cola, floral, banana, grape, peach, pear, pineapple, liquor, spice, and vanilla flavorings for beverages, ice cream, ices, candy, baked goods, gelatin desserts, chewing gum, and icings. The oil is used in perfumes. May cause sensitivity to light. GRAS.

BETA-APO-8'-CAROTENAL. Coloring agent for solid or semisolid foods. Nontoxic.

BETA CAROTENE. See Carotene.

BETAINE, ANHYDROUS. A dietary supplement in food up to 100 mg per day. Occurs in the common beet and in many vegetables and animal substances. Has been used to treat muscle weakness and degeneration. No known toxicity.

BHA. See Butylated Hydroxyanisole.

BHT. See Butylated Hydroxytoluene.

BIACETYL. See Diacetyl.

BIOTIN. Vitamin B Factor. Vitamin H. An essential nutrient vital for growth and manufactured in the body. It is present in minute amounts in every living cell, but the richest source is in kidney and pancreas cells and in yeast and milk. Cancer cells have more biotin than do normal cells. It acts as a coenzyme in the formation of certain essential fatlike substances, and plays a part in reactions involving carbon dioxide. It is needed for healthy circulation and red blood cells. There is no official minimum daily requirement, but a diet of 150 to 300 mg. of biotin is considered adequate. GRAS

BIRCH. Sweet Oil and Tar Oil. A flavoring agent from the bark and wood of deciduous trees common in Northern Hemisphere. The oil is obtained by distillation. It is a clear, dark brown liquid with a strong leatherlike odor. Birch *sweet oil* is used in synthetic strawberry, pineapple, maple, nut, root beer, sarsaparilla, spice, wintergreen and birch beer flavorings for beverages, ice cream, ices, candy, baked goods, gelatins, puddings (4,300 ppm), and syrups. Birch *tar oil*, which is refined, is used in chewing gum, and has also been used for preserving leather and wood and for treating skin diseases. No known toxicity.

BITTER ASH EXTRACT. See Quassia Extract.

BITTER WOOD EXTRACT. See Quassia Extract.

BIXIN (Norbixin). The active ingredients of Annatto, both carotenoidlike compounds, but with five times the coloring power of carotene, and with better stability. They impart a yellow coloring to food. See Annatto.

BLACK CUTCH EXTRACT. See Catechu Extract.

BLACKBERRY BARK EXTRACT. A natural flavoring agent extracted from the woody plant. Used in berry, pineapple, grenadine, root beer, sarsaparilla, wintergreen, and birch beer flavorings for beverages, ice cream, candy, baked goods, and liquors (10,000 ppm). No known toxicity.

BLACKTHORN BERRIES. See Sloe Berries.

BLATTERALKOHOL. See 3-Hexen-1-ol.

BOIS DE ROSE. The volatile oil used as a flavoring agent, which is obtained by steam distillation from the chipped wood of the tropical rosewood tree. The oil is colorless to pale yellow, with a slight camphor odor. Used in citrus, floral, fruit, meat, and spice flavorings for beverages, ice cream, ices, candy, baked goods, and chewing gum. No known toxicity. GRAS

BOLETIC ACID. See Fumaric Acid.

BORIC ACID. See Boron Sources.

BORNEO CAMPHOR. See Borneol.

BORNEOL. A flavoring agent found naturally in coriander, ginger oil, oil of lime, rosemary, strawberries, thyme, citronella, and nutmeg. It has a peppery odor and burning taste. Used as a synthetic nut or spice flavoring for beverages, ice cream, ices, candy, baked goods, syrup, and chewing gum. Smells like camphor, and is used in perfumery. Can cause nausea, vomiting, convulsions, confusion, and dizziness. It has a toxicity similar to camphor.

BORNYL ACETATE. It may be obtained from various pine needle oils. Strong piney odor. As a yarrow herb and iva herb extract, it is used as a synthetic fruit and spice flavoring agent for beverages, ice cream, ices, candy, baked goods, syrups, gelatin desserts, puddings, and chewing gum. Toxicity may be similar to Borneol (*see*).

BORNYL FORMATE. *Formic Acid.* A synthetic fruit flavoring agent for beverages, ice cream, ices, candy, baked goods, and syrups. See Formic Acid for toxicity.

BORNYL ISOVALERATE. A synthetic flavoring agent with a camphorlike smell used in fruit flavoring for beverages, ice cream, candy, baked goods, and syrups. Also used medicinally as a sedative. No known toxicity.

BORNYL VALERATE. A synthetic fruit flavoring agent for beverages, ice cream, ices, candy, and baked goods. No known toxicity.

BORNYVAL. See Bornyl Isovalerate.

BORON SOURCES. *Boric Acid. Sodium Borate.* Boron occurs in the earth's crust (in the form of its compounds, not the metal) and borates are widely used as antiseptics even though toxicologists warn about possible adverse reactions. Boric acid and sodium borate are astringents and antiseptics. Borates are absorbed from mucous membranes and can cause symptoms such as gastrointestinal bleeding, skin rash, central nervous system stimulation. The adult lethal dose is 30 grams (1 oz). Infants and young children are more susceptible. Boron is used as a diet supplement up to 1 mg per day. Cleared for use by the FDA in modified hop extract up to 310 ppm.

BORONIA, ABSOLUTE. A synthetic violet and fruit flowering agent extracted from a plant. Used for beverages, ice cream, ices, candy, baked goods. No known toxicity.

BOSWELLIA SPECIES. See Olibanum Oil.

BRASSICA ALBA. See Mustard.

BRILLIANT BLUE. See FD and C Blue No. 1.

BROMATE. *Calcium* bromate is a maturing agent and dough conditioner in bromated flours and bromated whole wheat flour. *Potassium* bromate is a bread improver. Sugar contaminated with potassium bromate caused a food poisoning outbreak in New Zealand. The lethal dose is not certain, but 2 to 4 oz of a 2 percent solution causes serious poisoning in children. Death in animals and man apparently is due to kidney failure, but central nervous system problems have been reported.

BROMELIN. BROMELAIN. A protein-digesting and milk-clotting enzyme found in pineapple. Used for tenderizing meat, chill-proofing beer, and as an anti-inflammatory medication. "Solutions consisting of water, salt, monosodium glutamate, and approved proteolytic enzymes, applied or injected into cuts of beef shall not result in a gain of more than 3 percent above the weight of the untreated product." No known toxicity.

BROMINATED VEGETABLE OILS. Bromine, a heavy, volatile, corrosive, nonmetallic liquid element, added to vegetable oil or other oils. Dark brown or pale yellow, with a bland or fruity odor. These high-density oils are blended with low-density essential oils to make them easier to emulsify. Used largely in soft drinks, citrus-flavored beverages, ice cream, ices, and baked goods. The FDA has them on the "suspect list." See Bromate for toxicity.

BROOM EXTRACT. See Genet, Absolute.

BUCHU LEAF OIL. A natural flavoring agent from a South African plant. Used in berry, fruit, chocolate, mint, and spice flavorings for beverages, ice cream, ices, candy, baked goods, condiments, and liquors. Has been used as a urinary antiseptic and mild diuretic. No known toxicity.

BUFFER. Usually a solution whose acidity-alkalinity is relatively constant and unaffected by the addition of comparatively large amounts of acid or alkali. Frequently a buffer consists a weak acid mixed with the sodium salt of the weak acid and are frequently used to control acidity in soft drinks. A typical buffer solution would be hydrochloric acid (*see*) and sodium hydroxide (*see*).

BUTADIENE-STYRENE COPOLYMER. A component for a chewing gum base. Butadiene is produced largely from petroleum gases and is used in the manufacture of synthetic rubber. It may be irritating to the skin and mucous membranes and narcotic in high concentrations. Styrene, obtained from ethyl benzene, is an oily liquid with a penetrating odor. It has the same uses and toxicity.

BUTADIENE STYRENE RUBBER. *Latex.* A chewing gum base. No known toxicity.

BUTANAL. See Butyraldehyde.

BUTANDIONE. See Diacetyl.

BUTANE. A gas produced from petroleum and used as a household fuel, refrigerant, in the manufacture of synthetic rubber, and raw material for motor fuels. Narcotic in high concentrations. GRAS

1,4-BUTANEDICARBOXYLIC ACID. See Adipic Acid.

BUTANOIC ACID. See Butyric Acid.

1-BUTANOL. See Butyl Alcohol.

2,3-BUTANOLONE. See Acetoin.

(*trans*)-BUTENEDIOIC ACID. See Fumaric Acid.

BUTOXYPOLYETHYLENE. A synthetic antifoaming agent used in beet sugar manufacture. No known toxicity.

BUTTERS. *Acids, Esters, and Distillate.* Butter *acids* are synthetic butter and cheese flavoring agents for beverages, ice cream, ices, candy (2,800 ppm), and baked goods. Butter *esters* are synthetic butter, caramel, and chocolate flavoring agents for beverages, ice cream, ices, baked goods, toppings, and popcorn (1,200 ppm). Butter *starter distillate* is a synthetic butter flavoring agent for ice cream, ices, baked goods, and shortening (12,000 ppm). No known toxicity.

BUTYL ACETATE. A synthetic flavoring agent, a clear liquid with a strong, fruity odor, prepared from acetic acid and butyl alcohol. Used in raspberry, strawberry, butter, banana, and pineapple flavorings for beverages, ice cream, ices, candy, baked goods, gelatin desserts, and chewing gum. An irritant, which may cause conjunctivitis (pink eye). A central nervous system depressant and in high doses it is narcotic.

BUTYL ACETOACETATE. A synthetic berry and fruit flavoring agent for beverages, ice cream, candy, and baked goods. No known toxicity.

BUTYL ALCOHOL. A synthetic butter, cream, fruit, liquor, rum, and whiskey flavoring agent for beverages, ice cream, ices, candy, baked goods, cordials, and cream. Occurs naturally in apple and raspberries. Used as a solvent for waxes, fats, resins, and shellac. May cause irritation of the mucous membranes, contact dermatitis, headache, dizziness, and drowsiness.

BUTYL ALDEHYDE. See Butyraldehyde.

BUTYL ANTHRANILATE. A synthetic grape, mandarin, and pineapple flavoring agent for beverages, ice cream, ices, candy, and baked goods. No known toxicity.

BUTYL BUTYRATE. A colorless, synthetic flavoring agent prepared from butyl alcohol, with a fruity odor. Used in berry, butter, apple, banana, peach, pineapple, liquor, Scotch, and nut flavoring for beverages, ice cream, ices, candy, baked goods, gelatin desserts, and chewing gum (1,500 ppm). In high concentrations may be irritating and narcotic.

BUTYL BUTYRYLLACTATE. A synthetic flavoring agent, colorless, liquid, with a buttery odor. Used in butterscotch, fruit, nut, and vanilla flavorings for beverages, ice cream, ices, candy, and baked goods. No known toxicity.

α-BUTYL CINNAMALDEHYDE. A synthetic fruit, nut, spice, and cinnamon flavoring agent for beverages, ice cream, ices, candy, and baked goods. No known toxicity.

BUTYL CINNAMATE. A synthetic chocolate, cocoa, and fruit flavoring agent for beverages, ice cream, ices, candy, baked goods, and liquors. No known toxicity.

BUTYL 2-DECENOATE. A synthetic apricot and peach flavoring agent for beverages, ice cream, ices, candy, and chewing gum (2,000 ppm). No known toxicity.

BUTYL DECYLENATE. See Butyl 2-Decenoate.

BUTYL DODECANOATE. See Butyl Laurate.

BUTYL ETHYL MALONATE. A synthetic fruit and apple flavoring agent for beverages, ice cream, ices, candy, and baked goods. No known toxicity.

BUTYL FORMATE. Formic Acid. A synthetic fruit, plum, liquor, and rum flavoring agent for beverages, ice cream, ices, candy, gelatin desserts, and baked goods. See Formic Acid for toxicity.

BUTYL HEPTANOATE. A synthetic fruit and liquor flavoring agent for beverages, ice cream, ices, candy, and baked goods. No known toxicity.

BUTYL HEXANOATE. A synthetic butter, butterscotch, pineapple, and rum flavoring agent for beverages, ice cream, ices, candy, and baked goods. No known toxicity.

BUTYL p-HYDROXYBENZOATE. No specific flavor is indicated but it is a flavoring agent used in beverages and baked goods. No known toxicity.

BUTYL ISOBUTYRATE. A synthetic raspberry, strawberry, butter, banana, and cherry flavoring agent for beverages, ice cream, ices, candy, baked goods, and chewing gum (2,000 ppm). No known toxicity.

BUTYL ISOVALERATE. A synthetic chocolate and fruit flavoring agent for beverages, baked goods, ice cream, ices, candy, puddings, and gelatin desserts. No known toxicity.

2-BUTYL-5 (or 6) -KETO-1,4-DIOXANE. A synthetic fruit flavoring for beverages, ice cream, ices, candy, baked goods, and shortenings. No known toxicity.

BUTYL LACTATE. A synthetic butter, butterscotch, caramel, and fruit flavoring agent for beverages, ice cream, ices, candy, and baked goods. No known toxicity.

BUTYL LAURATE. A synthetic fruit flavoring agent for beverages, ice cream, ices, candy and baked goods. No known toxicity.

BUTYL LEVULINATE. A synthetic butter, fruit, and rum flavoring agent for beverages, ice cream, ices, candy, and baked goods. No known toxicity.

BUTYL PARASEPT. See Butyl p-Hydroxybenzoate.

BUTYL PHENYLACETATE. Synthetic butter, honey, caramel, chocolate, rose, fruit, and nut flavoring agent for beverages, ice cream, ices, candy, baked goods, gelatin desserts, and puddings. No known toxicity.

BUTYL PROPIONATE. A synthetic butter, rum butter, fruit, and rum flavoring agent for beverages, ice cream, ices, candy, and baked goods. May be an irritant.

BUTYL RUBBER. A synthetic rubber used as a chewing gum base component. No known toxicity.

BUTYL SEBACATE. See Dibutyl Sebacate.

BUTYL STEARATE. A synthetic antifoaming agent used in the production of beet sugar. Also a synthetic banana, butter, and liquor flavoring agent for beverages, ice cream, ices, candy, baked goods, chewing gum, and liqueurs. No known toxicity.

BUTYL SULFIDE. A synthetic floral, violet, and fruit flavoring agent for beverages, ice cream, ices, candy, and baked goods. No known toxicity.

BUTYL 10-UNDECENOATE. A synthetic butter, apricot, cognac, and nut flavoring agent for beverages, ice cream, ices, candy, baked goods, chewing gum, icing, and liquor. No known toxicity.

BUTYL VALERATE. A synthetic butter, fruit, and chocolate flavoring agent for beverages, baked goods, ice cream, ices, candy, puddings, and gelatin desserts. No known toxicity.

BUTYLATED HYDROXYANISOLE (BHA) A preservative and antioxidant used in many products, including beverages, chewing gum, ice cream, ices, candy, baked goods, gelatin desserts, soup bases, potatoes, glacéed fruits, potato flakes, sweet potato flakes, dry breakfast cereals, dry yeast, dry mixes for desserts and beverages, lard, shortening, unsmoked dry sausage, and in emulsions for stabilizers for shortenings. It is a white, or slightly yellow, waxy solid with a faint, characteristic odor. Insoluble in water. Total content of antioxidants is not so exceed .02 percent of fat or oil content of food; allowed up to 1,000 ppm. in dry yeast; 200 ppm in shortenings; 50 ppm in potato flakes; and 50 ppm with BHT (Butylated Hydroxytoluene; *see*) in dry cereals. Can cause allergic reactions. The FDA is pursuing further study of BHA. GRAS

BUTYLATED HYDROXYMETHYLPHENOL. A new antioxidant, a nearly white, crystalline, solid, with a faint characteristic odor.

Insoluble in water and propylene glycol; soluble in alcohol. No known toxicity but the formula, 4-Hydroxymethyl-2,6-di-tert-butylphenol contains phenol, which is very toxic.

BUTYLATED HYDROXYTOLUENE (BHT). An antioxidant employed in many foods. Used as a chewing gum base, added to potato and sweet potato flakes, and dry breakfast cereals, an emulsion stabilizer for shortenings, used in enriched rice, animal fats, and shortenings containing animal fats. White, crystalline, solid, with a faint characteristic odor. Insoluble in water. Total content of antioxidants in fat or oils not to exceed .02 percent. Allowed up to 200 ppm in emulsion stabilizers for shortenings, 50 ppm in dry breakfast cereals and potato flakes. Used also as an antioxidant to retard rancidity in frozen fresh pork sausage and freeze-dried meats up to .01 percent based on fat content. Can cause allergic reactions. Loyola University scientists reported on April 14, 1972, that pregnant mice fed a diet consisting of one half of one percent of BHT (or BHA, butylated hydroxyanisole) gave birth to offspring that frequently had chemical changes in the brain and subsequent abnormal behavior patterns. BHT and BHA are chemically similar. BHT is prohibited as a food additive in England. The FDA is pursuing further study of BHT. GRAS

1,3-BUTYLENE GLYCOL. A clear, colorless, viscous liquid with a slight taste, used as a solvent for natural and synthetic flavorings except where government standards preclude such use. It has a similar toxicity to ethylene glycol (*see*) which, when ingested, may cause transient stimulation of the central nervous system, then depression, vomiting, drowsiness, coma, respiratory failure, and convulsions; renal damage may proceed to uremia and death.

BUTYRALDEHYDE. A synthetic flavoring agent found naturally in coffee and strawberries. Used in butter, caramel, fruit, liquor, brandy, and nut flavorings for beverages, ice cream, ices, candy, baked goods, alcoholic beverages, and icings. Used also in the manufacture of rubber accelerators, synthetic resins, and plasticizers. May be an irritant and narcotic.

BUTYRIC ACID. A clear, colorless liquid present in butter at 4 to 5 percent with a strong penetrating rancid-butter odor. Butter, butterscotch, caramel, fruit, and nut flavoring agent for beverages, ice cream, ices, candy, baked goods, gelatin desserts, puddings, chewing gum, and margarine. Found naturally in apples, butter acids, geranium, rose oil, grapes, strawberries, and wormseed oil. It has a low toxicity but can be a mild irritant. GRAS

BUTYRIC ALDEHYDE. See Butyraldehyde.

BUTYRIN. See (*tri*) Butyrin.

(*tri-*) *BUTYRIN.* A synthetic flavoring agent found naturally in butter. Butter flavoring for beverages, ice cream, ices, candy (1000 ppm), baked goods, margarine, and puddings. No known toxicity.

BUTYROIN. See 5-Hydroxy-4-Octanone.

BUTYRONE. See 4-Heptanone.

BUXINE.® See α-Amylcinnamaldehyde.

BUXINOL. See α-Amylcinnamyl Alcohol.

C

CACAO SHELL. Cocoa shells of the seeds of trees grown in Brazil, Central America, and most tropical countries. Weak chocolatelike odor and taste, thin and peppery, with a reddish-brown color. Used in the manufacture of caffeine (*see*); also theobromine, which occurs in chocolate products and is used as a diuretic and nerve stimulant. Occasionally causes allergic reactions from handling. GRAS.

CACHOU EXTRACT. See Catechu Extract.

CACTUS ROOT EXTRACT. See Yucca.

CADINENE. A general fixative that occurs naturally in juniper oil and pepper oil. It has a faint, pleasant smell. Used in candy, baked goods (1200 ppm), and chewing gum (1,000 ppm). No known toxicity.

CAFFEINE. Guaranine, Methyltheobromine, Theine, 1, 3, 7-Trimethyl-2, 6-Dioxopurine. An odorless white powder with a bitter taste, it occurs naturally in coffee, cola, guarana paste, maté leaves, tea, and kola nuts. Obtained as a by-product of caffeine-free coffee. Used as a flavor in cola and root beer beverages (.02 per cent of weight). A central nervous system, heart, and respiratory stimulant. Can cause nervousness, insomnia, irregular heartbeat, noise in ears, and, in high doses, convulsions. Can alter blood sugar release and uptake by liver. Caffeine crosses the placental barrier and its effects on the fetus are under study. On the FDA list of additives to be studied for safety.

CAJEPUT OIL. A spice flavoring from the cajeput tree native to Australia. The leaves yield an aromatic oil. Used for beverages, ice cream, ices, candy, and baked goods. No known toxicity.

CAJEPUTENE. See d-Limonene.

CAJEPUTOL. See Eucalyptol.

CALAMUS. Sweet Flag. An aromatic flavoring from the dried root of a plant grown in Europe, North America, West Asia, Burma, and Ceylon. Used in bitters, vermouth, root beer, and spice flavorings for beverages, candy, baked goods, ice cream, cordials, and bitters. The *oil* is used in chocolate, fruit, benedictine, chartreuse, nut, root beer, sarsaparilla, spice, ginger ale, vanilla, wintergreen, and birch beer flavorings for beverages, ice cream, ices, candy, baked goods, gelatin desserts, puddings, and liquors. Calamus has been used against intestinal gas and as a vermifuge, an agent that causes expulsion of intestinal worms. No known toxicity.

CALCIFEROL. See Vitamin D_2.

CALCIUM ACID PHOSPHATE. See Calcium Phosphate.

CALCIUM ASCORBATE. A preservative and antioxidant prepared from ascorbic acid (Vitamin C) and calcium carbonate (*see*). Used in concentrated milk products, cooked, cured, or pulverized meat products; in pickles in which pork and beef products are cured and packed (up to 75 ounces per 100 gallons). See Ascorbic Acid for toxicity. GRAS

CALCIUM BROMATE. A maturing agent and dough conditioner used in bromated flours. See Bromate.

CALCIUM CARBONATE. A tasteless, odorless powder that occurs naturally in limestone, marble, and coral. Used as a white food dye, an alkali to reduce acidity in wine up to 2.5 percent, a neutralizer for ice cream and ice cream syrups up to .25 percent, in confections up to .25 percent, and in baking powder up to 50 percent. Employed also as a yeast food; a firming agent; a carrier used in candies, particularly hard candies, to prevent sticking; in fudge to promote creaming, in cereal flours; as a carrier for bleaching agents; and in bread, rolls, and buns. A gastric antacid, and antidiarrhea medicine, it may cause constiption. See Calcium Sources. GRAS

CALCIUM CASEINATE. See Casein.

CALCIUM CHLORIDE. White, hard, odorless grains, which absorb water. Used as a firming agent for sliced apples and other fruit, in apple pie mix, as a jelly ingredient, in certain cheeses to aid coagulation, in artificially sweetened fruit jelly, and in canned tomatoes. Used also to preserve wood, fireproof materials, in automobile antifreeze, and as a dust control on unpaved roads. Replaces the body's electrolytes, reduces body water, combats allergies, and is urinary acidifier. May cause stomach upset and heart irregularities. GRAS for packaging only.

CALCIUM CITRATE. A fine, white, odorless power prepared from citrus fruit. Used as a buffer to neutralize acids in confections, jellies, and jams, and in saccharine at the rate of 3 ounces per 100 pounds of the artificial sweetener. It is also used to improve the baking properties of flour. See Citrate Salts for toxicity. GRAS

CALCIUM DISODIUM (EDTA). A preservative and sequestrant, white, odorless, crystalline powder, with a faint, salty taste. Used in canned and carbonated soft drinks for flavor retention; in canned white potatoes and cooked canned clams for color retention; in crab meat to retard struvite (crystal) formation; in dressings as a preservative; in cooked and canned dried lima beans for color retention; in fermented malt beverages to prevent gushing; in mayonnaise and oleomargarine as a preservative; in processed dried pinto beans for color retention; and in sandwich spreads as a preservative. Used medically as a chelating agent to detoxify poisoning by lead and other heavy metals. May cause intestinal upsets, muscle cramps, kidney damage, and blood in urine. On the FDA priority list of food additives to be studied for mutagenic, teratogenic, subacute, and reproductive effects.

CALCIUM GLYCEROPHOSPHATE. A fine, white, odorless, nearly tasteless, powder used in dentifrices, baking powder, and as a food stabilizer and dietary supplement. A component of many over-the-counter nerve-tonic foods. Administered medicinally for numbness and debility. See Calcium Sources. GRAS

CALCIUM HEXAMETAPHOSPHATE. An emulsifier, sequestering agent, and texturizer used in breakfast cereals, angel food cake, flaked fish (prevents struvite), ice cream, ices, milk, bottled beer, reconstituted lemon juice, puddings, processed cheeses, artificially sweetened jellies and preserves, potable water supplies to prevent scale formation and corrosion, and in pickle for curing hams. No known toxicity. GRAS

CALCIUM HYDROXIDE. Calcium Hydrate. Slaked Lime. An alkali, a white powder with slightly bitter taste. Used as a firming agent for various fruit products, as an egg preservative, in water treatment, and for dehairing hides. It is also used in mortar, plaster, cement, and other building materials, and medically as a topical astringent. Calcium sucrate or saccharate (which is used to standardize the potassium iodide of iodized table salt, reduces the acidity in wine, and is a sour cream neutralizer) is made up of 3 parts sugar to 1 part calcium hydroxide. No known toxicity. GRAS

CALCIUM HYPOCHLORITE. A germicide and sterilizing agent, the active ingredient of chlorinated lime, used in the curd washing of cottage cheese, in sugar refining, as an oxidizing and bleaching agent, and as an algae killer, bactericide, deodorant, disinfectant, and fungicide. Sterilizes fruit and vegetables by washing in a 50 percent solution. Under various names, dilute hypochlorite is found in homes as laundry bleach and household bleach. Occasionally cases of poisoning occur when housewives mix household hypochlorite solution with various other household chemicals which causes the release of poisonous chlorine gas. As with other corrosive agents, calcium hypochlorite's toxicity depends upon its concentration. It is highly corrosive to skin and mucous membranes. Ingestion may cause pain and inflammation of the mouth, pharynx, esophagus, and stomach, with erosion particularly of the mucous membranes of the stomach.

CALCIUM IODATE. White, odorless, or nearly odorless power used as a dough conditioner and oxidizing agent in bread, rolls, and buns. It is a nutritional source of iodine in foods such as table salt, and used also as a tropical disinfectant and as a deodorant. Low toxicity, but may cause allergic reactions.

CALCIUM LACTATE. White, almost odorless crystals or powder, used as a buffer and as such is a constituent of baking powders and is employed in confections; also used in dentifrices and as a yeast food and dough conditioner. In medical use, given for calcium deficiency; may cause gastrointestinal and cardiac disturbances.

CALCIUM OXIDE. Quicklime. Burnt Lime. A hard, white or grayish white odorless mass or powder that is used as a yeast food and dough conditioner for bread, rolls, and buns. It is also an alkali for neutralizing dairy products (including ice cream mixes) and alkalizes sour cream, butter, and confections, and is used in the processing of tripe. Industrial uses are for bricks, plaster, mortar, stucco, dehairing hides, fungicides, insecticides, and for clarification of beet and cane sugar juices. A strong caustic, it may severely damage skin and mucous membranes. See Calcium Sources. GRAS

CALCIUM PANTOTHENATE. Pantothenic Acid Calcium Salt. A B-complex vitamin, pantothenate is a white, odorless powder, with a sweetish taste and bitter aftertaste. Pantothenic acid occurs everywhere in plant and animal tissue, and the richest common source is liver; jelly of the queen bee contains 6 times as much. Rice bran and molasses are other good sources. Acid derivatives sold commercially are synthesized. See *d*-Pantothenamide. Biochemical defects from lack of calcium pantothenate may exist undetected for some time, but eventually manifest themselves as tissue failures. The calcium chloride double salt of calcium pantothenate has been cleared for use in foods for special dietary uses. GRAS

CALCIUM PROPIONATE. A preservative. White crystals or crystalline solid with the faint odor of propionic acid. Mold and rope inhibitor in bread and rolls; used in poultry stuffing, chocolate products, processed cheese, cakes and cupcakes, and artificially sweetened fruit jelly and preserves. Has been used as an antifungal medication for the skin. The FDA requires further study for safety. GRAS

CALCIUM PHOSPHATE Di, Mono, and Tri-Basic. White, odorless, powders used as yeast foods, dough conditioners, and firming agents. *Tri-basic* is an anticaking agent used in table salt, powdered sugar, malted milk powder, condiments, puddings, meat, dry-curing mixtures, cereal flours, and vanilla powder. It is tasteless. Used as a gastric antacid, mineral supplement, and a clarifying agent for sugars and syrups. *Dibasic* is used to improve bread, rolls, buns, cereal flours; a carrier for bleaching; used as a mineral supplement in cereals, in dental products, and in fertilizers. *Monobasic* is used in bread, rolls, and buns, artificially sweetened fruit jelly, canned potatoes, canned sweet peppers, canned tomatoes, and as a jelling ingredient. Employed in fertilizer as an acidulant, in baking powders, and in wheat flours as a mineral supplement. Nontoxic. See Calcium Salts. GRAS

CALCIUM PYROPHOSPHATE. A fine, white, odorless, tasteless powder, used as a nutrient, buffer, and neutralizing agent. It is also an abrasive in dentifrices, a feed supplement, and a compound used in ceramic ware. No known toxicity. See Calcium Sources. GRAS

CALCIUM SALTS: Acetate, Chloride, Citrate, Diacetate, Gluconate, Phosphate (monobasic), Phytate, Sulfate. Emulsifier salts used in evaporated milk and frozen desserts. Also in enriched bread. Firming agent in potatoes and canned tomatoes. May be gastric irritants, but they have little oral toxicity. See separate listing for Calcium Sulfate and Calcium Phosphate. GRAS

CALCIUM SALTS OF FATTY ACIDS. Used as binders and anti-caking agents in foods.

CALCIUM SILICATE. An anticaking agent, white or slightly cream-colored, free-flowing powder. Up to 5 percent in baking powder and 2 percent of table salts. Absorbs water. Constituent of lime glass and cement, used in road construction. Practically nontoxic orally, except that inhalation may cause irritation of the respiratory tract. On the FDA list of additives that need further study for mutagenic, teratogenic, subacute, and reproductive effects. GRAS

CALCIUM SORBATE. A preservative and fungus preventative used in beverages, baked goods, chocolate syrups, soda-fountain syrups, fresh fruit cocktail, tangerine purée (sherbet base), salads (potato, macaroni, cole slaw, gelatin), cheesecake, pie fillings, cake, cheese in consumer-size packages, and artificially sweetened jellies and preserves. No known toxicity. GRAS

CALCIUM SOURCES (harmless calcium salts): Carbonate, Citrate, Glycerophosphate, Oxide, Phosphate, Pyrophosphate, Sulfate (See all). Calcium is a mineral supplement for breakfast cereals, white cornmeal, infant dietary formula, enriched flour, enriched bromated flour (see Bromate), enriched macaroni, noodle products, self-rising flours, enriched farina, cornmeal, and corn grits, and enriched bread and rolls. Calcium is a major mineral in the body. It is incompletely absorbed from the gastrointestinal tract when in the diet so its absorption is enhanced by calcium normally present in intestinal secretions. Vitamin D is also required for efficient absorption of calcium. Recommended daily requirements for adult females is 1.5 grams, for adult males 1.2 grams, and for children .8 gram. Calcium and phosphorus are the major constituents of teeth and bones. The ratio of calcium to phosphorus in cow's milk is approximately 1.2 to 1. In human milk the ratio is 2 to 1.

CALCIUM STEARYL-2-LACTYLATE. A free-flowing, white powder

dough conditioner in yeast-leavened bakery products and prepared mixes for yeast-leavened bakery products. Also a whipping agent in dried, liquid, and frozen egg whites. On the FDA list of additives requiring further safety information. No known toxicity.

CALCIUM SULFATE. Plaster of Paris. A fine, white to slightly yellow odorless, tasteless powder used as a firming agent and yeast food and dough conditioner. Utilized in brewing and other fermentation industries, in Spanish-type sherry, as a jelling ingredient, in cereal flours, as a carrier for a bleaching agent, in bread, rolls, and buns, in blue cheese and Gorgonzola cheese, artificially sweetened fruit, jelly, canned potatoes, canned sweet peppers, and canned tomatoes. Used also in creamed cottage cheese as an alkali, and employed industrially in cement, wall plaster, and insecticides. Because it absorbs moistures and hardens quickly, its ingestion may result in intestinal obstruction. Mixed with flour, it has been used to kill rodents. See Calcium Salts. GRAS

CALENDULA. Dried flowers of marigolds, grown in Southern Europe and in gardens everywhere. Used as a natural flavoring agent. See Marigold, Pot, for foods in which used. Formerly used to soothe inflammation of skin and mucous membranes. No known toxicity. GRAS

CALORIE. A unit used to express the heat output of an organism and the fuel or energy value of food. The amount of heat required to raise the temperature of one gram of water from 14.5 to 15.5 degrees C. at atmospheric pressure.

2-CAMPHANOL. See Borneol.

CAMPHENE. A synthetic spice and nutmeg flavoring agent for beverages, ice cream, ices, candy, and baked goods. Occurs naturally in calamus oil, citronella, ginger, lemon oil, mandarin oil, myrtle, petitgrain oil, and juniper berries. No known toxicity.

d-CAMPHOR. Occurs naturally in basil, ho oil, iva herb extract, and zedoary-bark extract. It is a synthetic mint flavoring agent for ice cream, ices, candy, baked goods, and condiments. No known toxicity.

CAMPHOR, JAPANESE WHITE OIL. Camphor Tree. Distilled from trees at least fifty years old grown in China, Japan, Formosa, Brazil, and Sumatra. Camphor tree is used in spice flavorings for beverages, baked goods, and condiments. It is also used in embalming fluid, as a preservative in cosmetics, in the manufacture of explosives, in lacquers, as a moth repellent, and topically (as a counterirritant) in liniments, cold medications, and anesthetics. Camphor ingestion may cause vertigo, mental confusion, delirium, clonic convulsions, coma, respiratory failure, and death. Salts of any kind are incompatible and should not be added to camphor water. Camphor is readily absorbed from all sites of administration. Ingestion of 2 grams generally produces dangerous effects in an adult. Ingestion by pregnant women has caused fetal death.

CANANGA OIL. A natural flavor extract obtained by distillation from the flowers of the tree. Light to deep yellow liquid, with a harsh, floral odor. Used in cola, fruit, spice, and ginger ale flavoring for beverages, ice cream, ices, candy, and baked goods. No known toxicity. GRAS

CANE SUGAR. See Sucrose.

CAPERS. A natural flavoring from the spiny shrub. The picked flower bud is used as a condiment for sauces and salads. No known toxicity. GRAS

CAPRALDEHYDE. See Decanal.

CAPRIC ACID. See Decanoic Acid.

CAPRIC ALDEHYDE. See Decanal.

CAPRINALDEHYDE. See Decanal.

CAPROALDEHYDE. See Hexanal.

CAPROIC ACID See Hexanoic Acid.

CAPROIC ALDEHYDE. See Hexanal.

CAPRONIC ETHER ABSOLUTE. See Ethyl Hexanoate.

CAPRYLIC ACID. An oily liquid with a rancid taste made by the oxidation of octanol (*see*). It is a fatty acid that occurs in sweat, fusel oil, in the milk of cows and goats, and in palm and coconut oil. Used as a preservative and in the manufacture of dyes. Cleared for use as a synthetic flavoring. No known toxicity. GRAS

CAPSICUM. African Chillies. Cayenne Pepper. Tabasco Pepper. The dried fruit of a tropical plant used as a natural spice and ginger ale flavoring for beverages, ice cream, ices, candy, and baked goods; also meats and sauces. The *oleoresin* form is used in sausage, spice, ginger ale, and cinnamon flavorings for beverages, candy, baked goods, chewing gum, meats, and condiments. Used internally as a digestive stimulant. Irritating to the mucous membrane, it can produce severe diarrhea and gastritis. GRAS

CARAMEL. Burnt sugar with a pleasant, slightly bitter taste. Made by heating sugar or glucose and adding small quantities of alkali, or a trace of mineral acid during heating. A flavoring and coloring. Used as brown coloring in ice cream, baked goods, soft drinks, confections. As a flavoring, it is used in strawberry, butter, butterscotch, caramel, chocolate, cocoa, cola, fruit, cherry, grape, birch beer, liquor, rum, brandy, maple, black walnut, walnut, root beer, spice, ginger, ginger ale, vanilla, and cream soda beverages (2,200 ppm), ice cream, candy, baked goods, syrups (2,800 ppm), and meats (2,100 ppm). The FDA has given caramel priority for testing its mutagenic, teratogenic, subacute, and reproductive effects. GRAS

CARAWAY. The dried ripe seeds of a plant common to Europe and Asia and cultivated in England, Russia, and the U.S. Volatile, colorless to pale yellow liquid. Used as liquor flavoring for beverages, ice cream, ices, baked goods (10,000 ppm) and condiments; also as a spice in baking. The *oil* is used in grape licorice, anisette, kummel, liver, sausage, mint, caraway, and rye flavorings for beverages, ice cream, ices, candy, baked goods, chewing gum, meats, condiments, and liquors. A mild carminative from 1 to 2 grams to break up intestinal gas. No known toxicity. GRAS

CARBON BLACK. Several forms of artificially prepared carbon or charcoal, including animal charcoal, furnace black, channel (gas) black, lampblack, activated charcoal. Animal charcoal is used as a black coloring in confectionery. Activated charcoal is used as an antidote for ingested poisons and as an absorbent in diarrhea. The others have industrial uses. Carbon black is not subject to certification for coloring by the FDA. No known toxicity.

CARBON DIOXIDE. Colorless, odorless, noncombustible gas with a faint acid taste. Used as a pressure-dispensing agent in gassed creams (pressure-dispensed whipped cream.) Also used in the carbonation of beverages and as dry ice for refrigeration in the frozen food industry. Used on stage to produce harmless smoke or fumes. May cause shortness of breath, vomiting, high blood pressure, and disorientation.

CARBONATE, POTASSIUM. See Potassium Carbonate.

CARBONATE, SODIUM. See Sodium Carbonate.

CARBOXYMETHYLCELLULOSE. See Sodium Carboxymethyl Cellulose. GRAS for packaging.

CARDAMOM. Grains of Paradise. A natural flavoring agent from the dried ripe seeds of trees common to India, Ceylon, and Guatemala. Used in butter, chocolate, liquor, spice, and vanilla flavorings for beverages, ice cream, ices, candy, baked goods (1,700 ppm), meats, and condiments (900). The seed *oil* is used in chocolate, cocoa, coffee, cherry, liquor, liver, sausage, root beer, sarsaparilla, cardamom, ginger ale, vanilla, and cream soda flavorings for beverages, ice cream, candy, baked goods, meats, chewing gum, condiments, liquors, pickles, and curry powder. It is a mild carminative (breaks up intestinal gas). No known toxicity.

CARMINE. Cochineal.   A crimson pigment derived from a Mexican species of scale insect (*Coccus cacti*) that feeds on various species of cacti. The dye is used in red apple sauce, confections, baked goods, meats, and spices. It was involved in an outbreak of salmonellosis (an intestinal infection), which killed one infant in a Boston hospital, and made twenty-two other patients seriously ill. Carmine, used in the diagnostic solution to test the digestive organs, was found to be the infecting agent. Also used as a lake (*see* FD and C Lakes).

CARMINIC ACID. Natural Red 4.   Coloring matter, the essential constituent of carmine (*see*). Used in color photography and as a pigment for artists; also as a bacterial stain and for coloring food products. Not subject to certification of dye batch by the FDA.

CARNAUBA WAX.   A candy glaze and polish from the dried exudate of the leaves and buds of a South American palm tree. The crude wax is yellow or dirty green, brittle, and very hard. It is used in many polishes and varnishes, and when mixed with other waxes, makes them harder and gives them more luster. Used in cosmetic materials such as depilatories and deodorant sticks; in the last stage in tablet coating. On the FDA list for further study for mutagenic, teratogenic, subacute, and reproductive effects. Skin sensitization or irritation seems infrequent.

CAROB BEAN.   See Gum, Carob Bean.

CAROTENE. Provitamin A Beta Carotene.   Found in all plants and in many animal tissues, it is the chief yellow coloring matter of carrots, butter, and egg yolk. Extracted as red crystals or crystalline powder, it is used as a vegetable dye in butter, margarine, shortening, skimmed milk, buttermilk, and cottage cheese. It is also used to manufacture Vitamin A and is a nutrient added to skimmed milk, vegetable shortening, and margarine at the rate of 5,000 to 13,000 USP units per pound. Insoluble in water, acids, and alkalies. Too much carotene in the blood (exceeding 200 micrograms per 100 milliliters of blood) can lead to carotinemia—a pale yellow-red pigmentation of the skin that may be mistaken for jaundice. It is a benign condition and withdrawal of carotene from the diet cures it.

CARRAGEENAN CHONDRUS EXTRACT. Irish moss derivative. Seaweedlike odor; gluey, salty taste. Used as a stabilizer and emulsifier in chocolate products, chocolate-flavored drinks, chocolate milk, gassed cream (pressure-dispensed, whipped), syrups for frozen products, confections, evaporated milk, cheese spreads and cheese foods, ice cream, frozen custard, sherbets, ices, French dressing, artificially sweetened jellies and jams. Completely soluble in hot water and not coagulated by acids. Salts of carrageenan, an extract of Irish moss, a mixture of 2 or more of the ammonium, calcium, potassium, or sodium salts, are used in beverages, baked goods, puddings, jelly, and syrups and are used also as a demulcent to soothe mucous membrane irritation. The use of Irish moss in food and medicine has been known in Ireland for hundreds of years. Its use in the United States began in 1835, but really became common during World War II as a replacement for Japanese Isinglass (Agar-Agar). Sodium Carrageenan is on the FDA list for further study for mutagenic, teratogenic, subacute, and reproductive effects. GRAS

CARROT OIL. A natural flavoring. The volatile oil is obtained by steam distillation from the crushed seeds of a widely cultivated plant. Light yellow to amber liquid, with a pleasant odor. Used in violet, fruit, rum, and spice flavorings for beverages, ice cream, ices, candy, baked goods, gelatin desserts, puddings, condiments, and soups. Nontoxic. GRAS

CARVACROL. A colorless to pale yellow liquid with a pungent, spicy odor, related to thymol, but more toxic. It is found naturally in oil of origanum, dittany of crete oil, oregano, lovage oil, marjoram, and savory. It is a synthetic flavoring used in citrus, fruit, mint, and spice flavorings for beverages, ice cream, ices, candy, baked goods, and condiments. It is used as a disinfectant and is corrosive; one gram by mouth can cause respiratory and circulatory depression and cardiac failure leading to death.

CARVACRYL ETHYL ETHER. A synthetic spice flavoring agent for beverages, ice cream, ices, candy, and baked goods. No known toxicity.

CARVEOL. A synthetic mint, spearmint, spice, and caraway, flavoring agent for beverages, ice cream, ices, candy, and baked goods. Found naturally in caraway and grapefruit. No known toxicity.

CARVOL. See *d-* or *l-*Carvone.

4-CARVOMENTHENOL. A synthetic citrus and spice flavoring agent for beverages, ice cream, ices, candy, and baked goods. Occurs naturally in cardamom oil, juniper berries. No known toxicity.

d- or l-CARVONE (CARVOL). *d-*Carvone is usually prepared by distillation from caraway seed and dillseed oil. It is colorless to light yellow, with an odor of caraway. *l-*Carvone occurs in several essential oils. It may be isolated from spearmint oil or synthesized commercially from *d-*limonene. It is a colorless to pale yellow, with the odor of spearmint. Carvol is a synthetic liquor, mint, and spice flavoring agent for beverages, ice cream, ices, candy, baked goods, and liqueur. Used also in perfumery and soaps. No known toxicity. GRAS

CARVYL ACETATE. A synthetic mint flavoring agent for beverages, ice cream, ices, candy, and baked goods. No known toxicity.

CARVYL PROPIONATE. A synthetic mint flavoring agent for beverages, ice cream, ices, candy, and baked goods. No known toxicity.

CARYOPHYLLENE ACETATE. A general fixative that occurs in many essential oils, especially in clove oil. Colorless, oily, with a clovelike odor. Used in beverages, ice cream, ices, candy, baked goods, and chewing gum. Practically insoluble in alcohol. No known toxicity.

β-CARYOPHYLLENE. A synthetic spice flavoring. Occurs naturally in cloves, black currant buds, yarrow herb, grapefruit, allspice, and black pepper. The liquid smells like oil of cloves and turpentine. Used for beverages, ice cream, ices, candy, baked goods, chewing gum, and condiments. No known toxicity.

CARYOPHYLLENE ALCOHOL. A flavoring that occurs in many essential oils, especially in clove oil. Colorless, oily, with a clovelike odor. Used as a synthetic mushroom flavoring for baked goods and condiments. No known toxicity.

CASCARA, BITTERLESS EXTRACT. A natural flavoring derived from the dried bark of a plant grown from northern Idaho to northern California. Used in butter, caramel, maple, and vanilla flavorings for beverages, ice cream, ices, and baked goods. Also used as a laxative. The freshly dried bark causes vomiting, and must be dried for a year before use, when the side effect has disappeared. It has a bitter taste and its laxative effect is due to its ability to irritate the mucosa of the large intestine.

CASCARILLA BARK. A natural flavoring agent obtained from the bark of a tree grown in Haiti, the Bahamas, and Cuba. The dried bark extract is added to smoking tobacco for flavoring and used in bitters and spice flavorings for beverages. The *oil*, obtained by distillation, is light yellow to amber, with a spicy odor. It is used in cola, fruit, root beer, and spice flavorings for beverages, ice cream, ices, candy, baked goods, and condiments. Cascarilla has no known toxicity. GRAS

CASEIN. Ammonium Caseinate. Calcium Caseinate. Potassium Caseinate, Sodium Caseinate. The principal protein of cow's milk, without odor or taste. Used as a texturizer for ice cream, frozen custard, ice milk, fruit sherbets, and in special diet preparations. Also used in the manufacture of plastic, adhesives, and paints. Nontoxic. GRAS for packaging only.

CASHOO EXTRACT. See Catechu Extract.

CASSIA. A flavoring from a tropical Asian tree used in bitters, fruit, liquor, meat, root beer, sarsaparilla, and spice flavorings for beverages, ice cream, candy, and baked goods (3,000 ppm). No known toxicity.

CASSIA BARK. Padang or Batavia. GRAS. See Cassia Bark, Chinese.

CASSIA BARK, CHINESE. A natural flavoring extract from cultivated trees. Used in cola, root beer, and spice flavorings for beverages, ice cream, ices, candy, and baked goods. The bark *oil* is used in berry, butter, chocolate, lemon, coffee, cola, cherry, peach, rum, peppermint, pecan, root beer, cassia, ginger ale, and cinnamon flavorings for beverages, ice cream, ices, baked goods, chewing gum, meats, and condiments. The *buds* are used in spice flavorings for beverages. Cassia bark can cause inflammation and erosion of the gastrointestinal tract. GRAS

CASSIE, ABSOLUTE. A natural flavoring from the flowers of the acacia plant. Used in blackberry, violet, vermouth, and fruit flavorings for beverages, ice cream, ices, candy, baked goods, and gelatin desserts. No known toxicity.

CASSIS. See Currant Buds, Absolute.

CASTOR OIL. A flavoring, pale yellow and viscous, obtained from castor oil plant seeds. Slightly acrid, sometimes nauseating taste. Used in butter and nut flavorings for beverages, ice cream, ices, candy, and baked goods. Also a release and anti-sticking agent in hard candy products. The raw material is a constituent of embalming fluid, a cathartic, and a topical emollient. It can produce pelvic congestion and induce abortions.

CASTOREUM EXTRACT. A natural plant extract used in gooseberry, raspberry, tutti-frutti, rum, wine, black walnut, and vanilla flavorings for beverages, ices, ice cream, candy, chewing gum, condiments, and toppings. The *liquid* is used in loganberry, raspberry, orange, balsam, rose, violet, cherry, grape, honey, rum, muscatel, whiskey, and vanilla flavorings for beverages, ice cream, ices, candy, baked goods, gelatin desserts, chewing gum, and toppings. No known toxicity. GRAS

CATALASE. An enzyme from bovine liver used in milk, for making cheese, and for the elimination of peroxide. It is used also in combination with glucose oxidase for treatment of food wrappers to prevent oxidative deterioration of food.

CATECHU EXTRACT. Black Cutch Extract. Cachou Extract. Cashoo Extract. Pegu Catechu Extract. Flavoring extract prepared from the heartwood of acacia catechu (*see* Acacia) grown in India, Hindustan, Ceylon, and Jamaica. Used in bitters, fruit, and drum flavorings for beverages, ice cream, ices, candy, baked goods, and chewing gum. Used also for staining wood and dyeing fabrics. The *powder* is used in fruit, rum, and spice flavorings for beverages, ice cream, candy, baked goods, and chewing gum. Incompatible with iron compounds, gelatin, lime water, and zinc sulfate. Catechu has been used as an astringent in diarrhea. No known toxicity.

CAYENNE PEPPER. Pepper, Red. A condiment made from the pungent fruit of the plant. Used in sausage and pepper flavorings for beverages, ice cream, ices, candy, condiments, meats (910 ppm), and soups. Reported to retard growth of Mexicans and South Americans and Spanish who eat a great deal of these peppers. Rats fed the ingredient of pepper, a reddish-brown liquid called capsaicin, used in flavoring vinegar and pickles, were stunted in growth.

CEDAR LEAF OIL. The volatile oil is a natural flavoring obtained by steam distillation from the fresh leaves of a variety of evergreen trees. It is a colorless to yellow liquid, with a sagelike odor. Used in fruit and spice flavorings for beverages, ice cream, ices, candy, baked goods, meats, and liquors. Has been used to produce abortion, sometimes with fatal results. Similar toxicity to camphor (*see*). May cause sensitivity to light.

CEDRO OIL. See Lemon Oil.

CELERY SEED. A yellowish to greenish brown liquid, having a pleasant aromatic odor, distilled from the dried ripe fruit of the plant grown in southern Europe. *Celery seed* is used in sausage and celery flavorings for beverages (1,000 ppm), baked goods, condiments (2,500 ppm), soups, meats, and pickles. *Celery seed extract* is used in celery, meat, and spice flavorings for beverages, ice cream, ices, candy, baked goods (1,900 ppm), condiments, meats, and soups. *Celery seed solid extract* is used in celery, maple, meat, and spice flavorings for beverages, candy, baked goods, condiments, and maple syrup. *Celery seed oil* is used in fruit, honey, maple, sausage, nut, root beer, spice, vanilla, and cream soda flavorings for beverages, ice cream, ices, candy, baked goods, chewing gum, condiments, meats, soups, and pickles. Celery seed may cause a sensitivity to light. GRAS

CELLULOSE ACETATE. Obtained by treating cellulose with a food starch modifier, it is insoluble in water, alcohol, and ether. Used in the manufacture of rubber and celluloid substitutes, airplane dopes, varnishes, and lacquer. No known toxicity. GRAS in packaging only.

CETONE D. See Methyl β-Naphthyl Ketone.

CETONE V. See Allyl α-Ionone.

CETYL ALCOHOL. See 1-Hexadeconal.

CETYLIC ACID. See Palmitic Acid.

CEYLON CINNAMON. See Cinnamon.

CEYLON CINNAMON LEAF OIL. See Cinnamon Leaf Oil.

CHAMOMILE. Camomile. Roman, English, or Hungarian flowers; English chamomile *oil* is used as a natural flavoring in chocolate, fruit, and liquor flavorings for beverages, ice cream, ices, candy, and baked goods. Roman chamomile *extract* is a natural flavoring in berry, fruit, vermouth, maple, spice, and vanilla flavorings for the same foods as above. Roman chamomile *oil* is used in chocolate, fruit, vermouth, and spice flavorings for beverages, ice cream, ices, candy, baked goods, gelatin desserts, and liquors. Hungarian chamomile *oil* is used in chocolate, fruit, and liquor flavorings for beverages, ice cream, ices, candy, baked goods, chewing gum, and liquors. Chamomile may cause vomiting. GRAS

CHECKERBERRY EXTRACT. See Wintergreen.

CHECKERBERRY OIL. See Wintergreen.

CHERRY LAUREL OIL. A fruit and nut flavoring from the cultivated European shrub. Used in baked goods, Maraschino cherries, and extracts.

CHERRY BARK (WILD) EXTRACT. A natural flavoring extracted from a variety of cherry trees and used in berry, chocolate, cola, cherry, peach, wild cherry, liquor, nut, root beer, and vanilla flavorings for beverages, ice cream, ices, candy, baked goods, gelatin desserts, puddings, syrups, and liquors (800 ppm). No known toxicity.

CHERRY PIT EXTRACT. A natural flavoring extracted from the pits of sweet and sour cherries used in cherry flavoring for beverages, ice cream, and ices. No known toxicity.

CHERVIL. A natural flavoring extracted from an aromatic Eurasian plant and used in spice flavorings for beverages, ice cream, ices, baked goods, and condiments. No known toxicity. GRAS

CHICLE. The gummy, milky resin obtained from trees grown in Mexico and Central America. Rubberlike and quite soft at moderate temperatures. Used in the manufacture of chewing gum, insulation, and waterproofing. No known toxicity.

CHICORY EXTRACT. A natural flavor extract from a plant, usually with blue flowers and leaves. Used in butter, caramel, chocolate, coffee, maple, nut, root beer, sarsaparilla, vanilla, wintergreen, and birch beer flavorings for beverages, ice cream, candy, and baked goods. The root of the plant is dried, roasted, and ground for mixing with coffee. No known toxicity.

CHILTE. A chewing gum base component of vegetable origin. No known toxicity.

CHINA BARK EXTRACT. See Quillaja.

CHINESE CINNAMON. See Cinnamon.

CHINESE CINNAMON LEAF OIL. See Cinnamon Leaf Oil.

CHIVES. A member of the onion family, native to Eurasia. The leaves are used for a seasoning. No known toxicity. GRAS

CHLORINE GAS. Flour bleaching agent and an aging and oxidizing agent. Also used in water purification. Found in the earth's crust, it is a greenish yellow gas with a suffocating odor. A powerful irritant, dangerous to inhale, and lethal. 30 ppm will cause coughing. *CHLORINE DIOXIDE.* Flour bleacher and oxidizing agent. A yellow to reddish yellow gas, with an unpleasant odor, highly irritating and corrosive to the skin and mucous membranes of respiratory tract. Reacts violently with organic materials. It can kill. *CHLORITE.* See Calcium Hypochlorite.

CHLOROPHYLL. The green coloring matter of plants which plays an essential part in the photosynthesis process. It imparts a greenish color to certain fats and oils, notably olive and soybean oils. Most of the green coloring is removed during the processing of oils. No known toxicity.

CHLORTETRACYCLINE. Aoreomycin. Biomycin. Biomitsin. A preservative, an antibiotic, used in a dip for uncooked poultry. One of the reasons for increased resistance to antibiotics in patients is believed to be the widespread use of antibiotics in food animals. In 1969, the British restricted the veterinary use of antibiotics. In 1972, an FDA appointed committee to study the use of antibiotics in animals recommended curbs on use. Many strains of bacteria are now known to be resistant to tetracycline. The use of this antibiotic has caused permanent discoloration of the permanent teeth in children given the drug prior to the eruption of their second teeth. The drug can also cause skin rash, gastrointestinal upsets, and inflammations in the ano-genital area.

CHOLIC ACID. A colorless or white crystalline powder that occurs in the bile of most vertebrates and is used as an emulsifying agent in dried egg whites and as a choleretic to regulate the secretion of bile. Bitter taste; sweetish aftertaste. No known toxicity. GRAS

CHOLINE BITARTRATE. A dietary supplement included in the B complex and found in the form of a thick syrupy liquid in most animal tissue. It is necessary to nerve function and fat metabolism and can be manufactured in the body but not at a sufficient rate to meet health requirements. Dietary choline protects against poor growth, fatty liver, and renal damage in many animals. Choline deficiency has not been demonstrated in man but the National Academy of Sciences lists 500 to 900 mg per day as sufficient for the average man. GRAS

CHOLINE CHLORIDE. Ferric Choline Citrate. A dietary supplement with the same function as Choline Bitartrate (*see*). GRAS

CINCHONA BARK, RED. A natural flavoring from the bark of a South American tree used in bitters, fruit, rum, vermouth, and spice flavorings for beverages, ice cream, ices, candy, liquors, and bitters (1,000 ppm). Yellow cinchona bark is a natural flavoring from the bark of a species of South American tree used in bitters, fruit, and vermouth flavorings for liquors and bitters. The yellow *extract* is used as a bitters flavoring for beverages. Cinchona is grown also in Java and India and at one time was used as an antimalarial. May rarely cause allergies.

CINENE. See *d*-Limonene.

CINEOLE. See Eucalyptol.

CINNAMAL. See Cinnamaldehyde.

CINNAMALDEHYDE. Cinnamic Aldehyde. A flavoring, a yellowish oily liquid with a strong odor of cinnamon, the chief ingredient of the oil of cinnamon. Found naturally in cassia bark, cinnamon bark, and cinnamon root. Used in cola, apple, cherry, liquor, rum, nut, pecan, spice, cinnamon, vanilla, and cream soda flavorings for beverages, ice cream, ices, candy, baked goods, chewing gum (4,900 ppm), condiments, and meats. Also used in perfume industry. An irritant, especially in undiluted form. Can cause inflammation and erosion of gastrointestinal tract. GRAS.

CINNAMALDEHYDE ETHYLENE GLYCOL ACETAL. Cinncloval. Spice, cassia, cinnamon, and clove flavorings for beverages, ice cream, ices, candy, baked goods, and condiments. See Cinnamaldehyde for toxicity.

CINNAMEIN. See Benzyl Cinnamate.

CINNAMIC ACID. A cherry, honey, spice, cassia, and cinnamon flavoring agent for beverages, ice cream, ices, candy, baked goods, and chewing gum. Occurs naturally in cassia bark, strawberries, and vanilla. Used medicinally to combat intestinal worms. Main use is in the perfume industry. No known toxicity.

CINNAMIC ALCOHOL. See Cinnamyl Alcohol.

CINNAMIC ALDEHYDE. See Cinnamaldehyde.

CINNAMON (CEYLON, CHINESE, SAIGON). Dried bark of cultivated trees. Used in bitters, cola, apple, plum, vermouth, sausage, eggnog, cinnamon, and vanilla flavorings for beverages, ices, ice cream, candy (4,000 ppm), baked goods (1,900 ppm), condiments, meats, and apple butter. Used to break up intestinal gas and as an antidiarrheal. See Cinnamaldehyde for toxicity. GRAS

CINNAMON BARK. Extract and Oil. From the dried bark of cultivated trees. The *extract* is used in cola, eggnog, root beer, cinnamon, and ginger ale for beverages, ice cream, baked goods, condiments, and meats. The *oil* is used in berry, cola, cherry, rum, root beer, cinnamon, and ginger ale flavorings for beverages, condiments, and meats. No known toxicity. GRAS

CINNAMON LEAF OIL. A volatile oil obtained by steam distillation from cinnamon leaves. Used in cola, apricot, rum, root beer, cinnamon, and ginger ale flavorings for beverages, ice cream, ices, candy, baked goods, chewing gum, gelatin desserts, condiments, pickles, and sliced fruits. No known toxicity.

CINNAMYL ACETATE. A synthetic flavoring, colorless to slightly yellow, liquid, with a sweet floral odor. Occurs naturally in cassia bark. Used in berry, apple, apricot, cherry, grape, peach, pineapple, cinnamon, and vanilla flavorings for beverages, ice cream, ices, candy, baked goods, condiments, and chewing gum. No known toxicity.

CINNAMYL ALCOHOL. A synthetic flavoring, white to slightly yellow, liquid, with a balsamic odor. Occurs naturally in storax, balsam Peru, and cinnamon leaves. Used in raspberry, strawberry, apricot, peach, plum, prune, grape, liquor, brandy, nut, black walnut, spice, and cinnamon flavorings for beverages, ice cream, candy, baked goods, chewing gum, gelatin desserts, and brandy. Also used in perfumery and as a deodorant. No known toxicity.

CINNAMYL ANTHRANILATE. A synthetic flavoring, reddish yellow powder with a fruity taste. Used in cherry, grape, honey, and vanilla flavorings for beverages, ice cream, ices, candy, baked goods, gelatin desserts, and chewing gum. No known toxicity.

CINNAMYL BENZOATE. A synthetic butter, caramel, and fruit flavoring agent for beverages, ice cream, ices, candy, baked goods, condiments, and chewing gum. No known toxicity.

CINNAMYL BUTYRATE. A synthetic citrus, orange, and fruit flavoring agent for beverages, ice cream, ices, candy, baked goods, and gelatin desserts. No known toxicity.

CINNAMYL CINNAMATE. A synthetic fruit flavoring agent for beverages, ice cream, ices, candy, and baked goods. No known toxicity.

CINNAMYL FORMATE. Formic Acid. A synthetic flavoring, color-less to yellow liquid, with a faint cinnamon odor. Used in banana, cherry, pear, and spice flavorings for beverages, ice cream, ices, candy, baked goods, and chewing gum. See Formic Acid for toxicity.

CINNAMYL ISOBUTYRATE. A synthetic strawberry, citrus, apple, banana, grape, peach, pear, and pineapple flavoring agent for bev-erages, ice cream, ices, candy, baked goods, gelatin desserts, chewing gum, and toppings. No known toxicity.

CINNAMYL ISOVALERATE. A synthetic flavoring, colorless to yel-low liquid, with a spicy, fruity, floral odor. Used in strawberry, choco-late, apple, apricot, cherry, grape, maple, nut, spice, peach, pineapple, and plum flavorings for beverages, ice cream, ices, candy, baked goods, gelatin desserts and chewing gum. No known toxicity.

CINNAMYL PHENYLACETATE. A synthetic chocolate, honey, and spice flavoring agent for beverages, ice cream, ices, candy, and baked goods. No known toxicity.

CINNAMMYL PROPIONATE. A synthetic flavoring, colorless to yellow liquid, with a fruity-floral odor. Used in berry, apple, choco-late, currant, grape, peach, pear, and pineapple flavorings for bev-erages, ice cream, ices, candy, baked goods, gelatin desserts, and chewing gum. No known toxicity.

CINNCLOVAL. See Cinnamaldehyde Ethylene Glycol Acetal.

CIRE D'ABEILLE, ABSOLUTE. See Beeswax, Bleached.

CITRAL. A flavoring agent, light, oily, with a strong lemon odor. Occurs naturally in grapefruit, orange, peach, ginger, oil of lemon, oil of lime. Either isolated from citral oils or made synthetically. Used in strawberry, lemon, lime, orange, apple, cherry, grape, spice, ginger, and vanilla flavorings for beverages, ice cream, ices, candy, baked goods, and chewing gum. Used also in the synthesis of Vitamin A. Causes discoloration of white soaps. No known toxicity. GRAS

CITRAL DIEMETHYL ACETAL. A synthetic citrus, lemon, and fruit flavoring agent for beverages, ice cream, ices, candy, fruit, and chewing gum. No known toxicity.

CITRAL DIETHYL ACETAL. A synthetic citrus flavoring agent for beverages, ice cream, ices, candy, and condiments. No known toxicity.

CITRATE, CALCIUM. See Calcium Citrate.

CITRATE, ISOPROPYL. See Isopropyl Citrate.

CITRATE SALTS. Softening agents for cheese spreads; emulsifier salts to blend pasteurized processed cheeses and cheese foods. Citrates may interfere with the results of laboratory tests including tests for pancreatic function, abnormal liver function, and blood alkalinity-acidity.

CITRATE, SODIUM. See Sodium Citrate.

CITRATE, MONOGLYCERIDE. See Monoglyceride Citrate.

CITRATE, STEARYL. See Stearyl Citrate.

CITRIC ACID. One of the most varied additives. Used in the United States for nearly a century. Colorless or white, with a strong acid taste. Widely distributed in plant and animal tissues and fluids, it is produced commercially from the fermentation of crude sugars. It is also extracted from citrus fruits and occurs naturally in coffee and peaches. It is a fruit flavoring for beverages (2,500 ppm), ice cream, ices, candy (4,300 ppm), baked goods, and chewing gum (3,600 ppm.). Citric acid is used to neutralize lye employed in peeling vegetables, as an adjuster of acid-alkalinity in fruit juices, wines, jams, jellies, jelly candies, canned fruit, carbonated beverages, frozen fruit, canned vegetables, frozen dairy products, cheese spreads, sherbet, confections, canned figs, dried egg white, mayonnaise, salad dressing, fruit butter, preserves, and fresh beef blood. Employed in curing meats, for firming peppers, potatoes, tomatoes, and lima beans and to prevent off-flavors in fried potatoes. Removes trace metals and brightens color in various commercial products. It has also been used to dissolve urinary bladder stones, and as a mild astringent. No known toxicity. GRAS

CITRIDIC ACID. See Aconitic Acid.

CITROFLEX A-4. See Tributyl Acetylcitrate.

CITRONELLA OIL. A natural flavoring extract from fresh grass grown in Ceylon. It consists of about 60 percent geraniol (*see*), 15 percent citronellol (*see*) and 10 to 15 percent camphene (*see*). Almost colorless, with a pleasant odor. Used in citrus, fruit, and ginger ale flavorings for beverages, ice cream, ices, candy, and baked goods. Has been used in perfumes and as an insect repellent. Can cause vomiting when ingested, cyanosis, convulsions, damage to intestinal mucosa and, when taken in sufficient amounts, death.

CITRONELLAL. A synthetic flavoring agent. The chief constituent of citronella oil (*see*). Also found in lemon and lemon grass oils. Colorless, liquid, with an intense lemon-rose odor. Used in citrus, lemon, fruit, cherry, and spice flavorings for beverages, ice cream, ices, candy, baked goods, gelatin desserts, and chewing gum. A mild irritant. See Citronella Oil for toxicity.

CITRONELLOL. A synthetic flavoring. Obtained from citronellal or geraniol, geranium rose oil, or citronella oil (*see all*). Colorless, liquid, with a roselike odor. The *d* form is more oily and is the major ingredient of rhodinol (*see*). Used in berry, citrus, cola, fruit, rose, and floral flavorings for beverages, ice cream, ices, candy, baked goods, gelatin desserts, and chewing gum. See Citronella Oil for toxicity.

CITRONELLOXY ACETALDEHYDE. A synthetic floral, rose, and fruit flavoring agent for beverages, ice cream, ices, candy, and baked goods. See Citronella Oil for toxicity.

CITRONELLYL ACETATE. A synthetic flavoring agent, colorless liquid, with a fruity odor. Used in lemon, rose, apricot, banana, grape, pear, and raisin flavorings for beverages, ice cream, ices, candy, baked goods, gelatin desserts, and chewing gum. A major ingredient of rhodinyl acetate (*see*). No known toxicity.

CITRONELLYL BUTYRATE. A synthetic flavoring, colorless, liquid, with a strong fruit-rose odor. Used in cola, floral, rose, apple, pineapple, plum, prune, and honey flavorings for beverages, ice cream, ices, candy, baked goods, gelatin desserts, and chewing gum. A major ingredient of rhodinyl butyrate (*see*). No known toxicity.

CITRONELLYL FORMATE. Formic Acid. A synthetic flavoring, colorless liquid, with a strong fruity odor. Used in orange, apple, apricot, peach, plum and honey flavorings for beverages, ice cream, ices, candy, baked goods, and chewing gum. A major ingredient of rhodinyl formate (*see*). See Formic Acid for toxicity.

CITRONELLYL ISOBUTYRATE. A synthetic flavoring, colorless liquid, with a rose-fruit odor. Used in raspberry, strawberry, floral, rose and grape flavorings for beverages, ice cream, ices, candy, baked goods, and gelatin desserts. A major ingredient of rhodinyl isobutyrate (*see*). No known toxicity.

CITRONELLYL PHENYLACETATE. A synthetic butter, caramel, rose, fruit, and honey flavoring agent for beverages, ice cream, ices, candy, and baked goods. A major ingredient of rhodinyl phenylacetate (*see*). No known toxicity.

CITRONELLYL PROPIONATE. A synthetic flavoring, colorless liquid, with a rose-fruit odor. Used in lemon and fruit flavorings for beverages, ice cream, ices, candy, baked goods, and chewing gum. A major ingredient of rhodinyl propionate (*see*). No known toxicity.

CITRONELLYL VALERATE. A synthetic fruit flavoring used in beverages, ice cream, ices, candy, and baked goods. No known toxicity.

CITRUS BIOFLAVONOIDS. Vitamin P complex, a nutrient supplement up to one gram per day. Occurs naturally in plant coloring and in the tonka bean; also in lemon juice. High concentrates can be obtained from all citrus fruits, rose hips, and black currants. Commercial methods extract rinds of oranges, tangerines, lemons, limes, kumquats, and grapefruits. P Vitamin is related to healthy blood vessels and skin. At one time it was thought to prevent colds.

CITRUS PEEL EXTRACT. A natural flavor extract from citrus fruits used in bitters, lemon, lime, orange, vermouth, beer, and ginger ale flavorings for beverages, ice cream, ices, candy, and baked goods. No known toxicity. GRAS

CITRUS RED NO. 2. Monoazo. Used only for coloring orange skins that are *not* intended for processing, and that meet minimum maturity standards established by or under laws of the states in which the oranges are grown. Oranges colored with Citrus Red No. 2 are not supposed to bear more than 2 ppm of the color additive calculated on the weight of the whole fruit. Citrus Red No. 2 toxicity is far from determined even though, theoretically, consumers would not ingest the dye because they peel the orange before eating. The 2-naphthol constituent of the dye if ingested in quantity can cause eye lens clouding, kidney damage, vomiting, and circulatory collapse. Application to the skin can cause peeling, and deaths have been reported after application to the skin. See FD and C Colors.

CIVET, ABSOLUTE. Flavoring derived from the unctuous secretion from the receptacles between the anus and genitalia of both male and female civet cats. Semisolid, yellowish to brown, with an unpleasant, acrid, bitter taste. Used in raspberry, butter, caramel, grape, and rum flavorings for beverages, ice cream, ices, candy, baked goods, gelatin desserts, and chewing gum. A fixative in perfumery. No known toxicity.

CLARIFICATION. Removal from liquid of small amounts of suspended matter, for example, the removal of particles and traces of copper and iron from vinegar and certain beverages.

CLARY. Clary Sage. A natural extract of an aromatic herb grown in Southern Europe and cultivated widely in England. The herb is a vermouth and spice flavoring agent in vermouth (500 ppm). Clary *oil* is used in butter, black cherry, grape, licorice, vermouth, wine, root beer, birch beer, spice, vanilla, and cream soda flavorings for beverages, ice cream, ices, candy, baked goods, condiments, and vermouth. No known toxicity. GRAS

CLAY. Kaolin. China Clay. Used to clarify liquids (see Clarification) and as a filler for paper. Also used in the manufacture of porcelain and pottery, as an emollient, and as a poultice and gastrointestinal adsorbent. Nontoxic. GRAS for packaging.

CLOVE BUD EXTRACT. A natural flavor extract from the pungent, fragrant, reddish-brown dried flower buds of a tropical tree. Used in berry, fruit, meat, root beer, and spice flavorings for beverages, ice cream, ices, candy, baked goods, condiments, and meats. Cloves are used also as a dental analgesic and germicide. They may cause intestinal upsets. Rats poisoned with clove oil have shown paralysis of hind legs and jaws, with prostration and eventually death. The FDA has given toxicity studies of clove additives top priority. GRAS

CLOVE BUD OIL. The volatile, colorless or pale yellow oil obtained by steam distillation from the dried flower buds of a tropical tree. A characteristic clove odor and taste. Used in raspberry, coffee, cola, banana, cherry, peach, plum, rum, sausage, eggnog, pecan, root beer flavorings for beverages, ice cream, ices, baked goods, gelatin desserts, chewing gum (1,800 ppm), condiments, meats, liquors, spiced fruit (830 ppm), and jelly. See Clove Bud Extract for toxicity. GRAS

CLOVE BUD OLEORESIN. A natural resinous, viscous flavoring extract from the tree that produces clove buds. Used in fruit, meat, and spice flavorings for meat. See Clove Bud Extract for toxicity.

CLOVE LEAF OIL. The volatile pale yellow oil obtained by steam distillation of the leaves of the tropical tree that produces clove buds. Used in loganberry, cherry, root beer, sarsaparilla, and cinnamon flavorings for beverages, ice cream, ices, candy, baked goods, gelatin desserts, condiments, meats, pickles, and apple butter. See Clove Bud Extract for toxicity. GRAS

CLOVE STEM OIL. The volatile yellow to light brown oil obtained by steam distillation from the dried stems of the tropical tree that produces clove buds. Characteristic odor and taste of cloves. Used in berry, cherry, root beer, ginger ale, and ginger beer flavorings for beverages, ice cream, ices, candy, baked goods, and condiments. See Clove Bud Extract for toxicity. GRAS

CLOVER. An herb, a natural flavoring extract, from a plant characterized by three leaves and flowers in dense heads. Used in fruit flavoring for beverages, ice cream, ices, candy, and baked goods. May cause a sensitivity to light. GRAS

COBALT SOURCES: Carbonate, Chloride, Gluconate, and Sulfate. Cobalt is a metal occurring in the earth's crust. It is gray, hard, and magnetic. All here are used as a mineral supplement at the rate of 1 mg. per day. Excess administration can produce an overproduction of red blood cells plus toxic symptoms in the gastrointestinal tract. GRAS

COBALTOUS SALTS: Acetate, Chloride, and Sulfate. From the metal cobalt (see Cobalt Sources). Used in fermented malt beverages such as beer to prevent foaming or gushing. Ingestion can cause nausea and vomiting. Acts locally on gastrointestinal tract and may cause flushing of face and ears, mild low blood pressure, rash, ringing in the ears, and nerve deafness. Chronic administration of cobaltous salts has produced goiter and affected thyroid activity. During 1965 and 1966, there appeared to be an epidemic among apparently healthy Canadian, American, and Belgian men in their mid-forties who suddenly dropped dead. Autopsies showed they had a peculiar destruction of their heart muscle, which was traced to the cobalt added to beer.

COCA LEAF EXTRACT. Decocainized. Flavoring from the dried leaves of cocaine-containing plants grown in Bolivia, Brazil, Peru, and Java. Used in bitters and cola flavoring for beverages, ice, ice cream, and candy. Once a central nervous system stimulant. No known toxicity. GRAS

COCHINEAL. See Carmine.

COCONUT OIL. Refined. A white semisolid highly saturated fat expressed from the kernels of the coconut palm. Used in chocolate, candies, in baking, instead of lard, and in self-basting turkeys. Believed to be a precursor of hardening of the arteries. No known toxicity.

COGNAC OIL. Wine Yeast Oil. The volatile oil obtained from distillation of wine, with the characteristic aroma of cognac. *Green*

cognac oil is used as a flavoring for beverages, ice cream, candy, baked goods, chewing gum, condiments, liquors. *White cognac oil,* which has the same constituents as green oil, is used in berry, cherry, grape, brandy, and rum flavorings for beverages, ice cream, ices, candy, baked goods, and gelatin desserts. No known toxicity. GRAS

COLLOIDAL SILICON DIOXIDE. Practically insoluble in water. A free-flowing agent in salt, seasoned salt, and sodium bicarbonate. Also included in vitamin products, dietary products, spices, meat-curing compounds, flavoring powders, dehydrated honey, dehydrated molasses, and dehydrated nondiastatic malt. Percentages range from 1 percent in salt, to 2 percent in dehydrated products. Prolonged inhalation of the silicon dust can cause fibrosis of the lungs. Increases susceptibility to tuberculosis. Chemically and biologically inert when ingested. See Silicon Dioxide.

COPPER. One of the earliest known metals. Used as a mineral supplement. An essential nutrient for all mammals. Naturally occurring or experimentally produced copper deficiency in animals leads to a variety of abnormalities, including anemia, skeletal defects, and muscle degeneration. Copper deficiency is extremely rare in man. The body of an adult contains from 75 to 150 mg of copper. Concentrations are highest in the brain and liver and heart. A copper intake of 2 mg per day appears to maintain a balance in adults. An ordinary diet provides 2 to 5 mg daily. Copper itself is nontoxic, but soluble copper salts, notably copper sulfate, are highly irritating to the skin and mucous membranes and cause serious vomiting. Copper salts include copper carbonate, chloride, gluconate, hydroxide, orthophosphate, oxide, pyrophosphate, and sulfate. GRAS

CORLANDER. Coriander. The dried ripe fruit of a plant grown in Asia and Europe. Colorless or pale yellow liquid with the characteristic odor and taste of coriander. Used as a natural flavoring agent in raspberry, bitters, fruit, meat, spice, and ginger ale and vanilla flavorings for beverages, ice cream, candy, baked goods (880 ppm), condiments, meats (1,300 ppm), and liquors (1,000 ppm). The *oil* is used in blackberry, raspberry, chocolate, coffee, cola, fruit, liquor, sausage, root beer, spice, ginger ale and vanilla flavorings for beverages, ice cream, ices, candy, baked goods, chewing gum, condiments, meats, and liquors. Corlander is used as a weak medication (up to 1 gram) to break up intestinal gas. No known toxicity. GRAS

CORN DEXTRIN®. Dextri-Maltose. A white or yellow powder obtained by enzymatic action of barley malt on corn flours, and used as a modifier or thickening agent in milk and milk products. Nontoxic. GRAS for packaging only.

CORN SUGAR (CORN SYRUP). Dextrose. Used in maple, nut, and root beer flavorings for beverages, ice cream, ices, candy, and baked goods. Corn syrup is used for envelopes, stamps, sticker tapes, ale, aspirin, bacon, baking mixes, powders, beers, bourbon, breads, breakfast cereals, pastries, candy, carbonated beverages, catsups, cheeses, cereals, chop suey, chow mein, confectioners' sugar, cream puffs, fish products, ginger ale, hams, jellies, processed meats, peanut butters, canned peas, plastic food wrappers, sherbets, whiskeys, and American wines. May cause allergies. GRAS

CORNSTARCH. Many containers are powdered with cornstarch to prevent sticking. The dietetic grade is marketed as Maizena, Mondamin. It is an absorbent dusting powder, and a demulcent for irritated colon. May cause allergic reactions such as inflamed eyes, stuffy nose, and perennial hayfever. GRAS for packaging only.

CORPS PRALINE. See Maltol.

COSTMARY. Virgin Mary. A natural flavoring derived from an herb native to Asia. Its yellow aromatic flowers are shaped like buttons. Used as a pot herb and salad plant. Infrequently used today as a flavoring in beer and ale. Regarded as sacred to the Virgin Mary. No known toxicity.

COSTUS ROOT OIL. The volatile oil obtained by steam distillation from the dried roots of an herb. Light yellow to brown viscous liquid, with a persistent violetlike odor. A natural fruit and vanilla flavoring for beverages, ice cream, ices, candy, baked goods, and gelatin desserts. No known toxicity.

COTTONSEED FLOUR. Cooked, partly defatted and toasted flour used for pale yellow coloring. Sometimes used to make gin. The *oil* is used in most salad oils and oleomargarines and most mayonnaises and salad dressings. Lard compounds and lard substitutes are made with cottonseed oil. Sardines may be packed in it. Most commercial fried products such as potato chips and doughnuts are fried in cottonseed oil, and restaurants almost universally use it for cooking. Candies, particularly chocolates, often contain this oil and it is used to polish fruits at stands. It is known to cause allergies and because it is used in a wide variety of products without notice, it may be hard to avoid.

COTTONSEED OIL. See Cottonseed Flour.

COUCH GRASS. See Dog Grass Extract.

CREAM OF TARTAR. See Tartrate.

CREOSOL. See 2-Methoxy-4-Methylphenol.

p-CRESOL. A synthetic nut and vanilla flavoring agent. Obtained from coal tar. It occurs naturally in tea, and is used in beverages, ice cream, ices, candy, and baked goods. It is more powerful than phenol and less toxic. Phenol is an extremely toxic acid obtained from coal tar which has many industrial uses, including use as a disinfectant for toilets and as an anesthetic.

4-CRESOL. See p-Cresol.

o-CRESYL ACETATE. See o-Tolyl Acetate.

p-CRESYL ACETATE. See p-Tolyl Acetate.

CRETAN DITTANY. See Dittany of Crete.

CROCUS EXTRACT. See Saffron.

CUBEBS. Tailed Pepper. Java Pepper. The mature, unripe, sun-dried fruit of a perennial vine grown in South Asia, Java, Sumatra, the Indies, and Ceylon. It has a strong, spicy odor and is used in fruit flavoring for beverages (800 ppm). The volatile *oil* is obtained by steam distillation from the fruit and is colorless to light green with the characteristic spicy odor and a slightly acrid taste. It is used in berry, fruit, and ginger flavorings for beverages, ice cream, candy, baked goods, condiments, and meats. Java pepper was formerly used to stimulate healing of mucous membranes. The fruit has been used as a stimulant and diuretic and sometimes is smoked in cigarettes. No known toxicity.

CUMALDEHYDE. See Cuminaldehyde.

CUMIN. Cummin. A natural flavoring obtained from the seeds of an Old World plant. Used in spice and sausage flavorings for baked goods (2,500 ppm), condiments (3,900 ppm), and meats. A volatile *oil*, light yellow to brown, with a strong, disagreeable odor, is distilled from the plant. It is used in berry, fruit, sausage, and spice flavorings, for beverages, ice cream, ices, candy, chewing gum, baked goods, condiments, meats, and pickles. No known toxicity. GRAS

CUMINAL. See Cuminaldehyde.

CUMINALDEHYDE. The constituent of eucalyptus, myrrh, cassia, cumin, and other essential oils, it is a synthetic flavoring used in berry, fruit, and spice flavorings for beverages, ice cream, ices, candy, baked goods, chewing gum, and condiments. Used in perfumery. No known toxicity.

CUMINIC ALDEHYDE. See Cuminaldehyde.

CUPRIC CHLORIDE. See Copper.

CUPRIC OXIDE. See Copper.

CUPRIC SULFATE. See Copper.

CUPROUS IODIDE. See Iodine Sources.

CURACAO PEEL EXTRACT. A natural flavoring extracted from a plant native to the Caribbean Island. Used in orange and liquor flavorings for beverages (1,700 ppm). GRAS

CURACAO PEEL OIL. Obtained from the plant and used in berry, lime, orange, and liquor flavorings for beverages, ice cream, ices, candy and baked goods. No known toxicity.

CURRANT BUDS, ABSOLUTE. A natural flavoring from a variety of small raisins grown principally in Greece. Used in fruit, berry, and raspberry flavorings for beverages, ice cream, ices, candy, and baked goods. No known toxicity.

CYANOCOBALAMIN. See Vitamin B_{12}.

CYANODITHIOIMIDOCARBONATE, DISODIUM. Bacteria-killing component in the processing of sugar cane. Many organic cyano compounds are decomposed in the body to yield highly toxic cyanide.

CYCLAMATES. Sodium Cyclamate, and Calcium Cyclamate. Artificial sweetening agents about 30 times as sweet as refined sugar, removed from the market September 1, 1969, because they were found to cause bladder cancer in rats. At the time 175 million Americans weer swallowing cyclamates in significant doses in many products ranging from chewing gum to soft drinks.

CYCLOHEXANEACETIC ACID. A synthetic butter and fruit flavoring agent for beverages, ice cream, ices, candy, and baked goods. Cyclohexane in high concentrations may act as a narcotic and a skin irritant.

CYCLOHEXANEETHYL ACETATE. A synthetic fruit and honey flavoring agent for beverages, ice cream, candy, and baked goods. See Cyclohexaneacetatic Acid for toxicity.

CYCLOHEXYL ANTHRANILATE. A synthetic apple, banana, and grape flavoring agent for beverages, ice cream, ices, candy, baked goods, and gelatin desserts. Some cyclohexyl compounds are irritating to the skin.

CYCLOHEXYL BUTYRATE. A synthetic strawberry, apple, apricot, banana, and peach flavoring agent for beverages, ice cream, ices, candy, baked goods, and gelatin desserts. See Cyclohexyl Anthranilate for toxicity.

CYCLOHEXYL CINNAMATE. A synthetic apple, apricot, peach, and prune flavoring agent for beverages, ice cream, ices, candy, and baked goods. See Cyclohexyl Anthranilate for toxicity.

CYCLOHEXYL FORMATE. Formic Acid. A synthetic cherry flavoring for beverages, ice cream, ices, candy, and baked goods. See Formic Acid and Cyclohexyl Anthranilate for toxicity.

CYCLOHEXYL ISOVALERATE. A synthetic strawberry and apple flavoring agent for beverages, ice cream, ices, candy, and baked goods. See Cyclohexyl Anthranilate for toxicity.

CYCLOHEXYL PROPIONATE. A synthetic fruit flavoring for beverages, ice cream, ices, candy, baked goods, and gelatin desserts. See Cyclohexyl Anthranilate for toxicity.

CYCLOPENTADECANOLIDE. See ω-Pentadecalactone.

CYCLOTENE. See Methylcyclopentenolone.

CYMENE. See p-Cymene.

p-CYMENE. A synthetic flavoring, a volatile hydrocarbon solvent occurring naturally in anise star, coriander, cumin, mace oil, oil of mandarin, and origanum oil. Used in citrus and spice flavorings for beverages, ice cream, ices, candy, baked goods, chewing gum, and condiments. Ingestion may cause a burning sensation in the mouth and stomach, nausea, vomiting, and salivation, headache, giddiness, vertigo, confusion, and coma. Contact with liquid may cause blisters of the skin and inflammation of mucous membranes.

CYMOL. See p-Cymene.

CYMOPHENOL. See Carvacrol.

CYSTEINE. L-form. An essential amino acid (*see*) derived from hair. Soluble in water, used in bakery products as a nutrient. Use allowed up to .009 part for each 100 parts of flour. Has been used to promote wound healing. On the FDA list of additives to be studied. GRAS

CYSTINE. L and DL forms. Nonessential amino acid (*see*) found in urine and in horsehair. Colorless, practically odorless white crystals. Used as a nutrient supplement. On the FDA list for further study. GRAS

D

DANDELION ROOT, EXTRACT. A natural extract from the dandelion plant, cultivated as a lawn weed in North America and native to Eurasia. Dandelion coffee is made from the dried roots of the plant. The *root* extract is used in bitters, butter, caramel, floral, fruit, root beer, and vanilla flavorings for beverages, ice cream, ices, candy, and baked goods. The *fluid* extract is used in butter, caramel, fruit, maple, and vanilla flavorings for beverages, ice cream, ices, candy, and baked goods. There is no known toxicity from ingestion of dandelions.

DAUCUS CAROTA. See Carrot Oil.

DAVANA OIL. A plant extract used in fruit flavoring for beverages, ice cream, ices, candy, baked goods, and chewing gum. No known toxicity.

γ-DECALACTONE. A synthetic flavoring agent, colorless, with a fruity odor, used in citrus, orange, coconut, and fruit flavorings for beverages, ice cream, ices, baked goods, and gelatin desserts. No known toxicity.

δ-DECALACTONE. A synthetic flavoring agent. Occurs naturally in butter, cream, and milk. Colorless, with a fruity odor. Used in coconut and fruit flavorings for beverages, ice cream, ices, candy, baked goods, and toppings. No known toxicity.

DECANAL. A synthetic flavoring agent. Occurs naturally in oranges, sweet orange peel, sweet mandarin oil, grapefruit oil, orris, and coriander. Colorless to light yellow, with a definite fatlike odor that becomes florallike when diluted. Used in berry, citrus, lemon, orange, fruit, and honey flavorings for beverages, ice cream, ices, candy, baked goods, gelatin desserts, and chewing gum. No known toxicity. GRAS

DECANAL DIMETHYL ACETAL. A synthetic citrus, liquor, brandy, and cognac flavoring agent for beverages, ice cream, ices, candy, baked goods, gelatin desserts, puddings, and alcoholic beverages. No known toxicity. GRAS

DECANOIC ACID. A synthetic flavoring agent. Occurs naturally in anise, butter acids, oil of lemon, and oil of lime. Used in butter, coconut, fruit, liquor, whiskey, and cheese flavorings for beverages, ice cream, ices, baked goods, candy, gelatin desserts, puddings, and shortenings. No known toxicity.

1-DECANOL. A synthetic flavoring agent. Occurs naturally in sweet orange and ambrette seed. Used in butter, lemon, orange, coconut, and fruit flavorings for beverages, ice cream, ices, candy, baked goods, and chewing gum. No known toxicity.

DECANYL ACETATE. See Decyl Acetate.

2-DECENAL. A synthetic fruit flavoring for beverages, ice cream, ices, candy, and baked goods. No known toxicity.

DECENALDEHYDE. See 2-Decenal.

DECYL ACETATE. A synthetic berry, orange, apple, peach, plum and honey flavoring agent for beverages, ice cream, ices, candy, baked goods, gelatin desserts, and chewing gum. No known toxicity.

DECYL ALCOHOL. See 1-Decanol.

DECYL BUTYRATE. A synthetic citrus and fruit flavoring agent for beverages, ice cream, ices, candy, and baked goods. No known toxicity.

DECYL PROPIONATE. A synthetic citrus and fruit flavoring agent used in beverages, ice cream, ices, candy, and baked goods. No known toxicity.

DECYLIC ACID. See Decanoic Acid.

DECYLIC ALCOHOL. See 1-Decanol.

DEHYDROACETIC ACID. See Sodium Dehydroacetate.

DEMULCENT. A soothing usually thick oily or creamy substance used to relieve pain in inflamed or irritated mucous surfaces. The gum acacia, for instance, is used as a demulcent.

DESOXYCHOLIC ACID. An emulsifying agent, white, crystalline, powdered, almost insoluble in water. Used in dried egg whites up to .1 percent. No known toxicity. GRAS

DEXTRAN. A term applied to polysaccharides produced by bacteria growing on sugar. Used as a foam stabilizer for beer, in soft-center confections, and as a substitute for barley malt. It has also been used as a plasma expander for emergency treatment of shock. Can cause cancer in rats. GRAS

DEXTRIN. British Gum, Starch Gum. White or yellow powder produced from starch. Used as a foam stabilizer for beer, a diluting agent for dry extracts and pills, in polishing cereals, for preparing emulsions and dry bandages, for thickening industrial dye pastes, and in matches, fireworks, and explosives. No known toxicity. GRAS

DEXTROSE. See Corn Sugar.

DIACETYL. A flavoring agent that occurs naturally in cheese, cocoa, pears, coffee, raspberries, strawberries, angelica root, coffee extract, and cooked chicken, but usually prepared by a special fermentation of glucose. It is a yellowish green liquid. Used as a carrier for aroma of butter, vinegar, and coffee. Also used in blueberry, raspberry, strawberry, butter, buttermilk, butterscotch, caramel, chocolate, coffee, fruit, cheese, cherry, liquor, rum, wine, nut, almond, spice, ginger ale, vanilla, and cream soda flavorings for beverages, ice cream, ices, candy, baked goods, gelatin desserts, chewing gum, and shortening. Cleared by U.S. Department of Agriculture (Meat Inspection Division) to flavor oleomargarine in "amounts sufficient for the purpose." No known toxicity. GRAS

DIACETYL TARTARIC of Monoglycerides and Diglycerides. An emulsifying agent used to improve volume and uniformity in bakery products up to 20 percent by weight of the combination of such a preparation and the shortening. On the FDA list for further study. GRAS

DIALLYL DISULFIDE. See Allyl Disulfide.

DIALLYL SULFIDE. See Allyl Sulfide.

DIASMOL. See 1,3-Nonanediol Acetate (mixed esters).

DIATOMACEOUS EARTH. Kieselguhr. A porous and relatively pure form of silica formed from fossil remains of diatoms—one-celled algae with shells. Inert when ingested. Used in dentifrices, as a clarifying agent, as an absorbent for liquids because it can absorb about four times its weight in water, and for acid-proofing food packaging. The dust can cause lung damage after long exposure to high concentrations. GRAS

DIBENZYL ETHER. A synthetic fruit and spice flavoring agent for beverages, ice cream, ices, candy, baked goods, and chewing gum. No known toxicity.

DIBENZYL KETONE. See 1,3-Diphenyl-2-Propanone.

4,4-DIBUTYL-γ-BUTYROLACTONE. A synthetic butter, coconut, and nut flavoring agent for ice cream, candy, ices, and baked goods. No known toxicity.

DIBUTYL SEBACATE. Sebacic Acid. A synthetic fruit flavoring agent usually obtained from castor oil and used for beverages, ice cream, ices, candy, and baked goods. No known toxicity.

DIBUTYL SULFIDE. See Butyl Sulfide.

DIETHYL PYROCARBONATE (DEP). A fermentation inhibitor in still wines, beer, and orange juice added before or during bottling at a level not to exceed 200 to 500 ppm. DEP has been widely used because it supposedly does its job of preserving and then decomposes within twenty-four hours. But instead of disappearing, it reacts with ammonia in the beverages and forms urethan, according to university of Stockholm researchers who reported DEP-caused urethan concentrations of 0.1 to 0.2 milligram per liter in orange juice and of approximately 1 milligram per liter in white wine and beer. Urethan since 1943 has been known to be capable of causing cancer. The FDA does not require the listing of DEP on the label, and does not know how many beverages are actually treated with the additive. Inhalation of DEP vapors and exposure to the eyes, skin, and mucous membranes can be dangerous.

DIETHYL MALATE. Malic Acid. A synthetic apple and rum flavoring agent for beverages, ice cream, ices, candy, baked goods, gelatin, and puddings. No known toxicity.

DIETHYL MALONATE. A synthetic berry, fruit, apple, grape, peach, and pear flavoring agent for beverages, ice cream, candy, and baked goods. No known toxicity.

DIETHYL SEBACATE. Sebacic Acid. A synthetic butter, coconut, apple, melon, peach, and nut flavoring agent for beverages, ice cream, ices, candy, baked goods, gelatin desserts, and chewing gum. No known toxicity.

DIETHYL SUCCINATE. A synthetic raspberry, butter, orange, and grape flavoring agent for beverages, ice cream, ices, candy, and baked goods. No known toxicity.

DIETHYL TARTRATE. See Tartaric Acid.

DIETHYLSTILBESTROL (DES). Stilbestrol. A synthetic estrogen fed to cattle and poultry to "fatten them." A proven carcinogen, hormonal in nature, according to the FDA which has given top priority to the study of the safety of DES. The FDA stipulates a zero tolerance for the compound after a proper withdrawal period. In 1971, three Harvard scientists linked DES to a rare form of vaginal cancer in the daughters of women who had taken DES during pregnancy. An estimated 100,000 to 150,000 head of cattle containing residues of the hormone are apparently getting to market. The European Common Market, Italy, and Sweden have forbidden the use of DES in cattle.

DIGLYCERIDES. See Glycerides.

2,3-DIHYDRO-3-OXO-BENZISOSULFONAZOLE. See Saccharin.

DIHYDROACARVEOL. A synthetic flavoring agent occurring naturally in black pepper. Used in liquor, mint, spice, and caraway flavorings for beverages, ice cream, candy, baked goods, and alcoholic beverages. No known toxicity.

DIHYDROANETHOLE. See *p*-Propyl Anisole.

DIHYDROCARVYL ACETATE. Acetic Acid. A synthetic berry, fruit, mint, and spice flavoring agent for beverages, ice cream, ices, candy, baked goods, and condiments. No known toxicity.

DIHYDROCOUMARIN. A synthetic flavoring agent occurring naturally in tonka bean, oil of lavender, and sweet clovers. Used in butter, caramel, coconut, floral, fruit, cherry, liquor, rum, nut, root beer, spice, cinnamon, vanilla, cream soda, and tonka flavorings for beverages, ice cream, ices, candy, baked goods, gelatin desserts, puddings, and chewing gum. Prolonged feeding has revealed a possible trend toward liver injury.

2,3-DIKETOBUTANE. See Diacetyl.

DILAURYL THIODIPROPIONATE. An antioxidant, white, crystalline flakes with a sweet odor, in general food use to extend shelf life. In fat or oil up to .02 percent. On the FDA list for further study. GRAS

DILL. A natural flavoring agent from a European herb bearing a seedlike fruit. Used in sausage and spice flavorings for baked goods (4,800 ppm), condiments, meats, and pickles (8,200 ppm). Also used in medicine. Can cause sensitivity to light. GRAS

DILL OIL. The volatile oil obtained from the crushed, dried seeds or fruits of the herb. Slightly yellow, with a caraway odor and flavor. Used in strawberry, fruit, sausage, and dill flavorings for beverages, ice cream, ices, baked goods, gelatin desserts, chewing gum, condiments, meats, liquors, and pickles. See Dill for toxicity.

DILLSEED. Indian Dill. The volatile oil from a variety of dill herbs. Obtained by steam distillation. Light yellow, with a harsh carawaylike odor. Used in rye flavorings for baked goods, condiments, and meats. See Dill for toxicity.

1,2-DIMETHOXY-4-ALLYBENZENE. See Eugenyl Methyl Ether.

m-*DIMETHOXYBENZENE. Resorcinol.* A synthetic fruit, nut, and vanilla flavoring agent for beverages, ice cream, candy, and baked goods. Used on the skin as a bactericidal and fungicidal ointment. Has the same toxicity as phenol (extremely toxic), but causes more severe convulsions.

p-*DIMETHOXYBENZENE.* A synthetic raspberry, fruit, nut, hazel nut, root beer, and vanilla flavoring agent for beverages, ice cream, ices, candy, and baked goods. See above for toxicity.

3,4-DIMETHOXYBENZENECARBONAL. See Veratraldehyde.

DIMETHYL BENZYL CARBINOL. See a,a-Dimethylphenethyl Alcohol.

DIMETHYL ETHER PROTOCATECHUALDEHYDE. See Veratraldehyde.

DIMETHYL ETHER RESORCINOL. A benzene derivative, originally obtained from certain resins but now usually synthesized. See m-Dimethoxybenzene.

2,6-DIMETHYL-5-HEPTENAL. A synthetic fruit flavoring for beverages, ice cream, ices, candy, baked goods, gelatin desserts, and chewing gum. No known toxicity.

3,7-DIMETHYL-7-HYDROXYOCTANAL. See Hydroxycitronellal.

DIMETHYL KETONE. See Diacetyl.

2,6-DIMETHYL OCTANAL. A synthetic melon flavoring agent for beverages, ice cream, ices, candy, and baked goods. No known toxicity.

3,7-DIMETHYL-1-OCTANOL. A synthetic flavoring, colorless, with a sweet roselike odor. Used in floral, rose, and fruit flavorings for beverages, ice cream, ices, candy, and baked goods. No known toxicity.

DIMETHYL PHENETHYL CARBINYL ACETATE. See 2-Methyl-4-Phenyl-2-Butyl Acetate.

DIMETHYL POLYSILOXANE. Antifoam A. An antifoaming agent for use in processing foods in "amounts reasonably required to inhibit foaming." Used as a chewing gum base, in molasses, soft drinks, sugar distillation, skimmed milk, wine fermentation, syrups, soups, rendered fats, and curing solutions. Not to exceed 10 ppm in nonalcoholic beverages. No known toxicity.

DIMETHYL RESORCINOL. See *m*-Dimethozybenzene.

DIMETHYL SUCCINATE. Succinic Acid. A synthetic fruit flavoring agent for beverages, ice cream, ices, candy, baked goods, and chewing gum. No known toxicity.

a,a-DIMETHYLBENZYL ISOBUTYRATE. A synthetic fruit flavoring for beverages, ice cream, ices, candy, and baked goods. No known toxicity.

DIMETHYLGLYOXAL. See Diacetyl.

DIMETHYLKETOL. See Acetoin.

2,4-DIMETHYLACETOPHENONE. A synthetic grape, vanilla, and cream soda flavoring agent for beverages, ice cream, ices, candy, baked goods, and liquor. No known toxicity.

a,a-DIMETHYLPHENETHYL BUTYRATE. Butyric Acid. A synthetic fruit flavoring for beverages, ice cream, ices, candy, baked goods, puddings, and gelatins. No known toxicity.

a,a-DIMETHYLPHENETHYL ACETATE. Acetic Acid. A synthetic cherry and honey flavoring agent for beverages, ice cream, ices, candy, baked goods, and chewing gum. No known toxicity.

a,a-DIMETHYLPHENETHYL ALCOHOL. A synthetic fruit flavoring agent for beverages, ice cream, ices, candy, baked goods, chewing gum, jellies, and gelatin desserts. No known toxicity.

a,a-DIMETHYLPHENETHYL FORMATE. Formic Acid. A synthetic spice flavoring for beverages, ice cream, ices, and candy. See Formic Acid for toxicity.

2,6-DINTRO-3-METHOXY-1-METHYL-4-TERT-BUTYL-BEN-ZENE. See Musk; Ambrette.

DIOCTYL SODIUM SULFOSUCCINATE. A waxlike solid, or dissolved in a solution it is used as a wetting agent in industrial, pharmaceutical, cosmetic, and food applications. In foods and beverages it is used as a dispersing and solubilizing agent for gums, cocoa, and various hard-to-wet materials. Also a wetting agent in the cleaning of fruits, vegetables, and leafy plant material. Used in nonalcoholic beverages and sherbets at a rate not to exceed .5 percent of the weight of such ingredients. It is a stool softener in laxatives. Conjunctival irritation may result from use in ophthalmic preparations.

DIOXYMETHYLENE PROTOCATECHUIC ALDEHYDE. See Piperonal.

DIPENTENE. See *d*-Limonene.

DIPHENYL KETONE. See Benzophenone.

1,3-DIPHENYL-2-PROPANONE. A synthetic fruit, honey, and nut flavoring agent for beverages, ice cream, ices, candy, and baked goods. No known toxicity.

DIPOTASSIUM PHOSPHATE. A sequestrant, a white grain, very soluble in water. Used as a buffering agent to control the degree of acidity in antifreeze solutions and in the preparations of nondairy powdered coffee creams and in cheeses up to 3 percent by weight of cheese. It is a saline cathartic. No known toxicity. GRAS

DIPROPYL DISULFIDE. A synthetic flavoring agent. Colorless, insoluble in water. Occurs naturally in onion. Used in imitation onion flavoring for pickle products and baked goods. No known toxicity.

DIPROPYL KETONE. See 4-Heptanone.

DISODIUM CYANODITHIOMIDOCARBONATE. Bacteria-killing component in the processing of sugar cane. Any substance that releases the cyanide ion can cause poisoning. Sodium cyanide is one of the swiftest poisons known.

DISODIUM GUANYLATE. A flavor intensifier believed to be more effective than sodium inosinate and sodium glutamate. It is the disodium salt of 5'-guanylic acid, widely distributed in nature as a precursor of RNA and DNA. Can be isolated from certain mushrooms. No known toxicity.

DISODIUM PHOSPHATE (DIBASIC). A sequestrant used in evaporated milk, up to .1 percent by weight of finished product; in macaroni and noodle products at not less than .5 percent nor more than 1 percent. It is used as an emulsifier up to 3 percent by weight in specified cheeses. Cleared by the U.S. Department of Agriculture's Meat Inspection Department to prevent cooked-out juices in cured hams, pork shoulders and loins, canned hams, chopped hams, and bacon (5 percent in the pickling and 5 percent injected into the product). Used as a buffer to adjust acidity in chocolate products, beverages, sauces, and toppings, enriched farina. Incompatible with alkaloids. It is a mild saline cathartic and has been used in phosphorous deficiency treatment. It may cause mild irritation to the skin and mucous membranes, and can cause purging. GRAS

DISTILLED ACETYLATED MONOGLYCERIDES. Food emulsifiers and binders in nutrient capsules and tablets to make them palatable; also food-coating agents. Use is "at level not in excess of the amount reasonably required to produce the intended effect." Cleared by the U.S.D.A. Meat Inspection Department as an emulsifier for shortening. No known toxicity.

DITTANY OF CRETE. A natural flavoring extracted from a small herb grown in Crete. Used in spice flavorings for beverages and baked goods. No known toxicity.

γ-DODECALACTONE. A synthetic flavoring, colorless, with a coconut odor that becomes butterlike in low concentrations. Used in butter, butterscotch, coconut, fruit, maple, and nut flavorings for beverages, ice cream, ices, candy, baked goods, gelatin desserts, puddings, and jellies. No known toxicity.

δ-DODECALACTONE. A synthetic flavoring. Occurs naturally in butter, cream, and milk. Used in butter, fruit, and pear flavorings for candy, baked goods, oleomargarine, and toppings. Not to exceed 20 ppm in oleomargarine. No known toxicity.

DODECANOIC ACID. See Lauric Acid.

2-DODECENAL. A synthetic flavoring agent occurring naturally in oranges. Used in citrus flavoring for beverages, ice cream, ices, candy, and baked goods. No known toxicity.

DODECOIC ACID. See Lauric Acid.

DOG GRASS EXTRACT. A natural flavoring extract used in maple flavoring for beverages, ice cream, ices, candy, and baked goods. Derives its name from the fact that it is eaten by sick dogs. No known toxicity for humans. GRAS

DRACO RUBIN EXTRACT. See Dragon's Blood Extract.

DRAGON'S BLOOD EXTRACT. The resinous secretion of the fruit of trees grown in Sumatra, Borneo, and India. Almost odorless and tasteless and available in the form of red sticks, pieces, or caked. Makes a bright crimson powder. Used in bitters flavoring for beverages. Also used to color lacquers and varnishes. No known toxicity.

DRAYLIS ACID. See Benzoic Acid.

DRIED YEAST. A dietary source of folic acid. Used to enrich farina, cornmeals, corn grits, and bakery products. Dried yeast is cleared for use in food provided the total folic acid content of the yeast does not exceed .04 mg per gram of yeast. Nontoxic.

DRY MILK, NONFAT. See Nonfat Dry Milk.

DULSE. A natural flavoring extract from red seaweed. Used as a food condiment. No known toxicity. GRAS

DYMETHYL SULFIDE. See Methyl Sulfide.

E

ELDER FLOWERS. A natural flavoring from the small white flowers of a shrub or small tree. Used in fruit, wine, and spice flavorings for beverages, ice cream, ices, candy, baked goods, and wine. The leaves, shoot, and bark can cause nausea, vomiting, and diarrhea. GRAS

ELEMI. An oily resin derived from the tropical trees. The *gum* is used in fruit flavoring for beverages, ice cream, ices, candy, and baked boods. The *oil* is used in citrus, fruit, vermouth, and spice flavorings for beverages, ice cream, ices, candy, baked goods and soups. The *resins* are used industrially for making varnishes and inks. No known toxicity.

ELETTERIA CARDAMOMUM. See Cardamom.

EMOLLIENT. A substance which has a soothing, softening effect on the skin.

EMULSION. An emulsion is a mixture of two or more normally nonmixable liquids shaken so thoroughly together as to appear homogenized, for example, as is done with salad dressing. Most oils form emulsions with water.

ENANTHAL. See Heptanal.

ENANTHALDEHYDE. See Heptanal.

ENANTHIC ALCOHOL. See Heptyl Alcohol.

ENANTHYL ALCOHOL. See Heptyl Alcohol.

ENRICHED. A food term indicating that the original nutrients removed during the processing of a particular product have been restored, at least in part.

ENZACTIN.® See (tri-) Acetin.

EPICHLORHYDRIN. A modifier for food starch, which can be used up to a level of .3 percent. Insoluble in water. A strong skin irritant and sensitizer. Daily administration of .1 milligram per kilogram of body weight to skin killed all of a group of rats in 4 days, indicating a cumulative potential. Chronic exposure is known to cause kidney damage. A thirty-minute exposure to ambient air concentration of 8,300 ppm was lethal to mice. Poisoned animals showed cyanosis, muscular relaxation or paralysis, convulsions and death.

1,8-EPOXY-p-MENTHANE. See Eucalyptol.

EQUISETIC ACID. See Aconitic Acid.

ERIGERON CANADENSIS. See Erigeron Oil.

ERIGERON OIL. Horseweed, Fleabane Oil. Derived from the leaves and tops of a plant grown in the northern and central United States. Used in fruit and spice flavorings for beverages, ice cream, ices, candy, baked goods, and sauces. No known toxicity.

ERIODICTYON CALIFORNICUM. See Yerba Santa Fluid Extract.

ERYTHORBIC ACID. Isoascorbic Acid. White, slightly yellow crystals, which darken on exposure to light. An antioxidant used in pickling brine at a rate of 7.5 ounces per 100 gallons; in meat products at the rate of ¾ ounce per hundred pounds; in beverages; baked goods; cured cuts and cured pulverized products to accelerate color fixing in curing, to ¾ ounces 100 pounds. Isoascorbic acid contains one-twentieth of the Vitamin C activity of ascorbic acid (*see*). Nontoxic. GRAS

ERYTHROSINE. See FD and C Red No. 3.

ERYTHROXYLON COCA. See Coca Leaf Extract (decocainized).

ESSENCE. An extract of a substance that retains its fundamental or most desirable properties in concentrated form, such as a flavoring or fragrance.

ESSENTIAL OIL. The oily liquid obtained from plants through a variety of processes. The essential oil usually has the taste and smell of the original plant. Essential oils are called volatile because most of them are easily vaporized. The two theories, offered for calling such oils essential are (1) the oils were believed essential to life and (2) that they were the "essence" of the plant. A teaspoon may cause illness in an adult and less than an ounce may kill.

ESTRAGOLE. A colorless to light yellow oily liquid occurring naturally in anise, anise star, basil, estragon oil, and pimento oil. Used as a synthetic fruit, licorice, anise, and spice flavoring agent for beverages, ice cream, ices, baked goods, chewing gum, and condiments. No known toxicity. GRAS

ESTRAGON. Tarragon. A flavoring agent from the oil of leaves of a plant native to Eurasia and used in fruit, licorice, liquor, root beer, and spice flavorings for beverages, ice cream, ices, candy, baked goods, condiments, meats, and liquors. GRAS

ETHANAL. See Acetaldehyde.

ETHANOIC ACID. See Acetic Acid.

ETHANOL. An alcohol used as a solvent in candy, candy glaze, beverages, ice cream, ices, baked goods, liquors, sauces, and gelatin desserts. See Ethyl Alcohol for toxicity. GRAS

ETHONE. See 1-(*p*-Methoxyphenyl)-1-Penten-3-One.

ETHOVAN. See Ethyl Vanillin.

p-ETHOXYBENZALDEHYDE. A synthetic fruit and vanilla flavoring agent for beverages, ice cream, ices, candy, and baked goods. No known toxicity.

ETHYL ACETATE. Acetic Acid. A clear, volatile, flammable liquid with a fruity odor, occurring naturally in apples, bananas, grape juice (Concord), grapes, pineapple, raspberries, and strawberries. It is employed as a synthetic flavoring agent in blackberry, raspberry, strawberry, butter, lemon, apple, banana, cherry, grape, peach, pineapple, brandy, muscatel, rum, whiskey, mint, almond, and cream soda flavorings for beverages, ice cream, ices, baked goods, chewing gum, gelatins, puddings, and liquor. Industrially used in solvents, varnishes, and artificial leather. It is a mild local irritant and central nervous system depressant. Used medically to break up intestinal gas and as a stimulant to revive persons who have fainted. Its vapor is irritating. GRAS

ETHYL ACETOACETATE. Acetoacetic Ester. A synthetic flavoring that occurs naturally in strawberries. Pleasant odor. Used in loganberry, strawberry, apple, apricot, cherry, peach, liquor, and muscatel flavorings for beverages, ice cream, ices, candy, baked goods, chewing gum, and gelatin desserts. Moderately irritating to skin and mucous membranes.

ETHYL ACETONE. See 2-Pentanone.

ETHYL 2-ACETYL-3-PHENYLPROPIONATE. A synthetic fruit flavoring agent for beverages, ice cream, ices, and candy. No known toxicity.

ETHYL ACONITATE. Aconitic Acid. A synthetic fruit, liquor, and rum flavoring agent for beverages, ice cream, ices, candy, baked goods, and gelatin desserts. No known toxicity.

ETHYL ACRYLATE. A synthetic flavoring agent that occurs naturally in pineapple and raspberries. Used in fruit, liquor, and rum flavorings for beverages, ice cream, candy, baked goods, and chewing gum. Also used in the manufacture of water-resistant paint, paper coating, and leather finishes. Highly irritating to the eyes, skin, and mucous membranes and may cause lethargy and convulsions if concentrated vapor is inhaled.

ETHYL ALCOHOL. Contains ethanol (*see*), grain alcohol, and neutral spirits and is used as a solvent in candy glaze, beverages, ices, ice cream, candy, baked goods, liquors, sauces, and gelatin desserts. It is rapidly absorbed through the gastric and intestinal mucosa. For ingestion, within a few minutes, the fatal dose in adults is considered to be one and one half to two pints of whiskey (40 to 55 percent ethyl alcohol).

ETHYL p-ANISATE. A syntheic flavoring agent, colorless to slightly yellow, liquid, with a light fruity smell. Used in berry, fruit, grape, licorice, anise, liquor, rum, and vanilla flavorings for beverages, ice cream, ices, candy, and baked goods. No known toxicity.

ETHYL ANTHRANILATE. A synthetic flavoring agent, clear, colorless to amber, liquid, with an odor of orange blossoms. Used in berry, mandarin, orange, floral, jasmine, neroli, fruit, grape, peach, and raisin flavorings for beverages, ice cream, ices, candy, baked goods, gelatin desserts, and chewing gum. No known toxicity.

ETHYL BENZENECARBOXYLATE. See Ethyl Benzoate.

ETHYL BENZOATE. *Ethyl Benzenecarboxylate.* A synthetic flavoring agent, almost insoluble in water, with a pleasant odor. Used in currant, raspberry, strawberry, fruit, cherry, grape, liquor, nut, walnut, and vanilla flavorings for beverages, ice cream, ices, candy, baked goods, gelatin desserts, chewing gum, and liquors. No known toxicity.

ETHYL BENZOYLACETATE. A synthetic fruit flavoring agent for beverages, ice cream, ices, candy, and baked goods. It becomes yellow when exposed to light. Pleasant odor. No know toxicity.

ETHYL BENZYL ACETOACETATE. See Ethyl 2-Acetyl-3-Phenyl-propionate.

αETHYL BENZYL BUTYRATE. A synthetic fruit flavoring agent for beverages, ice cream, ices, candy, and baked goods. No known toxicity.

2-ETHYL BUTYL ACETATE. A synthetic fruit flavoring agent for beverages, ice cream, ices, and candy. No known toxicity.

ETHYL BUTYL KETONE. See 3-Heptanone.

ETHYL BUTYRATE. *Butyric Acid.* A synthetic flavoring agent, colorless, with a pineapple odor. Found naturally in apples and strawberries. In alcoholic solution it is known as pineapple oil. Used in blueberry, raspberry, strawberry, butter, caramel, cream, orange, banana, cherry, grape, peach, pineapple, rum, walnut, and eggnog flavorings for beverages, ice cream, ices, candy, baked goods, gelatins, puddings, and chewing gum (1,400 ppm). No known toxicity. GRAS

ETHYL CAPRATE. See Cognac Oil.

ETHYL CAPRYLATE. See Cognac Oil.

ETHYL CARVACROL. See Carvacryl Ethyl Ether.

ETHYL CELLULOSE. White granules prepared from wood pulp or chemical cotton and used as a binder and filler in dry vitamin preparations up to 35 percent; chewing gum up to .025 percent, and in confectionery up to .012 percent. Also used in the manufacture of plastics and lacquers. No known toxicity. GRAS for packaging.

ETHYL CINNAMATE. Cinnamic Acid. An almost colorless, oily liquid with a faint cinnamon odor, used as a synthetic flavoring in raspberry, strawberry, cherry, grape, peach, plum, spice, cinnamon, and vanilla flavorings for beverages, ice cream, ices, candy, baked goods, gelatin desserts, and chewing gum. Also a fixative for perfumes. No known toxicity.

ETHYL CITRATE. A bitter, oily sequestrant (see Sequestering) used in dried egg whites. No known toxicity.

ETHYL CYCLOHEXANEPROPIONATE. A synthetic pineapple flavoring agent for beverages, ice cream, ices, candy, and baked goods. No known toxicity.

ETHYL DECANOATE. Decanoic Acid. A synthetic flavoring occurring naturally in green and white cognac oils. Used in strawberry, cherry, grape, pineapple, liquor, brandy, cognac, and rum flavorings for beverages, ice cream, ices, candy, baked goods, gelatin desserts, and liquors. No known toxicity.

ETHYL DODECANOATE. See Ethyl Laurate.

ETHYL FORMATE. Formic Acid. A colorless, flammable liquid with a distinct odor occurring naturally in apples and coffee extract. Used as a yeast and mold inhibitor and as a fumigant for bulk and packaged raisins and dried currants; fungicide for cashew nuts, cereals, tobacco, and dried fruits. Also a synthetic flavoring agent for blueberry, raspberry, strawberry, butter, butterscotch, apple, apricot, banana, cherry, grape, peach, plum, pineapple, tutti-frutti, brandy, rum, sherry, and whiskey flavorings for beverages, ice cream, ices, candy, baked goods, liquor, gelatin, and chewing gum. Irritating to the skin and mucous membranes, and in high concentrations it is narcotic. See Formic Acid for further toxicity.

ETHYL 2-FURANPROPIONATE. A synthetic raspberry, apple, cherry, and pineapple flavoring agent for beverages, ice cream, ices, candy, and baked goods. No known toxicity.

ETHYL FURYLPROPIONATE. See Ethyl 2-Furanpropionate.

4-ETHYL GUAIACOL. A synthetic coffee and fruit flavoring agent for beverages, ice cream, ices, and gelatin desserts. No known toxicity.

ETHYL HEPTANOATE. A synthetic flavoring agent, colorless, with a fruity, winelike odor and taste, and a burning aftertaste. Used in blueberry, strawberry, butter, butterscotch, coconut, apple, cherry, grape, melon, peach, pineapple, plum, vanilla, cheese, nut, rum, brandy, and cognac flavorings for beverages, ice cream, ices, candy, baked goods, gelatin desserts, chewing gum, and liqueurs. No known toxicity.

2-ETHYL-2-HEPTENAL. A synthetic pineapple flavoring agent for beverages and candy. No known toxicity.

ETHYL HEXADECANOATE. See Ethyl Palmitate.

ETHYL 2,4-HEXADIENOATE. See Ethyl Sorbate.

ETHYL HEXANOATE. A synthetic flavoring agent that occurs naturally in apples, pineapples, and strawberries. Used in fruit, rum, nut, and cheese flavorings for beverages, ice cream, ices, candy, baked goods, gelatin desserts, chewing gum, and jelly. No known toxicity.

ETHYL α HYDROXYPROPIONATE. See Ethyl Lactate.

ETHYL ISOBUTYRATE. *Isobutyric Acid.* A synthetic strawberry, fruit, cherry, and butter flavoring agent for beverages, ice cream, ices, candy, baked goods, gelatin desserts, and toppings. No known toxicity.

ETHYL ISOVALERATE. *Isovaleric Acid.* A synthetic flavoring agent used in alcoholic solution for pineapple flavoring for beverages, ice cream, ices, candy, baked goods, gelatin desserts, and chewing gum. No known toxicity.

ETHYL LACTATE. *Lactic Acid.* A synthetic flavoring agent, colorless, with a characteristic odor. Used in strawberry, butter, butterscotch, coconut, grape, rum, maple, cheese, and nut flavorings for beverages, ice cream, candy, baked goods, gelatin desserts, chewing gum (3,100 ppm), syrup, and brandy (1,000 ppm). Used also as a solvent for cellulose acetate and nitrocellulose, which are used in the manufacture of explosives. No known toxicity.

ETHYL LAURATE. A synthetic flavoring agent, colorless, oily, with a light, fruity odor. Insoluble in water; very soluble in alcohol. Used in berry, coconut, fruit, grape, liquor, cognac, rum, nut, spice, nutmeg, and cheese flavorings for beverages, ice cream, ices, candy, baked goods, gelatin desserts, chewing gum, and liqueurs. No known toxicity.

ETHYL LEVULINATE. Levulinic Acid. A synthetic apple flavoring agent for beverages, ice cream, ices, candy, and baked goods. No known toxicity.

ETHYL MALATE. See Diethyl Malate.

4-ETHYL-2-METHOXYPHENOL. See 4-Ethyl Guaiacol.

ETHYL trans-2-METHYL-2-BUTENOATE. See Ethyl Tiglate.

ETHYL 2-METHYLBUTYRATE. A synthetic fruit flavoring agent for beverages, ice cream, ices, and candy. No known toxicity.

ETHYL 3-METHYL-3-PHENYLGLYCIDATE. Strawberry Aldehyde. A synthetic berry, loganberry, raspberry, strawberry, coconut, fruit, cherry, grape, pineapple, liquor, and wine flavoring agent for beverages, ice cream, ices, candy, baked goods, gelatin, pudding, and chewing gum. No known toxicity. GRAS

ETHYL MYRISTATE. A synthetic coconut, fruit, honey, and cognac flavoring agent for beverages, ice cream, ices, candy, baked goods, and liqueurs. No known toxicity.

ETHYL NITRITE. Sweet Spirit of Niter. Spirit of Nitrous Ether. A synthetic flavoring agent, colorless or yellowish, liquid, with a characteristic odor, and a burning, sweetish taste. Used in strawberry, cherry, pineapple, liquor, brandy, and rum flavorings for beverages, ice cream, ices, candy, baked goods, chewing gum, syrup, and icings. It may cause methemoglobinemia, in which oxygen is diminished in the red blood cells, low blood pressure, and, when it is in a high concentration, narcosis.

ETHYL NONANOATE. Nonanoic Acid. A synthetic fruit and rum flavoring agent for beverages, ice cream, ices, candy, baked goods, gelatin desserts, chewing gum, icings, and liqueurs. No known toxicity.

ETHYL 2-NONYNOATE. A synthetic berry, fruit, and melon flavoring agent for beverages, ice cream, ices, candy, and baked goods. No known toxicity.

ETHYL OCTANOATE. Octanoic Acid. A synthetic flavoring agent that occurs naturally in both cognac green and cognac white oils. Used in strawberry, butter, citrus, apple, pineapple, rum, nut, and cheese flavorings for beverages, ice cream, ices, candy, baked goods, gelatin desserts, and chewing gum. No known toxicity.

ETHYL OCTYNE CARBONATE. See Ethyl 2-Nonynoate.

ETHYL OLEATE. Oleic Acid. A synthetic flavoring agent, yellowish, oily, insoluble in water. Used in butter and fruit flavorings for beverages, ice cream, ices, candy, baked goods, gelatin desserts, and puddings. No known toxicity.

ETHYL 3-OXOBUTANOATE. See Ethyl Acetoacetate.

ETHYL OXYHYDRATE. See Rum Ether.

ETHYL PALMITATE. Ethyl Hexadecanoate. A synthetic butter and rum flavoring agent for ice cream, ices, candy, and baked goods. No known toxicity.

ETHYL PHENYLACETATE. Phenylacetic Acid. A synthetic flavoring agent, colorless or nearly colorless liquid, with a pleasant odor. Used in butter, honey, apricot, and cherry flavorings for beverages, ice cream, ices, candy, baked goods, and syrups. No known toxicity.

ETHYL PHENYLACRYLATE. See Ethyl Cinnamate.

ETHYL 4-PHENYLBUTYRATE. A synthetic fruit flavoring agent for beverages and candy. No known toxicity.

ETHYL 3-PHENYLGLYCIDATE. A synthetic berry, strawberry, fruit and cherry flavoring agent for beverages, ice cream, ices, candy, baked goods, and gelatin desserts. No known toxicity.

ETHYL 3-PHENYLPROPENOATE. See Ethyl Cinnamate.

ETHYL 3-PHENYLPROPIONATE. A synthetic fruit flavoring agent for beverages, ice cream, ices, candy, and baked goods. No known toxicity.

ETHYL 1-PROPENE-1,2,3-TRICARBOXYLATE. See Ethyl Aconitate.

ETHYL PROPIONATE. Propionic Acid. A synthetic flavoring agent, colorless, transparent liquid, with a fruity odor. Occurs naturally in apples. Used in butter, fruit, and rum flavorings for beverages, ice cream, ices, candy, baked goods, gelatin desserts, and chewing gum (1,100ppm). No known toxicity.

ETHYL PYRUVATE. Pyruvic Acid. A synthetic chocolate, fruit, rum, maple, and spice flavoring agent for beverages, ice cream, ices, candy, and baked goods. No known toxicity.

ETHYL SALICYLATE. Salicylic Ether. A synthetic flavoring agent that occurs naturally in strawberries, and has a pleasant odor. Used in fruit, root beer, sassafras, and wintergreen flavorings for beverages, ice cream, ices, candy, baked goods, chewing gum, gelatins, and puddings. At one time it was given medically to rheumatics. May interact with harmful results with medications such as anticoagulants, antidepressants, and medications for cancer such as Methotrexate. May cause allergic reaction in persons allergic to salicylates.

ETHYL SEBACATE. See Diethyl Sebacate.

ETHYL SORBATE. A synthetic fruit flavoring agent for beverages, ice cream, ices, candy, and baked goods. No known toxicity.

ETHYL TETRADECANOATE. See Ethyl Myristate.

ETHYL TIGLATE. Tiglic Acid. A synthetic raspberry, strawberry, pineapple and rum flavoring agent for beverages, ice cream, ices, candy, and baked goods. No known toxicity.

ETHYL 10-UNDECENOATE. A synthetic coconut, fruit, cognac, and nut flavoring agent for beverages, ice cream, ices, candy, baked goods, and liquor. No known toxicity.

ETHYL VALERATE. Valeric Acid. A synthetic butter, apple, apricot, peach, and nut flavoring agent for beverages, ice cream, ices, candy, baked goods, gelatin desserts, and chewing gum. No known toxicity.

ETHYL VANILLIN. Colorless flakes with a stronger odor and taste than vanillin (see). Used as a synthetic flavoring in raspberry, strawberry, butter, butterscotch, caramel, rum butter, chocolate, cocoa, citrus, coconut, macaroon, cola, fruit, cherry, grape, honey, liquor, muscatel, rum, maple, nut, pecan, root beer, vanilla, and cream soda for beverages, ice cream, ices, candy, baked goods, gelatin desserts, puddings, chewing gum, imitation vanilla extract (28,000 ppm), liquor, icings, and toppings. Also used in perfumery. No known toxicity. GRAS

ETHYLACETIC ACID. See Butyric Acid.

2-ETHYLBUTRYIC ACID. A synthetic fruit, nut, and walnut flavoring agent for beverages, ice cream, ices, candy, and baked goods. No known toxicity.

2-ETHYLBUTYRALDEHYDE. A synthetic chocolate flavoring agent for beverages, ice cream, ices, candy, and baked goods. No known toxicity.

ETHYLENE DICHLORIDE. Dutch Liquid. A solvent used in spice oleoresins (see) up to .005 percent, and for fats, oils, waxes, gums, and resins (*see*). Used in making tobacco extract. It burns with smoky flames. Has a pleasant odor and sweet taste, but its vapors are irritating. Deaths due to liver and kidney injury following ingestion of large amounts (30 to 70 grams) have been reported. Clouding of the eyes, hemorrhages, and destruction of the adrenal cortex have been reported in humans and dogs.

ETHYLENE OXIDE-METHYL FORMATE MIXTURE. A mold and yeast control agent in dried and glacéed fruits. Ethylene oxide is highly irritating to the mucous membranes and eyes. High concentrations may cause pulmonary edema. Inhalation of methyl formate vapor produces nasal and eye irritation, retching, narcosis, and death from pulmonary irritation. Exposure to 1 percent vapor for 2½ hours or 5 percent vapor for ½ hour is lethal.

ETHYLENEDIAMINE. Colorless, clear, thick and strongly alkaline. A component of a bacteria-killing component in processing sugar cane. Also used as a solvent for casein (*see*), albumin, and shellac. Has been used as a urinary acidifier. May be irritating to the skin and mucous membranes and has been known to cause sensitization leading to asthma and allergic skin rashes.

ETHYLENEDIAMINE TETRAACETATE (EDTA). A sequestrant (*see*) in carbonated beverages. EDTA salts are used in crab meat (cooked and canned) to retard struvite (crystal) formation and promote color retention. It is also used in nonstandardized dressings. A chelating agent, EDTA is on the FDA list to be studied for possible harmful effects. It may cause errors in a number of laboratory tests including those for calcium, carbon dioxide, nitrogen, and muscular activity. See Ethylenediamine for toxicity.

trans-1,2-ETHYLENEDICARBOXYLIC ACID. See Fumaric Acid.

ETHYLFORMIC ACID. See Propionic Acid.

EUBATUS, RUBUS. See Blackberry Bark Extract.

EUCALYPTOL. Eucalyptus Oil. A synthetic flavoring that occurs naturaly in allspice, star anise, basil, bay and bay leaf extract, cajaput oil, calamus and calamus oil, caraway, laurel leaf oil, peppermint oil, and pimento oil. Eucalyptus oil is 70–80 percent active eucalyptol. Eucalyptol is used in mint flavorings for beverages, ice cream, ices, candy, baked goods, and chewing gum. Fatalities have followed ingestion of doses as small as 3 to 5 milliliters and recovery has occurred after doses as large as 20 to 30 milliliters. Symptoms of poisoning are epigastric burning with nausea, weakness, water retention, and delirium.

EUCAYLPTUS OIL. *Dinkum Oil.* Volatile oil from the fresh leaves of an Australian dwarfish tree, cultivated in southern U.S. Colorless or pale yellow, smells like camphor, and has a pungent, spicy, cooling taste. Used in fruit, mint, root beer, spice, and ginger ale flavoring for beverages, ice cream, ices, candy, baked goods, and liquors. Has been used as an expectorant, vermifuge, and local antiseptic. As little as 1 milliliter has caused coma. Fatalities have followed doses as small as 3.5 milliliters. Symptoms include epigastric burning, with nausea. Symptoms have been reported to occur as long as two hours after ingestion.

EUCHEUMA COTTONI EXTRACT. A stabilizing and thickening agent in foods. In dairy products to suspend particles (*see* Hydrogenation) and for gelling. No known toxicity.

EUGENOL. The main constituent of such natural sources as carnation, cinnamon leaf, and clove oils. Colorless to pale yellow liquid with a strong odor of cloves; spicy pungent taste. Darkens and thickens upon exposure to air. Used as a defoamer in yeast production, in the manufacture of vanilla, and in perfumery. It is a synthetic fruit, nut, and spice flavoring agent for beverages, ice cream, ices, candy, baked goods, gelatin deserts, chewing gum, meats (2,000 ppm), and condiments. Acts as a local antiseptic and anesthetic when applied topically to control a toothache. When ingested in an aqueous emulsion, it can cause vomiting and gastric secretion of mucin (stomach cells). Toxicity is similar to phenol, which is highly toxic. Death in laboratory animals given eugenol is due to vascular collapse. GRAS.

EUGENYL ACETATE. *Acetic Acid.* A synthetic berry, fruit, mint, spice, and vanilla flavoring agent for beverages, ice cream, ices, candy, baked goods, chewing gum, and condiments. No known toxicity.

EUGENYL BENZOATE. A synthetic fruit and spice flavoring agent for beverages, ice cream, ices, candy, and baked goods. No known toxicity.

EUGENYL FORMATE. *Formic Acid.* A synthetic spice flavoring agent used in condiments. See Formic Acid for toxicity.

EUGENYL METHYL ETHER. A synthetic raspberry, strawberry, fruit, spice, clove, and ginger flavoring agent for beverages, ice cream, ices, candy, baked goods, and jellies. No known toxicity.

EVERNIA FURFURACEA. See Oak Moss, Absolute.
EVERNIA PRUNASTIC. See Oak Moss, Absolute.
EXALTOLIDE. See ω-Pentadecalactone.
EXTRACT. The solution that results from passing alcohol or an alcohol-water mixture through a substance. Examples would be the alcohol-water mixtures of vanilla, orange or lemon extracts found in bottles among the spices and flavorings on the supermarket shelf.

F

FARNESOL. A flavoring agent that occurs naturally in ambrette seed, star anise, linden flowers, oil of musk seed, oils of citronella, rose, lemon grass, and balsam. Used in berry, apricot, banana, cherry, melon, peach, citrus, fruit, raspberry, and strawberry flavorings for beverages, ice cream, ices, baked goods, candy, and gelatin desserts. Also used in perfumery to emphasize the odor of sweet floral perfumes, such as lilac. No known toxicity.

FAT. The most concentrated source of food energy and very necessary to health. Fat deposits provide insulation and protection for body structure as well as a storehouse for energy. Food fats are carriers of fat-soluble vitamins and include certain essential unsaturated fatty acid (*see*). *Saturated fats* contain only single bond carbon linkages and are the least active chemically. They are usually solid at room temperature. Most animal fats are saturated. The common saturated fats are acetic, butyric, caproic, caprylic, capric, lauric, myristic, palmitic, stearic, arachidic, behenic. Butterfat, coconut oil, and peanut oil are high in saturated fats. *Unsaturated fats* contain one or more double bond carbon linkages and are usually liquid at room temperature. Vegetable oils and fish oils most frequently contain unsaturated fats. Among the unsaturated fats are caproleic, lauroleic, myristoleic, palmitoleic, oleic, petroselinic, vaccenic, linoleic, linolenic, elaesostearic, gadoleic, arachidonic, erucic.

FATTY ACIDS. One or any mixture of liquid and solid acids, capric, caprylic, laurice, myristic, oleic, palmitic, and stearic. In combination with glycerin they form fat. Necessary for normal growth and skin. Commercially, used chiefly for making soaps and detergents. In foods they are used as emulsifiers, general food binders, lubricants, and defoamer components in the processing of beet sugar and yeast. *Polyglycerol esters* of fatty acids are prepared from edible fats, oils, corn, cottonseed, palm fruit, peanut, safflower, and soybean oils, lard and tallow. Used as emulsifiers and defoaming agents in beet sugar and yeast production, and as lubricant binders and components in the manufacture of other food additives. Fatty acid *salts* (one or more of the aluminum, ammonium, calcium, magnesium, potassium, and sodium salts of all of the above fatty acids) are used as emulsifiers, binders, and anticaking agents. A *free fatty acid* (FFA) is the uncombined fatty acid present in a fat. Some raw oils may contain as much as 3 percent FFA. These are removed in the refining process and refined fats and oils ready for use as foods usually have extremely low FFA content. No known toxicity.

FD AND C COLORS. (Food Drug and Cosmetic Colors). A color additive is a term to describe any dye, pigment, or other substance capable of coloring a food, drug, or cosmetic on any part of the human body. In 1900, there were more than 80 dyes used to color food. There were no regulations and the same dye used to color clothes could also be used to color candy. In 1906, the first comprehensive legislation for food colors was passed. There were only seven colors which, when tested, were shown to be composed of known ingredients which demonstrated no known harmful effects. Those colors were orange, erythrosine, ponceau 3R, amaranth, indigotine, naphthol yellow, and light green. A voluntary system of certification for batches of color dyes was set up. In 1938, new legislation was passed, superseding the 1906 act. The colors were given numbers instead of chemical names and every batch *had* to be certified. There were 15 food colors in use at the time. In 1950, children were made ill by certain coloring used in candy and popcorn. These incidents led to the delisting of FD and C Orange No. 1, Orange No. 2, and FD and C Red No. 32. Since that time, because of experimental evidence of possible harm, Red 1, Yellows 1,2,3, and 4 have also been delisted. However, Red No. 4 is still being used to color Maraschino cherries. In 1960, scientific investigations were required by law to determine the suitability of all colors in use for permanent listing. Today, Orange B (limited to 150 ppm) for coloring sausage casings and Citrus Red No. 2 (limited to 2 ppm) for coloring orange skins have been permanently listed; Blue No. 1, Red No. 3, Yellow No. 5, and Red No. 40 are permanently listed but without any restrictions the other food coloring additives are still on the "temporary list."

In 1959, the Food and Drug Administration approved the use of "lakes," in which the dyes have been mixed with alumina hydrate to make them insoluble. See FD and C Lakes. The only colors the World Health Organization finds 1A (or completely acceptable) for use in food are Red No. 2, Yellow No. 6, Yellow No. 5, Blue No. 1, and Green No. 3.

FD AND C BLUE NO. 1. Brilliant Blue. A coal tar derivative, it is used as a coloring in bottled soft drinks, gelatin desserts, ice cream, ices, dry drink powders, candy, confections, bakery products, cereals, and puddings. It may cause allergic reactions. It will produce malignant tumors at the site of injection in rats. On the FDA permanent list of color additives. Rated 1A for toxicology (completely vegetable). See FD and C Colors.

FD AND C BLUE NO. 2. Indigotine. Indigo Carmine. A dark-blue powder almost always containing sodium chloride or sulfate. Easily faded by light. Used in bottled soft drinks, bakery products, cereals, candy, confections, and dry drink powders. Also used as a dye in kidney tests and in testing milk. The World Health Organization gives it a toxicology rating of B—available data not entirely sufficient to meet requirements acceptable for food use. On the FDA provisional list of approved color additives. See FD and C Colors.

FD AND C CITRUS RED NO. 2. Found in 1960 to damage internal organs and to be a weak cancer-causing agent. Used to color orange skins. The World Health Organization said the color has been shown to cause cancer and that toxicological data available were inadequate to allow the determination of a safe limit; they recommended that it not be used as a food color. The FDA ruled on October 28, 1971 that results of several rodent studies and one dog study using both oral and injected Citrus Red No. 2 showed either no adverse effect or no adverse effect levels. No abnormalities in urinary bladders were reported. The FDA noted that a paper presented in 1965 by the University of Otago Medical School reported a significant level of urinary bladder cancers in rodents fed the dye for up to 24 months. The FDA said that since slides of the tissues in photographs were not yet available for examination, and since there has been no confirmation of the studies, "the listing of Citrus Red 2 should remain unchanged until the Otega results can be confirmed by examination." See FD and C Colors.

FD AND C GREEN NO. 1. Guinea Green B. A dull, dark green powder used as coloring in bottled soft drinks. The certified color industry did not apply for the extension of this color because of small demand for its use so it was automatically deleted from the list of color additives in 1966. Rated E by the World Health Organization, meaning it was found to be harmful and not to be used in food. See FD and C Colors.

FD AND C GREEN NO. 2. Light Green, S.F. YELLOW. Coloring used in bottled soft drinks. Because of lack of demand for this color, the certified color industry did not petition for extension and it was automatically deleted in 1966. It produces tumors at the site of injection under the skin of rats. See FD and C Colors.

FD AND C GREEN NO. 3. Fast Green. Used as coloring matter in mint-flavored jelly, frozen desserts, gelatin desserts, candy, confections, baking products, and cereals. Has been suspected of being a sensitizer in the allergic. On the FDA provisional list of approved color additives. Produces malignant tumors at the site of injection when introduced under the skin of rats. The World Health Organization gives it a toxicology rating of 1A, meaning completely acceptable. See FD and C Colors.

FD AND C LAKES. Aluminum or calcium lakes. Lakes are pigments prepared by combining FD and C colors with a form of aluminum or calcium, which makes the colors insoluble. Aluminum and calcium lakes are used in confection and candy products and for dyeing egg shells and other products that are adversely affected by water. See FD and C colors for toxicity.

FD AND C RED NO. 2. Amaranth. Red No. 2 accounts for 35 percent of all food coloring used. Dark, red-brown powder, used as coloring in dry drink powders, candy, bakery products, cereals, imitation jellies, gelatin desserts, Maraschino cherries, sausage, ice cream, sherbet, and puddings. It is derived from coal tar and is on the FDA list of approved color additives. The FDA has ordered processors using this coloring to submit data on all food, drug, and cosmetic products containing it. Two Russian scientists found Red No. 2 prevented some pregnancies and caused some still births in rats. The World Health Organization gives it a toxicology rating of 1A, meaning it has been found acceptable for use in food. The FDA ruled in the winter of 1972 that although Red No. 2 needed further study, it should not be delisted but restrictions are anticipated. See FD and C Colors.

FD AND C RED NO. 3. Erythrosine. A coal tar derivative, it is used in canned fruit cocktail, fruit salad, cherry pie mix (up to .01 percent), Maraschino cherries, gelatin desserts, ice cream, sherbets, candy, confectionery products, bakery products, cereals, and puddings. It is on the permanent list of color additives. It has been rated 1B by the World Health Organization indicating not enough data to make it completely acceptable for use in food. See FD and C Colors.

FD AND C RED NO. 4. Banned by the FDA in 1964 when it was shown to damage the adrenal glands and bladders of dogs, the agency relented and put it on the provisional list for use in Maraschino cherries. It is still in use in some drugs and cosmetics. It is a coal tar dye. The World Health Organization gives it a rating of IV E meaning it has been found to be harmful and should not be used in food. See FD and C Colors.

FD AND C RED NO. 40. Allura Red AC. The newest food coloring, approved for use in 1971. Allied Chemical has an exclusive patent on it. They expect it will have a wide use in coloring food in a range formerly enjoyed by Red No. 4 before that coloring was restricted only to Maraschino cherries. Permanently listed because, unlike the producers of the temporary colors, this producer supplied reproductive data. See FD and C Colors.

FD AND C VIOLET I. Used as coloring matter in gelatin desserts, ice cream, sherbets, carbonated beverages, dry drink powders, candy, confections, bakery products, cereals, puddings, and as the dye used for the Department of Agriculture's meat stamp. On the FDA provisional list of approved color additives. A Canadian study published in 1962 showed the dye caused cancer in 50 percent of the rats fed the dye in food. The FDA did not consider this valid evidence since the exact nature of the dye used could not be determined and all records and specimens are lost and not available for study. Furthermore, previous and subsequent studies have not confirmed evidence of Violet I causing cancer in rats. However, a two-year study with dogs did show non-cancerous lesions on the dog's ears after being fed Violet I. The FDA again felt the study was not adequate but that the ear lesions did appear to be dye-related and that perhaps two years may be too short a period to determine their eventual outcome. The FDA ruled on October 28, 1971, that Violet I should remain provisionally listed pending the outcome of a new dog study to be started as soon as possible and to last seven years.

FD AND C YELLOW NO. 5. *Tartrazine*. A coal tar derivative, it is used as a coloring in prepared breakfast cereals, imitation strawberry jelly, bottled soft drinks, gelatin desserts, ice cream, sherbets, dry drink powders, candy, confections, bakery products, spaghetti, and puddings. Causes allergic reactions in persons sensitive to aspirin. The certified color industry petitioned for permanent listing of this color in February 1966, with no limitations other than good manufacturing practice. However, in February 1966, the FDA proposed the listing of this color with a maximum rate of use of 300 ppm in food. The color industry objected to the limitation. Yellow No. 5 was recently permanently listed as a color additive without restrictions. Rated 1A by the World Health Organization—acceptable in food. See FD and C Colors.

FD AND C YELLOW NO. 6. *Monoazo*. *Sunset Yellow FCF*. A coal tar dye used as coloring matter in carbonated beverages, gelatin desserts, dry drink powders, candy and confectionery products that do not contain oils and fats, bakery products, cereals, puddings, and tablets. May cause allergic reactions. Rated 1A by the World Health Organization—acceptable in food. On the FDA provisional list of approved color additives. See FD and C Colors.

FENCHOL. See Fenchyl Alcohol.

***d*-FENCHONE.** A synthetic flavoring occurring naturally in common fennel (*see*). It is an oily liquid with a camphor smell and practically insoluble in water. Used in berry, liquor, and spice flavorings for beverages, ice cream, ices, candy, baked goods, and liquors. Used medically as a counterirritant.

FENCHYL ALCOHOL. A synthetic berry, lime, and spice flavoring agent in beverages, ice cream, ices, candy, and baked goods. No known toxicity.

FENNEL. A natural flavor extract from the dried ripe fruit of a variety of cultivated plants grown in Southern Europe and Western Asia. Colorless with the characteristic fennel taste. *Common fennel* is used as a sausage and spice flavoring for beverages, baked goods, condiments, and meats. *Sweet fennel* has the same function but includes ice cream, ices, candy. *Sweet fennel oil* is used in raspberry, fruit, licorice, anise, rye, sausage, root beer, sarsaparilla, spice, winter-green, and birch beer flavorings for beverages, ice cream, ices, candy, baked goods, gelatin desserts, condiments, meats, and liquors. May cause a sensitivity to light.

FENUGREEK. *Greek Hay.* A natural flavoring from an annual herb grown in Southern Europe, North Africa, and India for the seeds used in making curry. Fenugreek is a butter, butterscotch, maple, black walnut, and spice flavoring agent for beverages, ice cream, candy, baked goods, condiments, meats, and syrups. The *extract* (*see*) is a butter, butterscotch, caramel, chocolate, coffee, fruit, maple, meat, black walnut, walnut, root beer, spice, and vanilla flavoring agent for beverages, ice cream, ices, candy, baked goods, puddings, chewing gum, condiments, meats, syrups, pickles, liquors, and icings. The *oleoresin* (*see*) is a fruit, maple, and nut flavoring agent for beverages, ice cream, ices, candy, baked goods, puddings, and syrups. No known toxicity.

FERRIC CHOLINE CITRATE. See Iron Sources.

FERRIC ORTHOPHOSPHATE. See Iron Sources.

FERRIC PHOSPHATE. See Iron Sources.

FERRIC PYROPHOSPHATE. See Iron Sources.

FERRIC SODIUM PYROPHOSPHATE. See Iron Sources.

FERROUS FUMARATE. See Iron Sources.

FERROUS GLUCONATE. See Iron Sources.

FERROUS LACTATE. See Iron Sources.

FERROUS SULFATE. See Iron Sources.

FERULA ASSAFOETIDA. See Asafetida.

FIBER. Commonly termed "bulk"—the indigestible carbohydrates including cellulose, hemicellulose, and gums. Used in food to reduce calorie content, as a thickening agent, and a stabilizer. No known toxicity.

FICIN. An enzyme occurring in the latex of tropical trees. A buff-colored powder with an acrid odor. Absorbs water. Concentrated and used as a meat tenderizer. Ten to twenty times more powerful than papain tenderizers. Used to clot milk, as a protein digestant in the brewing industry, and as a chillproofing agent in beer. Also, in cheese as a substitute for rennet in the coagulation of milk; and for removing casings from sausages. Can cause irritation to the skin, eyes, and mucous membranes and in large doses can cause purging.

FILLED MILK. A combination of skim milk and vegetable oil to replace milk fat. Usually has the same amount of protein and calories as whole milk. Used as a milk substitute. It often contains the high cholesterol fatty acids (*see*) of coconut oil. Nontoxic.

FINOCHIO. See Fennel.

FISH OIL (HYDROGENATED). A fatty oil from fish or marine mammals used in soapmaking. GRAS for use in food packaging.

FIXATIVE. A chemical which reduces the tendency of an odor or flavor to vaporize. Patchouly, for instance, fixes the flavor of cola beverages and undecyl aldehyde fixes citrus flavors.

FLAVORING COMPOUND. A flavoring composed of two or more substances. The substances may be natural or synthetic and they are usually closely guarded secrets. Normally, a flavoring compound is complete, that is, it is added to a food without any additional flavorings being necessary. A strawberry flavoring compound, for example, may contain 28 separate ingredients before it is complete.

FLAXSEED. The seed of the flax plant may be "hidden" in cereals and milk of cows fed flaxseed. It is also in flaxseed tea and the laxative Flaxolyn. It is a frequent allergen when ingested, inhaled, or in direct contact. Flaxseed is the source of linseed oil.

FLEABANE OIL. *Oil of Canada Fleabane. Erigeron Oil.* The pale yellow volatile oil from a fresh flowering herb. It takes its name from its supposed ability to drive away fleas. Used in fruit and spice flavorings for beverages, ice cream, ices, candy, baked goods, and sauce. No known toxicity.

FLORENCE FENNEL. See Fennel.

FLUORINE SOURCES: *Calcium Fluoride; Hydrofluosilicic Acid; Potassium Fluoride; Sodium Fluoride and Sodium Silicofluoride.* All have been used in the fluoridation of water. Fluorides cross the placental barrier and the effects on the fetus are unknown. New clinical evidence shows that kidney disturbance sometimes is due to the amount of fluoride it contributes to the blood.

FOLIC ACID. A yellowish-orange compound, a member of the Vitamin-B complex, used as a nutrient. Occurs naturally in liver, kidney, mushrooms, yeast, green leaves, and grasses. Aids in cell formation, especially red blood cells and helps prevent pernicious anemia. Daily requirement is up to .10 mg. However, vitamin preparations containing more than .1 mg of folic acid per day cannot be purchased without a physician's prescription. No known toxicity.

FOOD STARCH, Modified. See Modified Starch.

FORMALDEHYDE(PARA). Paraformalhedyde is obtained by concentrating formaldehyde solution, used in embalming fluids. Formaldehyde is a component of a defoaming agent used in yeast and beet sugar production; also as a preservative (up to .01 ppm) in the final product. Generally a disinfectant, germicide, and fungacide for plants and vegetables. Ingestion can cause severe abdominal pain, internal bleeding, loss of the ability to urinate, vertigo, coma, and death. One ounce taken by mouth causes death within two hours.

FORMIC ACID. A synthetic flavoring, colorless, highly corrosive, which occurs naturally in apples, mace oil, peaches, raspberries, strawberries, tobacco leaves, and valerian root extract. Used in fruit flavoring for beverages, ice cream, ices, candy, and baked goods. It is a dangerous liquid which produces violent burns and local necrosis. Used as a decalcifier and for dehairing and plumping hides. Chronic absorption is known to cause albuminuria—protein in the urine. GRAS

FORMIC ETHER. See Ethyl Formate.

FORTIFIED. Fortification of food refers to the addition of nutrients such as Vitamin C to breakfast drinks and Vitamin D to milk. It actually increases the nutritional values of the original food.

FRANKINCENSE. Aromatic gum resin obtained from African and Asian trees and used chiefly as incense. For food use, see Olibanum Oil.

FUMARIC ACID. White, odorless, derived from many plants and essential to vegetable and animal tissue respiration; prepared industrially. An acidulant used as a leavening agent and a dry acid for dessert powders and confections (up to 3 percent). Also an apple, peach, and vanilla flavoring agent for beverages, baked goods, (1,300 ppm), and gelatin desserts (3,600 ppm). Used in baked goods as an antioxidant and as a substitute for tartaric acid (*see*). No known toxicity. GRAS

2-FURALDEHYDE. See Furfural.

2-FURANACROLEIN. See Furyl Acrolein.

FURCELLERAN: Sodium, Calcium, Potassium, and Ammonium Salts. Extracted from red seaweed grown in Northern European waters. The processed gum is a white odorless powder soluble in water. Used as an emulsifier, stabilizer, and thickener in foods. It is a natural colloid and gelling agent. Also used in puddings and jams, in products for diabetics, as a carrier for food preservatives, and bactericides. It is also used in over-the-counter drugs for weight reducing and toothpastes. On the FDA list of additives to be studied for mutagenic, teratogenic, subacute, and reproductive effects.

FURFURAL. Artificial ant oil. A synthetic flavoring that occurs naturally in angelica root oil, apples, coffee, peaches, skim milk (heated), oils of lime and lavender. Used in butter, butterscotch, caramel, coffee, fruit, brandy, rum, rye, molasses, nut, and cassia flavorings for beverages, ice cream, ices, candy, gelatin desserts, syrups (the biggest user: up to 30 ppm), and spirits. Used also as a solvent, insecticide, and fungicide. It irritates mucous membranes and acts on the central nervous system. Causes tearing and inflammation of eyes and throat irritation. Ingestion or absorption of .06 grams produces a persistent headache. Used continually, it leads to nervous disturbances and eye disorders (including photosensitivity).

FURFURYL ACETATE. Acetic Acid. A synthetic raspberry, fruit, spice, and ginger ale flavoring agent for beverages, ice cream, ices, candy, baked goods, and chewing gum. No known toxicity.

FURFURYL ALCOHOL. A synthetic flavoring obtained mainly from corncobs and roasted coffee beans. Has a faint burning odor and a bitter taste. Used in butter, butterscotch, caramel, coffee, fruit, and brandy flavorings for beverages, ice cream, ices, baked goods, and spirits. Also, an industrial solvent and wetting agent. It is poisonous.

FURFURYL MERCAPTAN. A synthetic flavoring that occurs naturally in coffee and is used in chocolate, fruit, coffee, and nut flavorings for beverages, ice cream, ices, candy, baked goods, gelatin desserts, and icings. No known toxicity.

2-FURFURYLIDENE BUTYRALDEHYDE. A synthetic fruit, liquor, rum, nut, and spice flavoring agent for beverages, ice cream, ices, candy, and baked goods. No known toxicity.

FURYL ACETONE. See (2-Furyl)-2-Propanone.

FURYL ACROLEIN. A synthetic coffee, fruit, cassia, and cinnamon flavoring agent for beverages, ice cream, ices, candy, baked goods, gelatin desserts, and puddings. No known toxicity.

4-(2-FURYL)-3-BUTEN-2-ONE. A synthetic nut, almond, and spice flavoring agent for beverages, ice cream, ices, candy, baked goods, and gelatin desserts. No known toxicity.

(2-FURYL)-2-PROPANONE. A synthetic fruit flavoring agent for ice cream, ices, candy, and baked goods. No known toxicity.

FUSEL OIL. Refined. A synthetic flavoring that occurs naturally in cognac oil. It is also a product of carbohydrate fermentation to produce ethyl alcohol (*see*) and varies widely in composition. Used in grape, brandy, cordial, rum, rye, Scotch, whiskey, and wine flavorings for beverages, ice cream, ices, candy, baked goods, chewing gum, gelatin desserts, puddings, and liquor. Commercial amyl alcohol (*see*) its major ingredient, is more toxic than ethyl alcohol, and as little as 30 milliliters has caused death. Smaller amounts can cause methemoglobinuria (blood cells in the urine), and kidney damage.

G

GALANGAL ROOT. East Indian Root. Chinese Ginger. The pungent, aromatic *oil* of the galangal root is a bitters, vermouth, spice, and ginger ale flavoring agent for beverages. The *extract* is a bitters, fruit, liquor, spice, and ginger ale flavoring agent for beverages, ice cream, ices, candy, baked goods, bitters, and liquors. Related to true ginger, it was formerly used in cooking and in medicine to treat colic. No known toxicity. GRAS

GALBANUM OIL. A yellowish to green or brown aromatic bitter gum resin from an Asiatic plant used as incense. The *oil* is a fruit, nut, and spice flavoring for beverages, ice cream, ices, candy, and baked goods. The *resin* is a berry, fruit, nut, and spice flavoring for beverages, ice cream, ices, candy, baked goods, and condiments. Has been used medicinally to break up intestinal gas and as an expectorant. No known toxicity.

GALLIC ACID. See Propyl Gallate.

GALLOTANNIC ACID. See Tannic Acid.

GAMBIR CATECHU. See Catechu Extract.

GAMBIR GUM. See Catechu Extract.

GARDEN ROSEMARY OIL. See Rosemary.

GARDENOL. See α-Methylbenzyl Acetate.

GARLIC OIL. Yellow liquid with a strong odor, obtained from the crushed bulbs or cloves of the plant. Used in fruit and garlic flavorings for beverages, ice cream, ices, candy, baked gods, chewing gum,

111

and condiments. Has been used medicinally to combat intestinal worms. The FDA has asked for further study of its safety. GRAS

GAS. A combustion product from the controlled combustion in air of butane, propane, or natural gas. It is used for removing or displacing oxygen in the processing, storage, or packaging of citrus products, vegetable fats, vegetable oils, coffee, and wine. No known toxicity when used in packaging.

GELATIN. A food thickener and stabilizer. A protein obtained by boiling animal skin, tendons, ligaments, or bones with water. Nutritionally, it is an incomplete protein lacking the amino acid tryptophan, and containing small amounts of other amino acids (see). It is colorless, or slightly yellow, and tasteless, and absorbs cold water 5 to 10 times its weight. Employed as a base for fruit gelatins, puddings, and chocolate milk, as well as chocolate-flavored beverages, cream (10 percent), and confections. It is an ingredient in cream cheese, Neufchâtel cheese, cheese spreads, cheese snacks, ice cream, frozen custard, fruit sherbet, and water ices. Used medicinally to treat malnutrition and brittle fingernails and as a blood plasma extender in treatment of shock. No known toxicity.

GENET, ABSOLUTE. A natural flavoring from flowers used in fruit and honey flavorings for beverages, ice cream, ices, candy, baked goods, and chewing gum. The extract is a raspberry and fruit flavoring for beverages. No known toxicity.

GENTIAN ROOT EXTRACT. The yellow or pale bitter root of Central and Southern European plants used in angostura, chocolate, cola, fruit, vermouth, maple, root beer, and vanilla flavorings for beverages, ice cream, ices, candy, and liquors. It has been used as a bitter tonic. No known toxicity.

GERANIAL. See Citral.

GERANIUM ROSE OIL. Derived from the leaves of Southern African granium herbs and rose petals added. Used in strawberry, lemon, cola, geranium, rose, violet, cherry, honey, rum, brandy, cognac, nut, vanilla, spice, and ginger ale flavorings for beverages, ice cream, ices, candy, baked goods, gelatin desserts, chewing gum, and jelly. A geranium root derivative has been used as an astringent and to treat chronic diarrhea in dogs. No known toxicity. GRAS

GERANIOL. A synthetic flavoring agent that occurs naturally in apples, bay leaves, cherries, coriander, grapefruit, oranges, tea, ginger, mace oil, and the oils of lavender, lavandin, lemon, lime, mandarin, and petitgrain. Sweet rose odor, and used in compounding artificial attar of roses in perfumery. A berry, lemon, rose, apple, cherry, peach, honey, root beer, cassia, cinnamon, ginger ale, and nutmeg flavoring for beverages, ice cream, ices, baked goods, candy, gelatin desserts, chewing gum, and toppings. Whereas no specific toxicity information is available, deaths have been reported from ingestion of unknown amounts of citronella oil (*see*) which is 93 per cent geraniol; gastric mucosa was found to be severely damaged. GRAS

GERANYL ACETATE. Acetic Acid. A synthetic flavoring agent that occurs naturally in oil of lavender and oil of lemon. A colorless liquid, with a flowery odor. Used in berry, lemon, orange, floral, apple, grape, peach, pear, honey, spice, and ginger ale flavorings for beverages, ice cream, ices, candy, baked goods, gelatin desserts, chewing gum, and syrup. No known toxicity but it is obtained from *geraniol* (*see*.)

GERANYL ACETOACETATE. A synthetic fruit flavoring agent for beverages, ice cream, ices, candy, and baked goods. See Geranyl Acetate for toxicity.

GERANYL BENZOATE. Benzoic Acid. A synthetic flavoring agent, slightly yellowish, liquid, with a floral odor. Used in floral and fruit flavorings for beverages, ice cream, ices, baked goods, and candy. See Geranyl Acetate for toxicity.

GERANYL BUTYRATE. Butyric Acid. A synthetic flavoring, colorless, liquid, with a rose or fruit odor. Used in berry, citrus, fruit, apple, cherry, pear, and pineapple flavorings for beverages, ice cream, ices, baked goods, gelatin desserts, and chewing gum. See Geranyl Acetate for toxicity.

GERANYL FORMATE. Formic Acid. A synthetic flavoring, colorless to pale yellow, liquid, with a fresh, leafy, rose odor. Used in berry, citrus, apple, apricot, and peach flavorings for beverages, ice cream, ices, candy, baked goods, gelatins, puddings, and chewing gum. See Geranyl Acetate for toxicity.

GERANYL HEXANOATE. Hexanoic Acid. A synthetic citrus and pineapple flavoring agent for beverages, ice cream, ices, candy, and baked goods. See Geranyl Acetate for toxicity.

GERANYL ISOBUTYRIC ACID. Isobutyric Acid. A synthetic floral, rose, apple, pear, and pineapple flavoring agent for beverages, ice cream, ices, candy, baked goods, gelatin desserts, puddings, and chewing gum. See Geranyl Acetate for toxicity.

GERANYL ISOVALERATE. A synthetic berry, lime, apple, peach, and pineapple flavoring agent for beverages, ice cream, ices, candy, and baked goods. See Geranyl Acetate for toxicity.

GERANYL PHENYLACETATE. Phenylacetic Acid. A synthetic flavoring, yellow, liquid, with a honey-rose odor. Used in fruit flavorings for beverages, ice cream, ices, candy, baked goods, and chewing gum. See Geranyl Acetate for toxicity.

GERANYL PROPIONATE. Propionic Acid. A synthetic flavoring, almost colorless, liquid, with a fruity-floral scent. Occurs naturally in oil of lavender. Used in berry, geranium, apple, pear, pineapple, and honey flavorings for beverages, ice cream, ices, candy, baked goods, gelatin desserts, and chewing gum. See Geranyl Acetate for toxicity.

GHATTI GUM. Indian Gum. The gummy exudate from the stems of a plant abundant in India and Ceylon. Used in butter, butterscotch, and fruit flavorings for beverages (2,000 ppm), ice cream, and ices. Has caused an occasional allergy, but when ingested in large amounts, it has not caused obvious distress. However, the FDA put ghatti gum on its priority list for short-term testing of mutagenic, teratogenic, subacute, and reproductive effects. In pharmaceutical preparations one part ghatti usually replaces two parts acacia (see). GRAS

GINGER. Derived from the rootlike stem of plants cultivated in all tropical countries, it is used in apple, plum, sausage, eggnog, pumpkin, ginger, ginger ale, and ginger beer flavorings for beverages, ice cream, ices, baked goods (2,500 ppm), and meats. The *extract* is used for cola, sausage, root beer, ginger, ginger ale, and ginger beer flavorings for beverages, ice cream, ices, candy, baked goods, condiments, and meats. The *oil* is used in root beer and ginger ale flavorings for the same products. Likewise the *oleoresin*, which is a ginger flavoring. Ginger has been used to break up intestinal gas and colic. No known toxicity. GRAS

GLUCONATE. Calcium and Sodium. A sequestrant derived from glucose, a sugar. Odorless, tasteless. Used as a buffer for confections, and a firming agent for tomatoes and apple slices. Sodium gluconate also is used as a nutrient and dietary supplement.

GLUCONIC ACID. A light, amber liquid with the faint odor of vinegar, produced from corn. It is water soluble and used as a dietary supplement and as a sequestrant. The magnesium salt of gluconic acid has been used as an antispasmodic. No known toxicity. GRAS

GLUCONO-DELTA-LACTONE. An acid with a sweet taste, fine, white, odorless. It is used as a leavening agent, in jelly powders and soft-drink powders where dry food acid is desired. Used in the dairy industry to prevent milk stone, and breweries to prevent beer stone, and is also a component of many cleaning compounds. Cleared by the U.S. Department of Agriculture's Meat Inspection Division for use at 8 ounces for each 100 pounds of cured, pulverized meat or meat food product to speed up the color-fixing process and to reduce the time required for smoking. No specific data on toxicity.

GLUCOSE. Occurs naturally in blood, grape, and corn sugars. A source of energy for plants and animals. Sweeter than sucrose. Glucose syrup is used to flavor sausage, hamburger, meat loaf, luncheon meat, chopped or pressed ham. It is also used as an extender in maple syrup. It is used medicinally for nutritional purposes and in the treatment of diabetic coma. No known toxicity.

GLUCOSE PENTAACETATE. A synthetic flavoring used in bitters flavoring for beverages and baked goods (1,500 ppm). No known toxicity.

GLUTAMATE. Ammonium and Monopotassium. Salt of glutamic acid. Used to impart meat flavor to foods and to enhance other natural food flavors and to improve the taste of tobacco. The FDA has asked for further studies on the glutamates as to their potential mutagenic, teratogenic, subacute, and reproductive effects. GRAS.

GLUTAMIC ACID. A white, practically odorless free-blowing crystalline powder, a non-essential amino acid (*see*) usually manufactured from vegetable protein. A salt substitute, it has been used to treat epilepsy and to correct low stomach acid. It is used to impart meat flavor to foods. Glutamic acid with hydrochloride (see Hydrochloric Acid) is used to improve the taste of beer, and is also used as a salt substitute. Both glutamic acid and glutamic acid hydrochloride are on the FDA list of additives to be studied for short-term testing of mutagenic, teratogenic, subacute, and reproductive effects.

GLUTEN. A mixture of proteins present in wheat flour, obtained as an extremely sticky yellowish-gray mass by making a dough and then washing out the starch. It consists almost entirely of two proteins, gliadin and glutelin, the exact proportions of which depend upon the variety of wheat. Contributes to the porous and spongy structure of bread. No known toxicity.

(MONO) GLYCERIDE CITRATE. Aids the action of and helps dissolve antioxidant formulations for oils and fats, such as shortenings for cooking. No known toxicity.

GLYCERIDES. Distilled. Food emulsifiers and binders in nutrient capsules and tablets; food-coating agent up to 5 percent of compound.

GLYCERIDES. Monoglycerides, Diglycerides, and Monosodium-glycerides of edible fats and oils. Emulsifying and defoaming agents. Used in bakery products to maintain "softness," in beverages, ice cream, ices, ice milk, milk, chewing gum base, shortening, lard, oleomargarine, confections, sweet chocolate, chocolate, rendered animal fat, and whipped toppings. The diglycerides are on the FDA list of food additives to be studied for possible mutagenic, teratogenic, subacute, and reproductive effects. GRAS

GLYCERIN. Glycerol. A sweet (about .6 times as cane sugar), warm-tasting substance which absorbs water from the air. Obtained from oils and fats as a by-product in the manufacture of soaps and fatty acids. Used as a humectant in tobacco and in marshmallows, pastilles, and jellylike candies; as a solvent for colors and flavors; as a bodying agent in combination with gelatins and edible gums; as a plasticizer in edible coatings for meat and cheese. It is also used in beverages, confectionery, baked goods, chewing gum, gelatin desserts, meat products, soda-fountain fudge. Also used in perfumery and as an emollient for the skin, and in suppositories for constipation. In concentrated solution it is irritating to the mucous membranes. Contact with strong oxidizing agent such as chromium trioxide, potassium chlorate, or potassium permanganate (*see*) may produce an explosion.

GLYCEROL. See Glycerin.

GLYCERYL ABIETATE. A density adjuster for citrus oil used in the preparation of alcoholic beverages and still and carbonated fruit drinks. Also cleared as a plasticizing material in chewing gum base. No known toxicity.

GLYCERYL LACTO ESTERS OF FATTY ACIDS. Food emulsifiers for use in shortening where free and combined lactic acid does not exceed 1.75 percent of shortening plus additive. No known toxicity.

GLYCERYL MONO- AND DI-ESTERS. Defoamers in yeast production. No known toxicity.

GLYCERYL TRIACETATE. See (*Tri-*) Acetin. GRAS

GLYCERYL TRIBUTYRATE. See (*Tri-*) Butyrin.

GLYCOCHOLIC ACID. An emulsifying agent for dried egg whites up to .1 percent. No known toxicity.

GLYCYRRHIZA. See Licorice, root.

GLYCYRRHIZA EXTRACT. See Licorice, extract.

GLYCYRRHIZIN, AMMONIATED. Licorice. Product of dried roots from the Mediterranean region used in licorice, anise, root beer, ginger beer, wintergreen, and birch beer flavorings for beverages, candy, and baked goods. Also used as a demulcent and expectorant and as a drug vehicle. On the FDA top priority list for short-term testing of mutagenic, teratogenic, subacute, and reproductive effects. Cases have been reported of avid licorice eaters who develop high blood pressure. See Licorice. GRAS

GRAINS OF PARADISE. Pungent aromatic seeds of a tropical African plant of the ginger family. It is a natural flavoring used in fruit, ginger, ginger ale, and pepper flavorings for beverages, ice cream, ices, and candy. No known toxicity.

GRAMINIS. See Dog Grass Extract.

GRAPEFRUIT OIL. The oil obtained by expression from the fresh peel of the grapefruit citrus Paradise. It is a yellow, sometimes reddish liquid used in grapefruit, lemon, lime, orange, and peach flavorings for beverages, ice cream, ices, candy, baked goods, gelatin desserts, chewing gum (1,500 ppm), and toppings. No known toxicity. GRAS

GRAPESKIN EXTRACT. Enocianina. A purple-red liquid extracted from the residue of grapes pressed for use in grape juice and wine. Used for coloring in still and carbonated drinks and ales, beverage bases, and alcoholic beverages. Regarding the spraying of grapes, specifications by the FDA restrict pesticide residues to not more than 10 ppm lead and not more than 1 ppm arsenic.

GUAIAC WOOD EXTRACT. A gum resin used in fruit and rum flavorings for beverages, ice cream, ices, candy, and baked goods. The *oil* is a raspberry, strawberry, rose, fruit, honey, ginger, and ginger ale flavoring for beverages, ice cream, candy, baked goods, gelatin desserts, and chewing gum. Formerly used to treat rheumatism. No known toxicity.

GUAIACYL ACETATE. A synthetic berry flavoring agent for beverages, ice cream, ices, candy, baked goods, gelatin, and chewing gum. No known toxicity.

GUAIYL ACETATE. *Guaiac Wood Acetate.* A synthetic tobacco and fruit flavoring agent for beverages, ice cream, ices, baked goods, and chewing gum. No known toxicity.

GUAIYL PHENYLACETATE. A synthetic berry, coffee, honey, tobacco, and smoke flavoring agent for beverages, ice cream, ices, candy, baked goods, and toppings. No known toxicity.

GUAR GUM. *Guar Flour.* From ground nutritive seed tissue of plants cultivated in India. A free-flowing powder, it is used as a stabilizer for frozen fruit, icings, glazes, and fruit drinks and as a thickener for hot and cold drinks. Has 5 to 8 times the thickening power of starch. Also, a binder for meats, confections, baked goods, cheese spreads, cream cheese, ice cream, ices, French dressing, and salad dressing. Keeps tablet formulations from disintegrating, and is used in lotions, creams, and tooth pastes; employed as a bulk laxative, appetite suppressant, and to treat peptic ulcer. On the FDA list of additives to be studied for short-term mutagenic, teratogenic, subacute, and reproductive effects. GRAS

GUARANA GUM. The dried paste consisting mainly of crushed seed from a plant grown in Brazil. Contains about 4 percent caffeine. Used in cola flavorings for beverages and candy. See Caffeine for toxicity.

GUARANINE. See Caffeine.

GUAVA. Extracted from the fruit of a small, shrubby American tree widely cultivated in warm regions. The fruit is sweet, sometimes acid, globular, and yellow. It is used to flavor jelly. No known toxicity. GRAS

GUINEA GREEN B. See FD and C Green No. 1.

GUM. True plant gums are the dried exudates from various plants obtained when the bark is cut or other injury is suffered. Gums are soluble in hot or cold water, and sticky. Today, the term gum, both for natural and synthetic sources, usually refers to water-soluble thickeners. Water-insoluble thickeners are referred to as resins. Gums are also used as emulsifiers, stabilizers, and suspending agents. No known toxicity.

GUM, CAROB BEAN. A thickener and stabilizer derived from the carob plant and used in chocolate milk, chocolate-flavored beverages, gassed cream (aerosol whipped cream), syrups for frozen products, confections, cream cheese, Neufchâtel cheese, ice cream, frozen custard, fruit sherbet, water ices, French dressing, and artificially sweetened jellies and preserves. Carob flour is an adsorbent-demulcent in diarrhea. On the FDA list of additives for short-term study of mutagenic, teratogenic, subacute, and reproductive effects. See Locust Bean Gum. GRAS

GUM ACACIA. See Acacia.

GUM ARABIC. See Acacia.

GUM BENJAMIN. See Benzoin.

GUM BENZOIN. See Benzoin.

GUM GUAIAC. Resin from the wood of the Guaiacum. Brown or greenish brown. Used as an antioxidant in edible fats or oils, beverages, rendered animal fat, or a combination of such fats and vegetable fats. It was formerly used in the treatment of rheumatism and other chronic diseases. No known toxicity.

GUM TRAGACANTH. The dried gummy exudation from plants found in Iran, Asia Minor, and Syria. A thickener and stabilizer, odorless, and with a gluelike taste. Used in fruit jelly, ornamental icings, fruit sherbets, water ices, salad dressing, French dressing, confections, and candy. Also employed in compounding drugs and pastes. One of the oldest known natural emulsifiers, its history predates the Christian era by hundreds of years; it has been recognized in the U.S. Pharmacopoeia since 1820. It has a long shelf life and is resistant to acids. Aside from occasional allergic reaction, it can be ingested in large amounts with little harm except for diarrhea, gas, or constipation. On the FDA list for study of its mutagenic, teratogenic, subacute, and reproductive effects. GRAS

H

HAW BARK. Black Extract. Extract of the fruit of a hawthorn shrub or tree. Used in butter, caramel, cola, maple, and walnut flavorings for beverages, ice cream, ices, candy, and baked goods. Has been used as a uterine antispasmodic. No known toxicity.

HEDEONA OIL. See Pennyroyal Oil.

HELIOTROPINE. See Piperonal.

HELIOTROPYL ACETATE. See Piperonyl Acetate.

HELIUM. This colorless, odorless, tasteless gas is used as propellant for foods packed in pressurized containers. No known toxicity. GRAS

HEMLOCK OIL. Spruce Oil. A natural flavoring extract from North American or Asian nonpoisonous hemlock. Used in fruit, root beer, and spice flavorings for beverages, ice cream, ices, candy, baked goods, gelatin puddings, and chewing gum. No known toxicity.

HENDECANAL. See Undecanal.

HENDECEN-9-ol. See 9-Undecanal.

10-HENDECENYL ACETATE. See 10-Undecen-1-yl-Acetate.

γ-HEPTALACTONE. A synthetic coconut, nut, and vanilla flavoring agent for beverages, ice cream, ices, candy, and baked goods. No known toxicity.

HEPTALDEHYDE. See Heptanal.

HEPTANAL. Heptyl Aldehyde. A synthetic flavoring agent, colorless to slightly yellow, with a penetrating, fruity odor. Obtained by distilling castor oil. Used in citrus, apple, melon, cognac, rum, and almond flavorings for beverages, ice cream, ices, candy, baked goods, and liqueurs. No known toxicity.

HEPTANAL DIMETHYL ACETAL. A synthetic fruit, melon, and mushroom flavoring agent for beverages, ice cream, ices, candy, baked goods, and condiments. No known toxicity.

HEPTANAL GLYCERYL ACETAL. A synthetic mushroom flavoring agent for beverages, ice cream, ices, candy, and baked goods. No known toxicity.

2, 3-HEPTANEDIONE. A synthetic raspberry, strawberry, butter, fruit, rum, nut, and cheese flavoring agent for beverages, ice cream, ices, candy, baked goods, and chewing gum. No known toxicity.

1-HEPTANOL. A synthetic flavoring agent, liquid, and miscible with alcohol and ether. See Heptyl Alcohol for use.

2-HEPTANONE. A synthetic flavoring agent, liquid, with a penetrating odor, used to give a "peppery" smell to such cheeses as Roquefort. Used in berry, butter, fruit, and cheese flavorings for beverages, ice cream, ices, candy, baked goods, and condiments (25 ppm). Used also in perfumery. Found naturally in oil of cloves and in cinnamon bark oil. The lethal concentration in air for rats is 4,000 ppm. In high doses it is narcotic, and a suspected irritant to human mucous membranes.

3-HEPTANONE. A synthetic melon flavoring agent for beverages, ice cream, ices, candy, and baked goods. See 2-Heptanone, which is a similar compound.

4-HEPTANONE. A synthetic strawberry and fruit flavoring agent for beverages, ice cream, ices, candy, baked goods, and gelatin desserts. See 2-Heptanone, which is a similar compound.

HEPTYL ACETATE. A synthetic berry, banana, melon, pear, and pineapple flavoring agent for beverages, ice cream, ices, candy, and baked goods. No known toxicity.

HEPTYL ALCOHOL. 1-Heptanol. A synthetic flavoring agent, colorless, with a fatty citrus odor, used in fruit flavorings for beverages, ice cream, ices, candy, and baked goods. No known toxicity.

HEPTYL ALDEHYDE. See Heptanal.

HEPTYL BUTYRATE. Butyric Acid. A synthetic raspberry, floral, violet, apricot, melon, and plum flavoring agent for beverages, ice cream, ices, candy, baked goods. No known toxicity.

γ-HEPTYL BUTYROLACTONE. See γ-Undecalactone.

HEPTYL ISOBUTYRATE. A synthetic coconut, apricot, peach, pineapple, and plum flavoring agent for beverages, ice cream, ices, candy, and baked goods. No known toxicity.

HEXADECANOIC ACID. See Palmitic Acid.

1-HEXADECANOL. Cetyl Alcohol. A synthetic chocolate flavoring agent for ice cream, ices, and candy. No known toxicity.

ω-6-HEXADECENLACTONE. Ambrettolide. 6-Hexadecenolide. A synthetic fruit flavoring agent for beverages, ice cream, ices, candy, baked goods, gelatin desserts, and chewing gum. No known toxicity.

6-HEXADECENOLIDE. See ω-6-Hexadecenlactone.

HEXADECYLIC ACID. See Palmitic Acid.

2, 4-HEXADIENOATE. See Allyl Sorbate.

HEXAHYDROPYRIDENE. See Piperidine.

HEXAHYDROTHYMOL. See Menthol.

γ-HEXALACTONE. A synthetic butter, fruit, honey, and vanilla flavoring agent for beverages, ice cream, ices, candy, and baked goods. No known toxicity.

HEXALDEHYDE. See Hexanal.

HEXANAL. Hexaldehyde. Hexoic Aldehyde. A synthetic flavoring agent occurring naturally in apples, coffee, cooked chicken, strawberries, tea, and tobacco leaves (oils). Used in butter, fruit, honey, and rum flavorings for beverages, ice cream, ices, candy, baked goods, gelatin desserts, and chewing gum. No known toxicity.

1-HEXANAL. See Hexyl Alcohol.

2, 3-HEXANDIONE. A synthetic strawberry, butter, citrus, banana, pineapple, rum, and cheese flavoring agent for beverages, ice cream, ices, candy, and baked goods. No known toxicity.

HEXANE. A colorless volatile liquid derived from distillation of petroleum and used as a solvent for spice oleoresins (*see*). Also used in low-temperature thermometers instead of mercury, usually with a blue or red dye. It is a mild central nervous system depressant which may be irritating to the respiratory tract.

HEXANEDIOIC ACID. See Adipic Acid.

HEXANOIC ACID. A synthetic flavoring agent that occurs naturally in apples, butter acids, cocoa, grapes, oil of lavender, oil of lavandin, raspberries, strawberries, and tea. Used in butter, butterscotch, chocolate, fruit, rum, pecan, and cheese, flavorings for beverages, ice cream, ices, candy, baked goods, chewing gum, and condiments. No known toxicity.

2-HEXEN-1-ol. A synthetic flavoring that occurs naturally in grapes; similar in compound to 3-Hexen-1-ol (*see*). Used in fruit and mint flavorings for beverages, ice cream, ices, candy, and baked goods. No known toxicity.

3-HEXEN-1-ol. Leaf Alcohol. A synthetic flavoring that occurs naturally in leaves of odoriferous plants and in grapefruit, raspberries, and tea. Strong odor. Used in fruit and mint flavorings for beverages, ice cream, ices, candy, and baked goods. No known toxicity.

2-HEXEN-1-yl ACETATE. A synthetic fruit flavoring agent for beverages, ice cream, ices, candy, and baked goods. No known toxicity.

2-HEXENAL. A synthetic berry and fruit flavoring agent that occurs naturally in apples and strawberries and is used for beverages, ice cream, ices, candy, and baked goods. No known toxicity.

cis-3-HEXENAL. A synthetic fruit flavoring agent for beverages, ice cream, ices, and candy. No known toxicity.

2-HEXENOIC ACID. See Methyl 2-Hexenoate.

HEXOIC ACID. See Hexanoic Acid.

HEXOIC ALDEHYDE. A synthetic berry, apple, pear, and pineapple flavoring agent for beverages, ice cream, ices, candy, baked goods, and chewing gum. No known toxicity. See Hexanal.

HEXYL ACETATE. *Acetic Acid. Hexyl Ester.* A synthetic berry, apple, pear, and pineapple flavoring agent for beverages, ice cream, ices, candy, baked goods, and chewing gum. No known toxicity.

2-HEXYL-4-ACETOXYTETRAHYDROFURAN. A synthetic fruit flavoring agent for beverages, ice cream, ices, candy, and baked goods. No known toxicity.

HEXYL ALCOHOL. *1-Hexanol.* A synthetic flavoring agent that occurs naturally in apples, oil of lavender, strawberries, and tea. Used in berry, coconut, and fruit flavorings for beverages, ice cream, ices, candy, baked goods, and gelatin desserts. Also used as a solvent. No known toxicity. GRAS

HEXYL ESTER. See Hexyl Acetate.

HEXYL FORMATE. *Formic Acid.* A synthetic raspberry and fruit flavoring agent for beverages, ice cream, ices, candy, and baked goods. See Formic Acid for toxicity.

HEXYL 2-FUROATE. A synthetic coffee, maple, and mushroom flavoring agent for candy and condiments. No known toxicity.

HEXYL HEXANOATE. *Hexanoic Acid.* A synthetic fruit flavoring agent for beverages, ice cream, ices, candy, and baked goods. No known toxicity.

2-HEXYL-5 (or 6)-KETO-1, 4-DIOXANE. A synthetic cream flavoring agent for beverages, ice cream, ices, candy, baked goods, and margarine. No known toxicity.

HEXYL OCTANOATE. *Octanoic Acid.* A synthetic fruit flavoring agent for beverages and puddings. No known toxicity.

HEXYL PROPIONATE. *Proprionic Acid.* A synthetic fruit flavoring agent for beverages, ice cream, ices, candy, and baked goods. No known toxicity.

α-HEXYLCINNAMALDEHYDE. A synthetic flavoring, pale yellow liquid, with a jasminelike odor. Used in berry, fruit, and honey flavorings for beverages, ice cream, ices, candy, baked goods, and gelatin desserts. No known toxicity.

HEXYLENE GLYCOL DIACETATE. See 1, 3-Nonanediol Acetate (mixed esters).

2-HEXYLIDENE CYCLOPENTANONE. A synthetic fruit flavoring agent for beverages, ice cream, ices, candy, and baked goods. No known toxicity.

HICKORY BARK EXTRACT. A natural flavoring extract from the hickory nut tree and used in butter, caramel, rum, maple, nut, spice, tobacco, and smoke flavorings for beverages, ice cream, ices, candy, baked goods, condiments, and liquors. No known toxicity. GRAS

HIPBERRY EXTRACT. See Rose Hips Extract.

HISTIDINE L and DL forms. One of the basic, essential amino acids (*see*), used as a nutrient. Soluble in water. (L-Histidine is the natural form.) Histidine is on the FDA list of additives that need further study. GRAS

HOPS. Extract. Carefully dried pineconelike fruit of the hop grown in Europe, Asia, and North America. Light yellow to greenish, oily, bitter, with an aromatic odor. Used especially in beer brewing and in fruit and root beer flavorings for beverages. A *solid extract* is used in bitters, fruit, and root beer flavorings for beverages, ice cream, ices, candy, and baked goods. Hops *oil* is used in raspberry, grape, whiskey, and spice flavorings for beverages, ice cream, ices, candy, baked goods, chewing gum, and condiments. Hops at one time were thought to be a sedative. No known toxicity. GRAS

HOREHOUND EXTRACT. Hoarhound. A flavoring extracted from a mintlike plant cultivated in Europe, Asia, and the United States. It has a very bitter taste and is used in maple, nut, and root beer flavorings for beverages, ice cream, ices, candy, and baked goods. It is also a bitter tonic and expectorant. No known toxicity.

HORSEMINT LEAVES EXTRACT. A flavoring extract from any of several coarse, aromatic plants, grown from New York to Florida, and from Texas to Wisconsin. Used in fruit flavorings for beverages (600 ppm). Formerly used as an aromatic stimulant and to break up intestinal gas. No known toxicity.

HORSERADISH. A condiment ingredient utilizing the grated root from the tall, coarse, white-flowered herb native to Europe. Often combined with vinegar or other ingredients. Contains ascorbic acid (*see*) and acts as a urinary antiseptic. No known toxicity. GRAS

HUMECTANT. A substance used to preserve the moisture content of materials. For example, glycerin (*see*) which is used to preserve moisture in confections and tobaccos.

HYACINTH, ABSOLUTE. A natural flavoring from the very fragrant common flower native to the Mediterranean. It is used in chewing gum. The bulb can cause severe gastrointestinal symptoms.

HYACINTHIN. See Phenylacetaldehyde.

HYDRATROPALDEHYDE. See 2-Phenylpropionaldehyde.

HYDRATROPALDEHYDE DIMETHYL ACETAL. See 2-Phenylpropionaldehyde Dimethyl Acetal.

HYDROCHLORIC ACID. An acid used as a modifier for food starch, in the manufacture of sodium glutamate (*see*) and gelatin, for the conversion of cornstarch to syrup (0.012 percent), and to adjust the pH (acid-alkalinity balance) in the brewing industry (0.02 percent). Concentrated solutions may cause severe burns, permanent eye damage, and skin rash. Inhalation of the fumes causes choking and inflammation of the respiratory tract; ingestion may corrode the mucous membranes, esophagus, and stomach, and cause diarrhea. Circulatory collapse and death can occur. GRAS

HYDROCINNAMIC ACID. See 3-Phenylpropionic Acid.

HYDROGEN PEROXIDE. A preservative and bacteria-killer for milk and cheese and a bleaching and oxidizing agent and modifier of food starch. Bleaches tripe and butter; used in the treatment of eggs before drying and in Cheddar and Swiss cheeses. Because it is a strong oxidizer, undiluted it can cause burns of the skin and mucous membranes. On the FDA list of additives to be studied for short-term mutagenic, teratogenic, subacute, and reproductive effects. GRAS

HYDROGENATED TALLOW. A component used in the production of beet sugar and yeast in amounts to inhibit foaming. See Hydrogenation. No known toxicity.

HYDROGENATED TALLOW ALCOHOL. See Hydrogenated Tallow, which has the same uses.

HYDROGENATION. The adding of hydrogen gas under high pressure to liquid oils. It is the most widely used chemical process in the edible fat industry. Used in the manufacture of margarine and shortening and in the extraction of petrol from coal. In the food industry its primary use is to convert liquid oils to semisolid fats, Crisco, for example, at room temperature. It retards rancidity in the compound and improves color. Usually, the higher the amount of hydrogenation, the lower the unsaturation in the fat and the less the possibility of flavor degradation due to rancidity. Hydrogenated oils still contain some unsaturated components which are susceptible to rancidity. Therefore, the addition of antioxidants is still necessary.

HYDROLYZED. Subject to hydrolysis or turned partly into water. Hydrolysis is derived from the Greek *hydro,* meaning "water," and *lysis* meaning "a setting free." It occurs as a chemical process in which the decomposition of a compound is brought about by water, resolving into simpler compound. Hydrolysis also occurs in the digestion of foods. The proteins in the stomach react with water in an enzyme reaction to form peptones, peptides, and amino acids.

HYDROQUINONE DIMETHYL ETHER. See *p*-Dimethoxybenzene.

3-HYDROXY-2-BUTANONE. See Acetoin.

2-HYDROXY-p-CYMENE. See Carvacrol.

5-HYDROXY-4-OCTANONE. A synthetic butter, butterscotch, fruit, cheese, and nut flavoring agent for beverages, ice cream, ices, candy, and baked goods. No known toxicity.

o-HYDROXYBENZALDEHYDE. See Salicylaldehyde.

p-HYDROXYBENZYL ACETONE. See 4-(p-Hydroxyphenyl)-2-Butanone.

2-HYDROXYCAMPHANE. See Borneol.

HYDROXYCITRONELLAL. *Laurine®.* A synthetic flavoring, colorless, liquid, with a sweet lily odor. Used in berry, citrus, linden, violet, and cherry flavorings for beverages, ice cream, ices, candy, baked goods, gelatin desserts, and chewing gum. No known toxicity.

HYDROXYCITRONELLAL DIETHYL ACETAL. A synthetic citrus and fruit flavoring agent for beverages, ice cream, ices, candy, and baked goods. No known toxicity.

HYDROXYCITRONELLAL DIMETHYL ACETAL. A synthetic flavoring, colorless, liquid, with a light floral odor. Used in fruit and cherry flavorings for beverages, ice cream, ices, candy, and baked goods. No known toxicity.

HYDROXYCITRONELLOL. A synthetic lemon, floral, and cherry flavoring agent for beverages, ice cream, ices, candy, baked goods, gelatin desserts, and chewing gum. No known toxicity.

4-HYDROXYUNDECANOIC ACID, γ-LACTONE. See γ-Undecalactone.

HYPNONE. See Acetophenone.

4-(p-HYDROXYPHENYL)-2-BUTANONE. A synthetic fruit flavoring for beverages, ice cream, ices, candy, baked goods, gelatin desserts, and chewing gum. No known toxicity.

HYPO. Prefix from the Greek meaning "under" or "below," as in hypoacidity—acidity in a lesser degree than is usual or normal.

HYSSOP. A synthetic flavoring from the aromatic herb. Used in bitters. The *extract* is a liquor flavoring for beverages, ice cream, ices, and liquors. The *oil* is a liquor and spice flavoring for beverages, ice cream, ices, candy, baked goods, and liquors. GRAS

I

IMITATION FLAVOR. A flavor containing any portion of nonnatural materials. For instance, unless a strawberry flavoring is made entirely from strawberries, it must be called imitation. When a processor fails to use all the standard ingredients in mayonnaise, he must call it salad dressing.

IMITATION MILK. Contains no milk derivatives. Usually contains water, sugar, and vegetable fat. A source of protein (such as soy bean) with various additive flavorings. Imitation milk contains 1 percent protein compared to 3.5 percent in whole cow's milk.

IMMORTELLE EXTRACT. A natural flavoring extract from a red-flowered tropical tree. The name derives from the French *Immortel*—"immortal" or "everlasting." Used in raspberry, fruit, and liquor flavoring for beverages, ice cream, ices, baked goods, candy, gelatin desserts, and chewing gum. GRAS

INDIAN GUM. See Ghatti Gum.

INDIAN TRAGACANTH. See Karaya Gum.

INDIGO CARMINE. See FD and C Blue No. 2.

INDOLE. A synthetic flavoring agent, white, lustrous, flaky, with an unpleasant odor, occurring naturally in jasmine oil and orange flowers. Also extracted from coal tar and feces; in highly dilute solutions the odor is pleasant, and it has been used in perfumery. Used in raspberry, strawberry, bitters, chocolate, orange, coffee, violet, fruit, nut, and cheese flavorings for beverages, ice cream, ices, candy, baked goods, and gelatin desserts. The lethal dose in dogs is 60 milligrams per kilogram of body weight.

INOSINATE. A salt of inosinic acid used to intensify flavor, as with sodium glutamate (*see*). Inosinic acid is prepared from meat extract; also from dried sardines. No known toxicity.

INOSITOL. A dietary supplement, a member of the Vitamin B complex. Found in plant and animal tissue. Isolated commercially from corn. Fine, white, crystalline powder, odorless, with a sweet taste, and stable in air. Also called muscle sugar. No known toxicity. GRAS

INVERT SUGAR. *Inversol. Nulomoline. Colorose.* A mixture of 50 percent glucose and 50 percent fructose. It is sweeter than sucrose. Commercially produced by "inversion" of sucrose. Honey is mostly invert sugar. Invert sugar is used in confectionery and in brewing. Like glycerin (*see*) it holds in moisture and prevents drying out. Used medicinally in intravenous solutions. No known toxicity. GRAS in packaging.

IODINE SOURCES: *Cuprous Iodide, Potassium Iodate, and Potassium Iodide.* Iodine occurs in solid earth crust. It is an integral part of the thyroid hormones which have important metabolic roles, and is an essential nutrient for man. Iodine deficiency leads to thyroid enlargement or goiter. Nutritionists have found that the most efficient way to add iodine to the diet is through the use of iodized salt. The FDA has ordered all table salts to specify whether the product contains iodide. However, many commercially prepared food items do not contain iodized salt. Iodized salt contains up to .01 percent; dietary supplements contain .16 percent. Cuprous and potassium iodides are used in table salts; potassium iodide is in some drinking water; and potassium iodate is used in animal feeds. Dietary iodine is absorbed from the intestinal tract, and man's main sources are from food and water. Seafoods are good sources, and dairy products may be good sources if the cows eat enriched grain. Adult daily iodine requirement is believed to be 110 to 150 mgs. Growing children and pregnant or lactating women may need more. Iodine has been found to cause allergic reaction in susceptible people.

IONONE. *Irisone.*® A flavoring agent that occurs naturally in Boronia, an Australian shrub; colorless to pale yellow, with an odor reminiscent of cedarwood or violets. α-Ionone is used in blackberry, loganberry, raspberry, citrus, orange, floral, fruit, cherry, spice, and vanilla flavorings for beverages, ice cream, ices, candy, baked goods, gelatin desserts, chewing gum, and icings. β-Ionone is used in blackberry, berry, loganberry, raspberry, strawberry, floral, violet, fruit, cherry, grape, pineapple, liquor, muscatel, nut, and pistachio flavorings for beverages, ice cream, ices, candy, baked goods, gelatin desserts, chewing gum, and Maraschino cherries. It may cause allergic reactions.

IRIS FLORENTINA. See Orris.

IRISH MOSS DERIVATIVE. See Carrageenan Chondrus Extract.

α-IRISONE.® See Ionone, α-Ionone.

β-IRISONE.® See Ionone, β-Ionone.

IRON. Ammonium Citrate, Carbonate, Chloride, Gluconate, Oxide, Phosphate, Pyrophosphate, Sulfate, and Reduced Iron. Iron occurs in the earth's crust. It is used as a mineral supplement and in prepared breakfast cereals, poultry stuffing, enriched flours, macaroni and noodle products, enriched farina, cornmeal, corn grits, and bread. The recommended daily allowance for children and adults is from .2 mg to 1.0 mg and 18 mg per day for pregnant women. Iron is potentially toxic in all its forms. GRAS

IRON OXIDE. Any of several natural or synthetic oxides of iron (iron combined with oxygen) varying in color from red brown or black to orange and yellow. Used for dyeing eggshells and for food coloring. See Iron for toxicity.

IRON SOURCES (IRON SALTS): Ferric Choline Citrate; Ferric Orthophosphate; Ferric Phosphate; Ferric Pyrophosphate, Ferric Sodium Pyrophosphate; Ferrous Fumarate; Ferrous Gluconate; Ferrous Lactate; and Ferrous Sulfate. Ferric phosphate is used as a food supplement, particularly in bread enrichment. Ferric pyrophosphate is a grayish blue powder used in ceramics. Ferric sodium pyrophosphate is used in prepared breakfast cerals, poultry stuffing, enriched flours, self-rising flours, farina, cornmeal, corn grits, bread, and rolls. Ferrous fumarate is used to treat iron deficiency anemia. Ferrous gluconate is used in food coloring (yellowish gray), as a flavoring agent, and to treat iron deficiency anemia. It may cause gastrointestinal disturbances. Ferrous lactate is greenish white with a sweet, iron taste. It is affected by air and light. It is also used to treat anemia. Ferrous sulfate is blue green and odorless, it oxidizes in air, and is used as a wood preservative, weed killer, and to treat anemia. Large quantities can cause gastrointestinal disturbances. For ferric choline citrate, see Choline Chloride.

α-IRONE. A synthetic flavoring derived from the violet family, and usually isolated from irises and orris oil. Light yellow, slightly viscous.

Used in berry, raspberry, strawberry, floral, violet, and fruit flavorings for beverages, ice cream, ices, candy, baked goods, and chewing gum. Also used in perfumery. See Orris Root Extract for toxicity.

IRRADIATED ERGOSTEROL. See Vitamin D_2.

ISO. Greek for "equal." In chemistry, it is a prefix added to the name of one compound to denote another composed of the same kinds and numbers of atoms but different from each other in structural arrangement.

ISOAMYL ACETATE. A synthetic flavoring agent that occurs naturally in bananas and pears. Colorless; pearlike odor and taste. Used in raspberry, strawberry, butter, caramel, coconut, cola, apple, banana, cherry, grape, peach, pear, pineapple, rum, cream soda, and vanilla flavorings for beverages, ice cream, ices, candy, baked goods, gelatin desserts, and chewing gum (2,700 ppm). Also used in perfuming shoe polish among other industrial uses. Exposure to 950 ppm for one hour has caused headache, fatigue, substernal pressure, and irritation of mucous membranes.

ISOAMYL ACETOACETATE. A synthetic fruit and apple flavoring agent for beverages, ice cream, ices, candy, and baked goods. No known toxicity.

ISOAMYL ALCOHOL. A synthetic flavoring agent that occurs naturally in apples, cognac, lemons, peppermint, raspberry, strawberry, and tea. Used in chocolate, apple, banana, brandy, and rum flavorings for beverages, ice cream, ices, candy, baked goods, gelatin desserts, chewing gum, and brandy. A central nervous system depressant. Vapor exposures have caused marked irritation of the eyes, nose, and throat, and headache. Amyl alcohols are highly toxic, and ingestion has caused human deaths from respiratory failure. Isoamyl alcohol may cause heart, lung, and kidney damage.

ISOAMYL BENZOATE. A synthetic berry, apple, cherry, plum, prune, liquor, rum, and maple flavoring agent for beverages, ice cream, ices, candy, gelatin desserts, baked goods, and chewing gum. Also used in perfumery and cosmetics. No known toxicity.

ISOAMYL CINNAMATE. A synthetic strawberry, butter, caramel, chocolate, cocoa, fruit, peach, pineapple, and honey flavoring agent for beverages, ice cream, candy, and baked goods. No known toxicity.

ISOAMYL FORMATE. Formic Acid. A synthetic flavoring agent, colorless, liquid, with a fruity smell. Used in strawberry, apple, apricot, banana, peach, and pineapple flavorings for beverages, ice cream, candy, baked goods, gelatin desserts, and chewing gum. See Formic Acid for toxicity.

ISOAMYL 2-FURANBUTYRATE. A synthetic chocolate, coffee, fruit, and whiskey flavoring agent for beverages, ice cream, ices, candy, baked goods, and gelatin. No known toxicity.

ISOAMYL 2-FURANPROPIONATE. A synthetic chocolate, coffee, fruit, and whiskey flavoring agent for beverages, ice cream, ices, candy, and baked goods. No known toxicity.

α-ISOAMYL FURFURYLACETATE. See Isoamyl 2-Furanpropionate.

α-ISOAMYL FURFURYLPROPIONATE. See Isoamyl 2-Furanbutyrate.

ISOAMYL ISOBUTYRATE. A synthetic fruit and banana flavoring agent for beverages, ice cream, ices, candy, baked goods, gelatin desserts, puddings, and chewing gum (2,000 ppm). Used in manufacture of artificial rum and fruit essences. No known toxicity.

ISOAMYL ISOVALERATE. A synthetic flavoring agent, clear, colorless, liquid, with an apple odor. Occurs naturally in bananas and peaches. Used in raspberry, strawberry, apple, apricot, banana, cherry, peach, pineapple, honey, rum, walnut, vanilla, and cream soda flavorings for beverages, ice cream, ices, candy, baked goods, gelatin desserts, puddings, chewing gum, jellies, and liqueurs. No known toxicity.

ISOAMYL LAURATE. A synthetic fruit and liquor flavoring agent for beverages, ice cream, ices, candy, and baked goods. No known toxicity.

ISOAMYL NONANOATE. A synthetic fruit, cognac, and rum flavoring agent for beverages, ice cream, ices, candy, and baked goods. No known toxicity.

ISOAMYL OCTANOATE. A synthetic chocolate, fruit, and liquor flavoring agent for beverages, ice cream, ices, candy, baked goods, and gelatin desserts. No known toxicity.

ISOAMYL PHENYLACETATE. A synthetic butter, chocolate, cocoa, peach, honey, licorice, and anise flavoring agent for beverages, ice cream, ices, candy, baked goods, toppings, and gelatin desserts. No known toxicity.

ISOAMYL PYRUVATE. A synthetic fruit, rum, and maple flavoring agent for beverages, ice cream, ices, candy, and baked goods. No known toxicity.

ISOAMYL SALICYLATE. A synthetic flavoring agent, colorless, liquid, with a pleasant odor. Used in root beer and fruit flavorings for beverages, ice cream, ices, candy, and baked goods. Also used in perfumery and soaps. See Salicylic Acid for toxicity.

ISOBORNEOL. A synthetic fruit and spice flavoring agent for beverages, ice cream, ices, candy, baked goods, and chewing gum. See Borneol for toxicity.

ISOBORNYL ACETATE. A synthetic fruit flavoring for beverages, ice cream, ices, candy, baked goods, and gelatin. No known toxicity.

ISOBUTYL ACETATE. A synthetic flavoring agent, clear, colorless, liquid, with a fruity odor. Used in raspberry, strawberry, butter, banana, and grape flavorings for beverages, ice cream, ices, candy, baked goods, gelatin desserts, chewing gum, and icings. May be mildly irritating to mucous membranes and in high concentrations it is narcotic.

ISOBUTYL ACETOACETATE. A synthetic berry and fruit flavoring agent for beverages, ice cream, ices, candy, and baked goods. See Isobutyl Acetate for toxicity.

ISOBUTYL ANTHRANILATE. A synthetic mandarin, cherry, and grape flavoring agent for beverages, ice cream, ices, candy, baked goods, and chewing gum (1,700 ppm). No known toxicity.

ISOBUTYL BENZOATE. A synthetic berry, cherry, plum, and pineapple flavoring agent for beverages, ice cream, ices, candy, and baked goods. No known toxicity.

ISOBUTYL BUTYRATE. A synthetic berry, apple, banana, pineapple, liquor, and rum flavoring agent for beverages, ice cream, ices, candy, baked goods, puddings, and liquor. No known toxicity.

ISOBUTYL 2-FURANPROPIONATE. A synthetic berry and pineapple flavoring agent for beverages, ice cream, ices, candy, baked goods, gelatin desserts, chewing gum, and icings. No known toxicity.

ISOBUTYL HEXANOATE. A synthetic apple and pineapple flavoring agent for beverages, ice cream, ices, baked goods, and chewing gum. No known toxicity.

ISOBUTYL ISOBUTYRATE. A synthetic strawberry, butter, fruit, banana, and liquor flavoring agent in beverages, ice cream, ices, candy, baked goods, gelatin desserts, puddings, and liquor. No known toxicity.

ISOBUTYL PHENYLACETATE. A synthetic butter, caramel, chocolate, fruit, honey, and nut flavoring agent for beverages, ice cream, ices, candy, baked goods, puddings, and Maraschino cherries. No known toxicity.

ISOBUTYL PROPIONATE. A synthetic strawberry, butter, peach, and rum flavoring agent for beverages, ice cream, candy, and baked goods. Used in the manufacture of fruit essences. No known toxicity.

ISOBUTYL SALICYLATE. A synthetic flavoring agent, colorless, liquid, with an orchid odor. Used in fruit and root beer flavorings for beverages, ice cream, ices, candy, and baked goods. See Salicylic Acid for toxicity.

ISOBUTYLENE-ISOPYRENE COPOLYMER. A chewing-gum base. Isobutylene is used to produce antioxidants for foods, food supplements, and packaging. Vapors may cause asphyxiation.

a-ISOBUTYLPHENETHYL ALCOHOL. A synthetic butter, caramel, chocolate, fruit, and spice flavoring agent for beverages, ice cream, ices, candy, baked goods, liqueurs, and chocolate. See Isoamyl Alcohol for toxicity.

ISOBUTYRALDEHYDE. A synthetic flavoring agent which occurs naturally in soy sauce, tea, tobacco, and coffee. It has a pungent odor. Used in berry, butter, caramel, fruit, liquor, and wine flavorings for beverages, ice cream, ices, candy, baked goods, and liquor. No known toxicity.

ISOBUTYRIC ACID. A synthetic flavoring agent which occurs naturally in bay, bay leaves, parsley, and strawberries. It has a pungent odor. Used in butter, butterscotch, fruit, liquor, rum, cheese, nut, vanilla, and cream soda flavorings for beverages, ice cream, ices, candy, baked goods, chewing gum, and margarine. It is a mild irritant.

ISOEUGENOL. A synthetic flavoring agent, pale yellow, viscous, with a floral odor. Occurs naturally in mace oil. Used in mint, fruit, spice, cinnamon, and clove flavorings for beverages, ice cream, ices, baked goods, chewing gum (1,000 ppm), and condiments. Used in the manufacture of vanillin (*see*). No known toxicity.

ISOEUGENYL ACETATE. A synthetic berry, fruit, and spice flavoring agent for beverages, ice cream, ices, candy, baked goods, and chewing gum. No known toxicity.

ISOEUGENYL ETHYL ETHER.   A synthetic flavoring agent, white crystals with a spicy, clovelike odor. Used in fruit and vanilla flavorings for beverages, ice cream, ices, candy, and baked goods. No known toxicity.

ISOEUGENYL FORMATE.   A synthetic spice flavoring agent used in condiments. See Formic Acid for toxicity.

ISOEUGENYL METHYL ETHER.   A synthetic raspberry, strawberry, cherry, and clove flavoring agent for beverages, ices, ice cream, candy, baked goods, gelatin desserts, and chewing gum. No known toxicity.

ISOEUGENYL PHENYLACETATE.   A synthetic fruit, honey, and spice flavoring agent for beverages, ice cream, ices, candy, and baked goods. No known toxicity.

ISOLATE.   In chemistry, a chemical or material obtained from a natural substance. For example, citral can be isolated from lemon oil or orange oil; geraniol can be isolated from the oil of geranium and oil of citronella. An extract, on the other hand, is a solution obtained by passing alcohol or an alcohol and water mixture through a substance.

ISOLEUCINE. L and DL forms.   An essential component in human nutrition. It is a product of almost every protein but is not synthesized in the human body. Isolated commercially from beet sugar. The FDA has asked for a further study of this nutrient. GRAS

ISOPROPYL CITRATE.   A sequestrant and antioxidant agent used in oleomargarine and salad oils. See Citrate Salts for toxicity.

ISOPROPYL FORMATE. Formic Acid.   A synthetic berry and melon flavoring agent for beverages, ice cream, candy, and baked goods. See Formic Acid for toxicity.

ISOPROPYL HEXANOATE.   A synthetic pineapple flavoring agent for beverages, ice cream, ices, candy, and baked goods. No known toxicity.

ISOPROPYL ISOBUTYRATE.   A synthetic pineapple flavoring agent for beverages, ice cream, ices, candy, and baked goods. No known toxicity.

ISOPROPYL ISOVALERATE.   A synthetic pineapple and nut flavoring agent for beverages, ice cream, ices, candy, and baked goods. No known toxicity.

ISOPROPYL PHENYLACETATE.   A synthetic butter, caramel, and honey flavoring agent for beverages, ice cream, ices, candy, and baked goods. No known toxicity.

ISOVINYL FORMATE. Formic Acid. A synthetic fruit flavoring agent for beverages, ice cream, ices, candy, and baked goods. See Formic Acid for toxicity.

ISOVINYL PROPIONATE. See Isovinyl Formate.

J

JASMINE. Oil and Spiritus (alcoholic solution). The *oil* is extracted from a tropical shrub and is used in raspberry, strawberry, floral, and cherry flavorings for beverages, ice cream, ices, candy, baked goods, gelatin desserts, chewing gum, and jelly. The *spiritus* is used in blackberry, strawberry, and fruit flavorings for beverages, ice cream, ices, candy, baked goods, gelatin, and cherries. No known toxicity.

JASMONYL. See 1,3-Nonanediol Acetate.

JUNIPER. Extract, Oil, and Berries. A flavoring from the dried ripe fruit of trees grown in Northern Europe, Asia, and North America. The greenish yellow *extract* is used in liquor, root beer, sarsaparilla, wintergreen, and birch beer flavorings for beverages, ice cream, ices, candy, and baked goods. The *oil* is used in berry, cola, pineapple, gin, rum, whiskey, root beer, ginger, and meat flavorings for beverages, ice cream, ices, candy, baked goods, gelatin desserts, chewing gum, meats, and liquors. The *berries* are used in gin flavoring for condiments and liquors. Juniper is used also in fumigating, and was formerly a diuretic for reducing body water. No known toxicity. GRAS

K

KADAYA. See Karaya Gum.

KARAYA GUM. Kadaya. Katilo. Kullo. Kuterra. Sterculia. Indian Tragacanth. Mucara. The dried exudate of a tree found in India. The finely ground white powder is used in gelatins and in gumdrops, prepared ices, and ice cream, and as a filler for lemon custard. Also a citrus and spice flavoring agent for beverages, ice cream, ices (1,300 ppm), candy, baked goods, meats, toppings (3,500 ppm), and emulsions (18,000 ppm). Used instead of the more expensive gum tragacanth (*see*) and in bulk laxatives. On the FDA high-priority list for short-term study of mutagenic, teratogenic, subacute, and reproductive effects. GRAS

KATILO. See Karaya Gum.

KAUTSCHIN. See *d*-Limonene.

KELP. See Algae, Brown.

KENTONAROME. See Methylcyclopentenolone.

KETONE C-7. See 2-Heptanone.

2-KETOPROPIONALDEHYDE. See Pyruvaldehyde.

α-KETOPROPIONIC ACID. See Pyruvic Acid.

KOLA NUT EXTRACT. *Guru Nut.* A natural extract from the brownish seed, about the size of a chestnut, produced by trees in Africa, the West Indies, and Brazil. Contains caffeine (*see*). Used in butter, caramel, chocolate, cocoa, coffee, cola, walnut, and root beer flavorings for beverages, ice cream, ices, candy, and baked goods. Has been used to treat epilepsy. GRAS

KRAMERIA EXTRACT. See Rhatany Extract.

KULLO. See Karaya Gum.

KUTEERAL. See Karaya Gum.

L

LABDANUM. *Absolute, Oil, and Oleoresin.* A synthetic flavoring agent, a volatile oil obtained by steam distillation from gum extracted from shrubs. Golden yellow, viscous, with a strong balsamic odor. The *absolute* is used in raspberry, fruit, and vanilla flavorings for beverages, ice cream, ices, candy, baked goods, gelatin desserts, and chewing gum. The *oil* is used in fruit and spice flavorings for beverages, ice cream, ices, candy, and baked goods. The *oleoresin* (*see*) is used in fruit and vanilla flavorings for beverages, ice cream, ices, candy, and baked goods. No known toxicity.

LACTIC ACID. *Butyl Lactate. Ethyl Lactate.* A colorless, nearly odorless liquid which occurs in sour milk as the result of lactic-acid bacteria; also found in molasses, due to partial conversion of sugars, in apples and other fruits, tomato juice, beer, wines, opium, ergot, foxglove, and other plants. It is produced commercially by fermentation of whey, cornstarch, potatoes, and molasses. Used as an acidulant in beverages, candy, olives, dried egg whites, cottage cheese, confections, bread, rolls, buns, cheese products, frozen desserts, sherbets, ices, fruit jelly, butter, preserves, jams (sufficient amounts may be added to compensate for the deficiency of fruit acidity), and in the brewing industry. Also used in infant-feeding formulas. Used in blackberry, butter, butterscotch, lime, chocolate, fruit, walnut, spice and cheese flavorings for beverages, ice cream, ices, candy, baked goods, gelatins, puddings, chewing gum, toppings, pickles, and olives (24,000 ppm). In concentrated solution it is caustic.

LACTOFLAVIN. See Riboflavin.

LAMINARIA. Seaweed from which algin is extracted. See Alginates. GRAS

LANOLIN. Wool fat, the secretion of the sebaceous glands of sheep, which is deposited onto the wool fibers. Chemically a wax instead of a fat. Contains about 25–30 percent water; yellowish white, slight odor. Mixes with about twice its weight of water. Used as a chewing gum base component and as a water absorbable ointment base in cosmetics. May cause allergic reactions.

LANTANA. See Oregano.

LARIXINIC ACID. See Maltol.

LAUREL. The fresh berries and leaf extract of the laurel tree. The berries are used as a flavoring for beverages and the leaf extract is a spice flavoring for vegetables. No known toxicity. GRAS

LAURIC ACID. Dodecanoic Acid. A common constituent of vegetable fats, especially coconut oil and laurel oil. A white, glossy powder, insoluble in water, and used in the manufacture of miscellaneous flavors for beverages, ice cream, candy, baked goods, gelatins, and puddings. Used chiefly in the manufacture of soaps, detergents, cosmetics, and lauryl alcohol. It is a mild irritant.

LAURINE®. See Hydroxycitronellal.

LAUROSTEARIC ACID. See Lauric Acid.

LAVANDIN OIL. A flavoring from a hybrid related to the lavender plant, pale yellow, liquid, with a camphor-lavender smell. Used in berry and citrus flavorings for beverages, baked goods, ice cream, ices, candy, and chewing gum. No known toxicity. GRAS

LAVENDER. The colorless liquid extracted from the fresh, flowery tops of the plant. Smells like lavender, and used in ginger ale flavoring for beverages. Lavender *absolute* is a fruit flavoring for beverages, ice cream, ices, candy, and baked goods. Lavender *concrete* is a fruit flavoring for beverages, ice cream, ices, candy, and baked goods. Lavender *oil* is a citrus, pineapple, and ginger ale flavoring for beverages, ice cream, ices, candy, baked goods, and chewing gum. Lavender was once used to break up stomach gas. Keeps moths away from clothes. Used in fumigating and in perfumery. May cause a sensitivity to light. GRAS

LEAF ALCOHOL.   See 3-Hexen-1-ol.

LEAVENING.   From the Latin "levare," to raise. It is a substance, such as yeast, acting to produce fermentation in dough or liquid. Leavening serves to lighten or enliven, such as baking soda when it produces a gas that lightens dough or batter.

LECITHIN.   From the Greek, meaning "egg yolk." Found in all living organisms, plant and animal. It is a significant constituent of nerve tissue and brain substance. Composed of units of choline, phosphoric acid, fatty acids, and glycerin (*see all*). Commercially isolated from eggs, soybeans, corn, and egg yolk and used as an antioxidant in prepared breakfast cereal, candy, sweet chocolate, bread, rolls, buns, and oleomargarine. *Hydroxylated* lecithin is a defoaming component in yeast and beet sugar production. Lecithin with or without *phosphatides* (components of fat) is an emulsifier for sweet chocolate, milk chocolate, bakery products, frozen desserts, oleomargarine, rendered animal fat or a combination of vegetable-animal fats. Nontoxic.

LEMON. Extract and Oil.   Lemon extract is used in lemon flavorings for beverages, ice cream, ices, candy, baked goods, and icings. Lemon *oil* is a blueberry, loganberry, strawberry, butter, grapefruit, lemon, lime, orange, cola, coconut, honey, wine, rum, root beer, and ginger ale flavoring for beverages, ice cream, ices, candy, baked goods, gelatin desserts, chewing gum (1,900 ppm), condiments, meats, syrups, icings, and cereals. Lemon oil is suspected of being a cancer-causing agent. GRAS

LEMON BALM.   See Balm Oil.

LEMON-GRASS OIL.   Volatile oil distilled from the leaves of the lemon grasses. A natural flavoring agent used in lemon and fruit flavorings for beverages, ice cream, ices, candy, baked goods, gelatin desserts, and chewing gum. Used chiefly in perfumery. Has killed a child, and autopsy showed gastric mucosa was severely damaged.

LEMON OIL, TERPENELESS. A lemon, fruit, ginger, and ginger ale flavoring agent for beverages, ice cream, ices, candy, baked goods, gelatin desserts, chewing gum, and toppings. Terpene, which is removed to improve flavor, is a class of unsaturated hydrocarbons. See Lemon for toxicity.

LEMON PEEL. From the outer rind, the extract is used as a flavor in medicines and in beverages, confectionery, and cooking. See Lemon for toxicity.

LEUCINE. L and DL forms. An essential amino acid (see) for human nutrition, not manufactured in the body. It is isolated commercially from gluten, casein, and keratin. It has a sweet taste. The FDA says it needs further study. GRAS

LICORICE, Extract, Extract Powder, and Root. Licorice extract, from the Mediterranean plant, used in fruit, licorice, anise, maple, and root beer flavorings for beverages, ice cream, ices, candy, baked goods, gelatin, chewing gum (29,000 ppm) and syrups. Licorice extract powder is used in licorice, anise, maple, and root beer flavorings for beverages, ice cream, ices, baked goods, candy (6,500 ppm), and chewing gum (22,000 ppm). Licorice root is used in licorice and root beer flavorings for beverages, candy, baked goods, chewing gum (3,200 ppm), tobacco, and medicines. Some people known to have eaten licorice candy regularly and generously had raised blood pressure, headaches, and muscle weakness. On the FDA list for further study for safety. GRAS

LIGHT GREEN SF YELLOWISH. See FD and C Green No. 2.

LIME OIL. A natural flavoring extracted from the fruit of a tropical tree. Colorless to greenish. Used in grapefruit, lemon, lemon-lime, lime, orange, cola, fruit, rum, nut, and ginger flavorings for beverages, ice cream, ices, candy, baked goods, gelatin desserts, chewing gum (3,100 ppm), and condiments. Terpeneless (see Lemon Oil) lime oil is used in lemon, lime, lemon-lime, cola, pineapple, ginger, and ginger ale flavorings for beverages, ice cream, ices, candy, baked goods, gelatin desserts, chewing gum, and syrups. May cause sensitivity to light. GRAS

LIMONENE. D, L, and DL forms. A synthetic flavoring agent that occurs naturally in star anise, buchu leaves, caraway, celery, oranges, coriander, cumin, cardamom, sweet fennel, common fennel, mace, marigold, oil of lavandin, oil of lemon, oil of mandarin, peppermint, petitgrain oil, pimento oil, orange leaf (absolute), orange peel (sweet oil), origanum oil, black pepper, peels of citrus, macrocarpa bunge, and hops oil. Used in lime, fruit, and spice flavorings for beverages, ice cream, ices, candy, baked goods, gelatin desserts, and chewing gum (2,300 ppm). A skin irritant and sensitizer. GRAS

LINALOE WOOD OIL. A natural flavoring agent, colorless to yellow, with a flowery odor. Used in berry, citrus, fruit, liquor, and ginger flavorings for beverages, ice cream, ices, candy, baked goods, and liquors. No known toxicity.

LINALOL. Linalool. A synthetic flavoring that occurs naturally in basil, bois de rose oil, cassia, coriander, cocoa, grapefruit, grapefruit oil, oranges, peaches, tea, bay and bay-leaf extract, ginger, lavender, laurel leaves, and other oils. Colorless, with a floral odor. Used in blueberry, chocolate, lemon, lime, orange, cola, grape, peach, cardamom, nutmeg, and meat flavorings for beverages, ice cream, ices, candy, baked goods, gelatin desserts, meats, and chewing gum. Used in perfumery instead of bergamot or French lavender. No known toxicity. GRAS

LINALYL ACETATE. A synthetic flavoring that occurs naturally in basil, jasmine oil, lavandin oil, lavender oil, lemon oil, peels of citrus, macrocarpa bunge, petitgrain oil, and lemon oil. Colorless, with a floral odor. Used in berry, citrus, peach, pear, and ginger flavorings for beverages, ice cream, ices, candy, baked goods, gelatin desserts, and chewing gum. Used in perfumery. No known toxicity. GRAS

LINALYL ANTHRANILATE. A synthetic berry, citrus, fruit, and grape flavoring agent for beverages, ice cream, ices, candy, and baked goods. No known toxicity.

LINALYL BENZOATE. A synthetic flavoring, brownish yellow, with a roselike odor. Used in berry, citrus, fruit, and peach flavorings for beverages, ice cream, ices, candy, baked goods, and gelatin desserts. No known toxicity.

LINALYL BUTYRATE. A synthetic flavoring used in loganberry, butter, caramel, citrus, floral, rose, fruit, grape, peach, pear, pineapple, plum, honey, nut, and spice flavorings for beverages, ice cream, ices, candy, baked goods, and gelatin desserts. No known toxicity.

LINALYL CINNAMATE. A synthetic loganberry, floral, rose, fruit, grape, and honey flavoring agent for beverages, ice cream, ices, candy, and baked goods. No known toxicity.

LINALYL FORMATE. Formic Acid. A synthetic flavoring that occurs naturally in oil of lavandin. Used in berry, apple, apricot, peach, and pineapple flavorings for beverages, ice cream, ices, candy, and baked goods. See Formic Acid for toxicity.

LINALYL HEXANOATE. A synthetic fruit flavoring agent for beverages, ice cream, ices, candy, and baked goods. No known toxicity.

LINALYL ISOBUTYRATE. A synthetic flavoring, colorless, slightly yellow, with a fruity odor. Used in berry, citrus, fruit, banana, black currant, cherry, pear, pineapple, plum, nut, and spice flavorings for beverages, ice cream, ices, candy, and baked goods. No known toxicity.

LINALYL ISOVALERATE. A synthetic flavoring, colorless to slightly yellow, with a fruity odor. Used in loganberry, apple, apricot, peach, pear, and plum flavorings for beverages, ice cream, ices, candy, baked goods, and gelatin desserts. No known toxicity.

LINALYL OCTANOATE. A synthetic citrus, rose, apple, pineapple, and honey flavoring agent for beverages, ice cream, ices, candy, and baked goods. No known toxicity.

LINALYL PROPIONATE. A synthetic currant, orange, banana, pear, and pineapple flavoring agent for beverages, ice cream, ices, candy, baked goods, and gelatin desserts. No known toxicity.

LINDEN FLOWERS. A natural flavoring from the flower of the tree grown in Europe and the United States. Used in raspberry and vermouth flavorings for beverages (2,000 ppm). No known toxicity. GRAS

LINOLEIC ACID. An essential fatty acid (*see*) prepared from edible fats and oils. Component of Vitamin F and a major constituent of many vegetable oils, for example, cottonseed, soybean, peanut, corn, sunflower, safflower seed, poppy seed, linseed, and perilla oils. Used in emulsifiers and vitamins. Large doses can cause nausea and vomiting. When given in large doses to rats, weight loss and progressive secondary anemia developed. GRAS

LIVER-STOMACH CONCENTRATE. With intrinsic factor complex. A dietary supplement containing Vitamin B_{12} activity and folic acid. In suitable dosage, liver extract increases the number of red blood cells in persons affected with pernicious anemia. May cause allergic reactions.

LOCUST BEAN GUM. St.-John's-bread. Carob Bean. A natural flavor extract from the seed of the carob tree cultivated in the Mediterranean area. The history of the carob tree dates back more than 2,000 years when the ancient Egyptians used locust bean gum as an adhesive in mummy binding. It is alleged that the "locusts [through confusion of the locusts with the carob] and wild honey" that sustained John the Baptist in the wilderness were carob beans, thus the name "St.-John's-bread." The carob pods are used as feed for stock today because of their high protein content. They are also eaten by some health food enthusiasts for the same purpose. They are also used as a thickener and stabilizer (*see* Gum, Carob Bean). Carob bean extract is used in raspberry, bitters, butter, butterscotch, caramel, chocolate, cherry, brandy, wine, maple, root beer, spice, vanilla, cream soda, and grape flavorings for beverages, ice cream, ices, candy, baked goods, gelatin desserts (600 ppm), icings, and toppings (1,000 ppm). On the FDA list of food additives requiring further study for mutagenic, subacute, reproductive, and teratogenic effects. GRAS

LOVAGE. Smallage. Flavoring obtained from the root of an herb native to southern Europe. Used in bitters, maple, and walnut flavorings for beverages, ice cream, ices, candy, baked goods, and table syrups. The *extract* is used in berry, butter, butterscotch, caramel, coffee, fruit, maple, meat, black walnut, and spice flavorings for the same foods as above, plus condiments and icings. The *oil*, yellow-brown and aromatic, is used in butter, butterscotch, caramel, coffee, fruit, licorice, liquor, maple, nut, walnut, and spice flavorings for the same foods as is the extract. No known toxicity.

LUPULIN. Hops. A natural flavoring extract from a plant (*Humulus lupulis*) grown in Europe, Asia, and North America. Used in beer brewing. Formerly used as aromatic bitters and as a sedative. At one time in veterinary usage it was recommended for treatment of nymphomania. No known toxicity. GRAS

LYSINE. L and DL forms. An essential amino acid (*see*) isolated from casein (*see*), fibrin, or blood. It is used for food enrichment for wheat-based foods. Lysine improves their protein quality and results in improved growth and tissue synthesis. Employed in the fortification of specialty bread and cereal mixes up to .25 percent to .5 percent of the weight of flour. On the FDA list for further study. GRAS

M

MACE. Obtained by steam distillation from the ripe dried seed of the nutmeg. Colorless to pale yellow, with the taste and odor of nutmeg. Used in bitters, meat, and spice flavorings for beverages, ice cream, ices, baked goods, condiments, and meats (2,000 ppm). The *oil* is used in chocolate, cocoa, coconut, cola, fruit, nut, spice, and ginger ale flavorings for beverages, ice cream, ices, candy, baked goods, chewing gum, condiments, and meats. The *oleoresin* (*see*) is used in sausage and spice flavorings for baked goods, condiments, meats, and pickles. See Nutmeg for toxicity.

MAGNESIUM: Magnesium Phosphate, Magnesium Sulfate, Magnesium Oxide, Magnesium Silicate, Magnesium Chloride, Magnesium Carbonate, Magnesium Cyclamate, and Magnesium Hydroxide. A silver-white, light, malleable metallic element that occurs abundantly in nature but is always found in combination in minerals, in sea and mineral waters, and in plants and animals. *Magnesium phosphate*, a white, odorless powder, and *magnesium sulfate* are used as mineral supplements for food. Recommended daily allowances, according to the National Academy of Sciences, are 40 mg for infants; 100 to 300 mg for children; 350 mg for adult males and females. *Magnesium sulfate* is used also as a corrective in the brewing industry and for fertilizers. *Magnesium oxide*, a white, bulky powder, is an alkali used as a neutralizer in frozen dairy products, butter, cacao products, and canned peas. *Magnesium silicate*, a fine, white, odorless and tasteless powder, is used in table salt and vanilla powder as an anticaking agent. In table salt it is limited to 2 percent. *Magnesium chloride* is used for color retention and as a firming agent in canned peas. *Magnesium carbonate*, a white powder or mass, is used as an alkali for sour cream, butter, ice cream, cacao products, and canned peas. It is also used as a drying agent and an anticaking agent. *Magnesium cyclamate* was banned in 1969 as an artificial sweetener. *Magnesium hydroxide*, a bulky, white powder, is used as an alkali in canned peas and as a drying agent and color retention agent for improved gelling in the manufacture of cheese. Toxic when inhaled. GRAS

MALEIC HYDRAZIDE. Inhibitor of the growth and sprouting of plants. Made from maleic acid and a hydrazine salt of strong inorganic acid. Highly toxic in humans. Has produced central nervous system disturbances and liver damage in experimental animals and is believed capable of causing mutations.

MALIC ACID. A flavoring agent and aid in aging wine; colorless, crystalline compound, with a strong acid taste that occurs naturally in a wide variety of fruit, including apples, cherries, peaches, and tomatoes, and coffee, rhubarb root, and vanilla. Used as an alkali in frozen dairy products, beverages, baked goods, confections, fruit, butter, and jelly and jam preserves "in amounts sufficient to compensate for the deficiency of fruit in artificially sweetened fruit." No known toxicity.

MALT EXTRACT. Extracted from barley which has been allowed to germinate, and then heated to destroy vitality, and dried. Contains diastase, dextrin, dextrose, protein bodies and salts from barley. The extract is prepared by mixing it with water and allowing the solution to evaporate. It is used as a food adjunct, or nutrient. It is also used widely in the brewing industry. No known toxicity. GRAS

MALTOL. A white, crystalline powder with a butterscotch odor, found in the bark of young larch trees, pine needles, chicory, wood tars, and in roasted malt. It imparts a "freshly baked" odor and flavor to bread and cakes. Used as a synthetic chocolate, coffee, fruit, maple, nut, and vanilla flavoring agent for beverages, ice cream, ices, candy, baked goods, gelatin desserts, chewing gum, and jelly. No known toxicity.

MANDARIN OIL. Obtained by expression of the peels of a ripe mandarin orange. Clear, dark orange to reddish yellow, with a pleasant orangelike odor. It is an orange, tangerine, cherry, and grape flavoring for beverages, ice cream, ices, candy, gelatin desserts, and chewing gum. No known toxicity. GRAS

MANGANESE SOURCES: Manganese Acetate, Manganese Carbonate, Manganese Chloride, Manganese Citrate, Manganese Gluconate, Manganese Sulfate, Manganese Glycerophosphate, Manganese Hypophosphite, and Manganous Oxide. A mineral supplement first isolated in 1774. It occurs in minerals and in minute quantities in animals, plants, and water. Many forms are used in dyeing. Toxic when inhalted. GRAS

MANNITOL. Widespread in plants but mostly prepared from seaweed. White, crystalline, solid, odorless, and sweet tasting. Used as a texturizer in chewing gum and in candy up to 5 percent. Has been used as a sweetener in "sugar free" products but has calories and carbohydrates. Used as a dusting or antisticking agent in a number of food products. When taken in excess, it can cause gastrointestinal disturbances. It may also induce or worsen kidney disease. On the FDA priority list of additives to be restudied.

MARGARINE. Oleomargarine. A butter substitute made from animal or vegetable fats or oils. If oils are used they are "hardened" into fats by the process of hydrogenation (*see*). Skimmed milk, water, salt, coloring matter (carotene, *see*), artificial flavors, lecithin (*see*), and small amounts of vitamins are usually added. By federal regulations, margarine contains at least 80 percent fat. No known toxicity.

MARIGOLD, POT. A natural plant extract. The oil is used in various flavorings for beverages, ice cream, ices, candy, and baked goods. No known toxicity. See Tagetes. GRAS

MARJORAM, POT. Sweet Marjoram. The natural extract of the flowers and leaves of two varieties of the fragrant marjoram plant. The *oleoresin* (*see*) is used in sausage and spice flavorings for condiments and meats. The *seed* is used in sausage and spice flavorings for meats (3,500 ppm) and condiments. Sweet marjoram is used in sausage and spice flavorings for beverages, baked goods (2,000 ppm), condiments, meats, and soups. The *sweet oil* is used in vermouth, wine, and spice flavorings for beverages, ice cream, ices, candy, baked goods, and condiments. No known toxicity. GRAS

MARSHMALLOW ROOT. See Althea Root.

MATÉ. Paraguay Tea. St. Bartholomew's Tea. Jesuit's Tea. A natural flavoring extract from small gourds grown in South America, where mate is a stimulant beverage. Among its constituents are caffeine, purines, and tannins. No specific flavors are specified. See Caffeine and Tannic Acid for toxicity. GRAS

MELISSA. See Balm Oil.

MELONAL. See 2,6-Dimethyl-5-Heptenal.

p-MENTHA-1,8-DIEN-7-OL. A synthetic citrus, fruit, mint, and vanilla flavoring agent for beverages, ice cream, ices, candy, and baked goods. It is found naturally in caraway. Can cause skin irritation.

MENTHOL. A flavoring agent that occurs naturally in raspberries, peppermint and other mints, as well as betel. Usually obtained from peppermint oil. Used in butter, caramel, fruit, peppermint, and spearmint flavorings for beverages, cream, ices, candy, baked goods, chewing gum (1,100 ppm), and liquor. Also used in perfumery, cigarettes, cough drops, and nasal inhalers. It is an antipruritic and mild local anesthetic (topical dose: 0.1 percent to 2 percent in skin preparations); it can cause severe abdominal pain, nausea, vomiting, vertigo, and coma when ingested in its concentrated form. The lethal dose in rats is 2.0 grams per kilogram of body weight. GRAS

(d)-neo-MENTHOL. A flavoring agent that occurs naturally in Japanese mint oil. Used in mint flavorings for beverages, ice cream, ices, candy, and baked goods. See Menthol for toxicity.

MENTHONE. A synthetic flavoring agent that occurs naturally in raspberries and peppermint oil. Bitter, with a slight peppermint taste. Used in fruit and mint flavorings for beverages, ice cream, ices, candy, baked goods, and chewing gum. May cause gastric distress.

MENTHYL ACETATE. A natural flavoring agent that occurs naturally in peppermint oil. Colorless, with a mint odor. Used in fruit, mint, and spice flavorings for beverages, ice cream, ices, candy, baked goods, and chewing gum; also in perfumes and toilet waters. No known toxicity. GRAS

METHANETHIOL. Methyl Mercaptan. A pesticide and fungicide isolated from the roots of a plant. Occurs in the "sour" gas of West Texas, in coal tar, and in petroleum. Produced in the intestinal tract by action of bacteria. Found in urine after ingestion of asparagus. Its odor may cause nausea and it may be narcotic in high concentrations.

METHIONINE. An essential amino acid (*see*) not synthesized in the human body. It is used in special dietary foods and in animal feeds. Used in fat. Rutgers University researchers have patented a process to impregnate a carrier material with methionine for use in deep-fried cooking oil to impart a "fresh" potato or potato chip flavor to snack foods, soups, or salad dressings. On the FDA list of additives requiring further study. GRAS

p-METHOXY BENZYL ACETATE. See Anisyl Acetate.

p-METHOXY BENZYL ALCOHOL. See Anisyl Alcohol.

2-METHOXY-4-METHYLPHENOL. Creosol. A synthetic flavoring that occurs naturally in cassie and is used in fruit, rum, nut, and clove flavorings for beverages, ice cream, ices, candy, baked goods, and liqueurs. About the same toxicity as phenol, a highly caustic, poisonous compound derived from benzene.

1-METHOXY-4-PROPENYLBENZENE. See Anethole.

2-METHOXY-4-PROPENYLPHENOL. See Isoeugenol.

METHOXYACETOPHENONE. See Acetanisole.

METHOXYBENZENE. See Anisole.

o-METHOXYBENZALDEHYDE. A synthetic flavoring agent that occurs naturally in cassia oil and is used in spice and cinnamon flavorings for beverages, baked goods, and chewing gum. No known toxicity.

p-METHOXYBENZALDEHYDE. Anisaldehyde. A synthetic flavoring agent that occurs naturally in hawthorn, fennel, oil of anise, star anise, and Tahiti vanilla beans. Used in raspberry, strawberry, butter, caramel, chocolate, apricot, cherry, peach, licorice, anise, nut, black walnut, walnut, spice, and vanilla flavorings for beverages, ice cream, ices, candy, baked goods, gelatin desserts, and chewing gum. No known toxicity.

p-METHOXYBENZYL FORMATE. See Anisyl Formate.

4'-METHYL ACETOPHENONE. A synthetic fruit, almond, and vanilla flavoring agent for beverages, ice cream, ices, candy, baked goods, Maraschino cherries, chewing gum, and condiments. No known toxicity.

METHYL ACETATE. Acetic Acid. A synthetic flavoring agent that occurs naturally in coffee. Colorless liquid with a pleasant odor. Used in fruit, rum, and nut flavorings for beverages, ice cream, ices, candy, baked goods, gelatin desserts, puddings, and liquor. Also used industrially as a solvent for many resins and oils. May be irritating to the respiratory tract and, in high concentrations, it may be narcotic.

METHYL ACRYLATE. Transparent, elastic substance used in packaging. Practically odorless. Used also to coat paper and plastic film. Can be highly irritating to the eyes, skin, and mucous membranes. Convulsions occur if vapors are inhaled in high concentration. GRAS for packaging.

METHYL AMYL KETONE. See 2-Heptanone.

METHYL ANISATE. Anisic Acid. A synthetic fruit, melon, liquor, root beer, and spice flavoring agent for beverages, ice cream, ices, candy, and baked goods. No known toxicity.

METHYL ANTHRANILATE. A synthetic flavoring, colorless to pale yellow, liquid, with a grape odor. Occurs naturally in grapes, Concord grape juice, jasmine oil, lavender oil, lemon oil, orange flowers, petitgrain oil, peels of macrocarpa bunge, and tuberose. Used in loganberry, strawberry, orange, floral, rose, violet, cherry, grape, melon, liquor, wine, and honey flavorings for beverages, ice cream, ices, candy, baked goods, gelatin desserts, chewing gum (2,200 ppm), and liqueurs. Used in perfumes. No known toxicity. GRAS

METHYL BENZOATE. Oil of Niobe. A synthetic flavoring agent, colorless, transparent, with a pleasant odor. Used in fruit, liquor, rum, nut, spice, and vanilla flavorings for beverages, ice cream, ices, candy, and baked goods. Also used in perfumes. No known toxicity.

METHYL BUTYRATE. A synthetic flavoring agent that occurs naturally in apples. Colorless. Used in fruit and rum flavorings for beverages, ice cream, candy, and baked goods. No known toxicity.

METHYL p-ter-BUTYPHENYLACETATE. A synthetic chocolate, fruit, and honey flavoring agent for beverages, ice cream, ices, candy, and baked goods. No known toxicity.

METHYL CINNAMATE. A synthetic strawberry, butter, cream, cherry, grape, peach, plum, and vanilla flavoring agent for beverages, ice cream, ices, candy, baked goods, gelatin desserts, chewing gum, and condiments. See Cinnamic Acid for toxicity.

METHYL DISULFIDE. A synthetic onion flavoring agent for baked goods, condiments, and pickle products. No known toxicity.

METHYL ETHYL CELLULOSE. A foaming, aerating, and emulsifying agent prepared from wood pulp or chemical cotton. Used in vegetable-fat whipped topping. Used as a bulk laxative but absorbed from the bowel. For toxicity see Sodium Carboxymethyl Cellulose.

METHYL GLUCOSIDE OF FATTY ACIDS OF EDIBLE COCONUT OIL. Used in the manufacture of beet sugar and as an aid in crystallization of sucrose and dextrose. No known toxicity except that coconut oil is thought to contribute to cholesterol clogging of the arteries.

METHYL HEPTANOATE. A synthetic berry, grape, peach, and pineapple flavoring agent for beverages, ice cream, ices, candy, and baked goods. No known toxicity.

6-METHYL-5-HEPTEN-2-ONE. A synthetic flavoring agent that occurs naturally in oil of lavender and oil of lemon. Used in berry, citrus, banana, melon, pear, peach, and pineapple flavorings for beverages, ice cream, ices, candy, baked goods, and gelatin desserts. No known toxicity.

METHYL HEXANOATE. A synthetic pineapple flavoring agent for beverages, ice cream, ices, candy, and baked goods. No known toxicity.

METHYL 2-HEXENOATE. A synthetic fruit flavoring agent for beverages and candy. No known toxicity.

METHYL-p-HYDROXY-BENZOATE. Methylparaben. A preservative in beverages, baked goods, candy, and artificially sweetened jellies and preserves. Methylparaben may cause allergic skin reaction. On the FDA list of additives requiring further study. GRAS

METHYL ISOBUTYL KETONE. A synthetic fruit flavoring agent for beverages, ice cream, ices, candy, and baked goods. Used as a solvent for cellulose and lacquer. Similar in toxicity to methyl ethyl ketone which is irritating to eyes and mucous membranes, but likely more toxic. Causes intestinal upsets and central nervous system depression.

METHYL ISOBUTYRATE. A synthetic fruit flavoring agent for beverages, ice cream, ices, candy, and baked goods. No known toxicity.

METHYL LAURATE. A synthetic floral flavoring agent for beverages, ice cream, ices, candy, and baked goods. No known toxicity.

METHYL MERCAPTAN. A synthetic flavoring agent that occurs naturally in caseinate, cheese, skim milk, coffee, and cooked beef. Used in coffee flavoring for beverages, ice cream, ices, candy, and baked goods. See Methanethiol for toxicity.

METHYL β-NAPHTHYL KETONE. Oranger Crystals. 2'Acetonaphthone. A synthetic flavoring agent used in berry, strawberry, citrus, fruit, grape, and vanilla flavorings for beverages, ice cream, ices, candy, baked goods, gelatin desserts, and chewing gum. See Methyl Isobutyl Ketone for toxicity.

METHYL NONANOATE. A synthetic berry, citrus, pineapple, honey, and cognac flavoring agent for beverages, ice cream, ices, candy, and baked goods. No known toxicity.

METHYL 2-NONENOATE. A synthetic berry and melon flavoring agent for beverages, ice cream, ices, candy, and baked goods. No known toxicity.

METHYL 2-NONYNOATE. A synthetic berry, floral, violet, fruit, banana, and melon flavoring agent for beverages, ice cream, ices, candy, baked goods, gelatin desserts, and condiments. No known toxicity.

METHYL OCTANOATE. A synthetic flavoring agent that occurs naturally in pineapple. Used in pineapple and berry flavorings for beverages, ice cream, ices, candy, and baked goods. No known toxicity.

149

METHYL 2-OCTYNOATE. A synthetic flavoring agent used in berry, raspberry, strawberry, floral, violet, fruit, peach, liquor, and muscatel flavorings for beverages, ice cream, ices, candy, baked goods, gelatin desserts, chewing gum, and jellies. No known toxicity.

4-METHYL-2-PENTANONE. A synthetic fruit flavoring for beverages, ice cream, ices, candy, and baked goods. No known toxicity.

2-METHYL-4-PHENYL-2-BUTYL ACETATE. A synthetic fruit and tea flavoring agent for beverages, ice cream, ices, candy, and baked goods. No known toxicity.

METHYL PHENYLACETATE. A synthetic colorless flavoring with a strong odor of honey. Used in strawberry, chocolate, peach, and honey flavorings for beverages, ice cream, ices, baked goods, candy, gelatin desserts, chewing gum, and syrup. No known toxicity.

2-METHYL-4-PHENYLBUTYRALDEHYDE. A synthetic nut flavoring agent for beverages, ice cream, ices, candy, and baked goods. No known toxicity.

3-METHYL-2-PHENYLBUTYRALDEHYDE. A synthetic fruit flavoring for beverages, ice cream, ices, and candy. No known toxicity.

METHYL 4-PHENYLBUTYRATE. A synthetic strawberry, fruit, and honey flavoring agent for beverages, ice cream, ices, candy, and baked goods. No known toxicity.

METHYL SALICYLATE. Salicylic Acid. Wintergreen Oil. Found naturally in sweet birch, cassie, and wintergreen. Used in strawberry, grape, mint, walnut, root beer, sarsaparilla, spice, wintergreen, birch beer, and vanilla flavorings for beverages, ice cream, ices, candy, baked goods, chewing gum (8,400 ppm), and syrup. Used in perfumery. Ingestion of relatively small amounts may cause severe poisoning and death. The average lethal dose in children is 10 milliliters. Symptoms are nausea, vomiting, acidosis, and pulmonary edema. Salicylates interact with a number of drugs with potentially lethal combinations. Among the deadly combinations are methyl salicylate and anticoagulants, tricylic antidepressants, the arthritis drug, Indocin, and the cancer drug, methotrexate. The FDA proposed that linaments and other liquid preparations containing more than 5 percent methyl salicylate be marketed in special child-resistant containers. As little as one teaspoon of methyl salicylate has been reported to be fatal.

METHYL SULFIDE. A synthetic flavoring agent that occurs naturally in caseinate, cheese, coffee, coffee extract, and skim milk.

Disagreeable odor. Used in chocolate, cocoa, coffee, fruit, and molasses flavorings for beverages, ice cream, ices, candy, baked goods, gelatin desserts, and syrups. Used also as a solvent for minerals. No known toxicity.

METHYL 9-UNDECENOATE. A synthetic citrus and honey flavoring agent for beverages, ice cream, ices, candy, and baked goods. No known toxicity.

METHYL 2-UNDECYNOATE. A synthetic floral and violet flavoring agent for beverages, ice cream, ices, candy, and baked goods. No known toxicity.

METHYL VALERATE. A synthetic flavoring agent that occurs naturally in pineapple. Used in fruit flavorings for beverages, ice cream, ices, candy, and baked goods. No known toxicity.

2-METHYL VALERIC ACID. A synthetic chocolate flavoring agent for candy. No known toxicity.

METHYLACETALDEHYDE. See Propionaldehyde.

METHYLACETIC ACID. See Propionic Acid.

2-METHYLALLYL BUTYRATE. A synthetic pineapple flavoring for beverages, ice cream, ices, candy, and baked goods. No known toxicity.

METHYLBENZYL ACETATE. A synthetic flavoring agent, colorless, with a gardenia odor. Used in cherry and fruit flavorings for beverages, ice cream, ices, candy, baked goods, gelatin desserts, and chewing gum. See Methyl Acetate for toxicity.

α-METHYLBENZYL ACETATE. Acetic Acid. A synthetic berry and fruit flavoring agent for beverages, ice cream, ices, candy, baked goods, chewing gum, and toppings. See Methyl Acetate for toxicity.

α-METHYLBENZYL ALCOHOL. A synthetic flavoring agent, colorless, with a hyacinth odor. Used in strawberry, rose, fruit, and honey flavorings for beverages, ice cream, ices, candy, baked goods, gelatin desserts, and chewing gum. Methyl alcohol is wood alcohol, a widely used solvent in paints, varnishes, and paint removers. Readily absorbed from the gastrointestinal tract; as little as two teaspoonfuls is considered toxic if ingested. The fatal dose lies between 2 and 8 ounces.

α-METHYLBENZYL BUTYRATE. A synthetic berry and fruit flavoring agent for beverages, ice cream, ices, candy, and baked goods. No known toxicity.

α-METHYLBENZYL ISOBUTYRATE. A synthetic fruit flavoring

agent for beverages, ice cream, ices, candy, and baked goods. No known toxicity.

α-METHYLBENZYL FORMATE. Formic Acid. A synthetic fruit and berry flavoring agent for beverages, ice cream, ices, candy, and baked goods. See Formic Acid for toxicity.

2-METHYLBUTYRALDEHYDE. A synthetic flavoring agent that occurs naturally in coffee and tea. Used in chocolate and fruit flavorings for beverages, ice cream, ices, candy, and baked goods. No known toxicity.

3-METHYLBUTYRALDEHYDE. A synthetic flavoring agent that occurs naturally in coffee extract, oil of lavender, and peppermint oil. Used in butter, chocolate, cocoa, fruit, and nut flavorings for beverages, ice cream, ices, candy, baked goods, and gelatin desserts. No known toxicity.

2-METHYLBUTYRIC ACID. A synthetic fruit flavoring agent for beverages, ice cream, ices, and candy. No known toxicity.

METHYLCELLULOSE. A thickening agent and stabilizer prepared from wood pulp or chemical cotton. Commercial product has a methoxyl content of 29 percent. Used as a bodying agent for beverages and canned fruits sweetened with artificial sweeteners; a thickener for Kosher food products; a bulking agent for low-calorie crackers; a binder in nonwheat baked goods for nonallergic diets; a beer foam stabilizer; a condiment carrier; in food products for diabetics and low-calorie dietetic products; an edible film for food products; a leavening agent for prepared mixes; a clarifier for vinegar and beverages; in imitation jellies and jams; processed cheese; confectionery; and toppings. It is a bulk laxative. For toxicity see Sodium Carboxymethyl Cellulose. GRAS

6-METHYLCOUMARIN. A synthetic flavoring agent used in butter, caramel, coconut, fruit, nut, root beer, and vanilla flavorings for beverages, ice cream, ices, candy, baked goods, gelatin desserts, puddings, and chewing gum. Unlike methylcoumarin, which is listed as "generally recognized as safe" by the Flavor Extract Manufacturers Association, coumarin, once widely used in foods, is banned. Prolonged feeding of coumarin causes liver injury.

METHYLCYCLOPENTENOLONE. A synthetic flavoring agent used in berry, butter, butterscotch, caramel, maple, hazelnut, pecan, walnut, fruit, and vanilla flavorings for beverages, ice cream, ices, candy, baked goods, gelatin desserts, chewing gum, and syrups. No known toxicity.

5-METHYLFURFURAL. A synthetic honey, maple, and meat flavoring agent for beverages, ice cream, ices, candy, and baked goods. No known toxicity.

o-METHYLANISOLE. A synthetic fruit and nut flavoring agent for beverages, ice cream, ices, candy, and baked goods. No known toxicity.

p-METHYLANISOLE. A synthetic berry, maple, black walnut, walnut, and spice flavoring agent for beverages, ice cream, ices, candy, baked goods, gelatin desserts, puddings, condiments, and syrups. No known toxicity.

2-METHYLOCTANAL. A synthetic citrus flavoring agent for beverages, ice cream, ices, candy, and baked goods. No known toxicity.

METHYLPARABEN. See Methyl-p-Hydroxy Benzoate.

2-METHYLPENTANOIC ACID. See 2-Methyl Valeric Acid.

β-METHYLPHENETHYL ALCOHOL. A synthetic berry, rose, melon, and honey flavoring agent for beverages, ice cream, ices, candy, and baked goods. Methyl alcohol is absorbed from the gastrointestinal tract. As little as two teaspoonfuls can be fatal.

METHYLPHENYL ETHER. See Anisole.

METHYLPROTOCATECHUIC ALDEHYDE. See Vanillin.

4-METHYLQUINOLINE. A synthetic butter, caramel, fruit, honey, and nut flavoring agent for beverages, ice cream, ices, candy, and baked goods. No known toxicity.

METHYLTHEOBROMINE. See Caffeine.

2-METHYLUNDECANAL. A synthetic flavoring agent, colorless, with a fatty odor. Used in a variety of foods. No known toxicity.

4(p-METHOXYPHENYL)-2-BUTANONE. A synthetic fruit, licorice, and anise flavoring agent for beverages, ice cream, ices, candy, baked goods, and gelatin desserts. No known toxicity.

1-(p-METHOXYPHENYL)-1-PENTEN-3-ONE. A synthetic butter, cream, fruit, maple, nut, and vanilla flavoring agent for beverages, ice cream, ices, candy, and baked goods. No known toxicity.

1-(p-METHOXYPHENYL)-2-PROPANONE. A synthetic flavoring agent that occurs naturally in star anise. Used in fruit and vanilla flavorings for beverages, ice cream, ices, candy, and baked goods. No known toxicity.

p-METHOXYTOLUENE. See p-Methylanisole.

MEXICAN SAGE. See Oregano.

MILFOIL. See Yarrow.

MILK. Milk may be a hidden ingredient in cream of rice, macaroni, filled candy bars, Ovaltine, Junket, prepared flours, frankfurters, and other sausages. Some people are allergic to milk. See also Nonfat Dry Milk.

MIMOSA, ABSOLUTE. A natural flavoring agent extracted from mimosa trees, herbs, and shrubs, which are native to warm regions and have small white or pink flowers. Used in raspberry and fruit flavorings for beverages, ice cream, ices, candy, and baked goods. No known toxicity.

MINERAL OIL. A distillate of petroleum used as a defoaming component in the processing of beet sugar and yeast; as a coating for fresh fruits and vegetables; a lubricant and binder for capsules and tablets supplying small amounts of flavor, spice, condiments, and vitamins. Also employed as a lubricant in food-processing equipment, a dough-divider oil, pan oil; a lubricant in meat-packing plants. It is also used in confectionery as a sealant. May inhibit absorption of digestive fats and it has a mild laxative effect.

MODIFIED STARCH. Ordinary starch that has been altered chemically to modify such properties as thickening or jelling. Babies have difficulty in digesting starch in its original form. Modified starch is used in baby food on the theory that it is easier to digest. Questions about safety have arisen because babies do not have the resistance of adults to chemicals. Among chemicals used to modify startch are propylene oxide, succinic anhydride, 1-octenyl succinic anhydride, aluminum sulfate, and sodium hydroxide (*see all*). On the FDA top priority list for reevaluation.

MOLASSES EXTRACT. Extract of sugar cane, a thick, brown, viscid syrup. Separated from raw sugar in the successive processes of sugar manufacture and graded according to its quality. It is a natural flavoring agent for candy, baked goods, ice cream, and medicines. No known toxicity.

MOLYBDENUM. A dietary supplement. The dark gray powdered mineral is a trace element in animal and plant metabolism. Resembles chromium and tungsten in many of its properties. Low order of toxicity.

MONARDA SPECIES. See Horsemint Leaves Extract.

MONO AND DI-GLYCERIDES OF FATS OR OILS. See Glycerides.

4-MONOAMINOPHOSPHATIDE. See Lecithin.

MONOAMMONIUM GLUTAMATE. See Glutamate, Ammonium.

MONOGLYCERIDE CITRATE. Aids the action of and helps dissolve antioxidant formulations which retard rancidity in oils and fats. See Citrate Salts for toxicity.

MONOPOTASSIUM GLUTAMATE. See Glutamate, Monopotassium.

MONOSODIUM GLUTAMATE. MSG. The monosodium salt of glutamic acid (*see*), one of the amino acids. Occurs naturally in seaweed, sea tangles, soybeans, and sugar beets. Used to intensify meat and spice flavorings in meats, condiments, pickles, soups, candy, and baked goods. Believed responsible for the so-called "Chinese Restaurant Syndrome" in which diners suffer from chest pain, headache, and numbness after eating a Chinese meal. Causes brain damage in young rodents and brain damage effects in rats, rabbits, chicks, and monkeys. Baby food processors removed MSG from baby food products. On the FDA list of additives needing further study for mutagenic, teratogenic, subacute, and reproductive effects. GRAS

MONOSODIUM PHOSPHATE. A derivative of edible fat. Used as an emulsifying agent in food products and as a buffer in prepared cereal. Cleared by the USDA's Meat Inspection Department to decrease the amounts of cooked-out juices in canned hams, pork shoulders, pork loins, chopped hams, and bacon. Monosodium phosphate is a urinary acidifier but has no known toxicity. GRAS

MORELLONE. See 3-Benzyl-4-Heptanone.

MORPHOLINE. Salt of Fatty Acid. Coating on fresh fruits and vegetables. Broad industrial uses. A strong alkali, corrosive to the skin, irritating to the eyes and mucous membranes. May cause liver and kidney injury.

MOSCHUS MOSCHIFERUS. See Musk, tonquin.

MOUNTAIN MAPLE EXTRACT. Extract from a tall shrub or bushy tree found in the eastern United States. Used in chocolate, malt, and maple flavorings for beverages, ice cream, ices, candy, and baked goods. No known toxicity.

MSG. See Monosodium Glutamate.

MUSK. Dried secretions from the glandular sac of a small, hornless Central Asian male deer. Musk is a brown, unctuous, smelly substance. As *musk ambrette* it is used in fruit, cherry, maple, mint, nut, black walnut, pecan, spice, and vanilla flavorings for beverages, ice cream, ices, candy, baked goods, gelatin desserts, pudding, and chewing gum. As *musk tonquin* it is used in fruit, maple, and molasses flavorings for beverages, ice cream, ices, candy, baked goods, and syrups. As *musk ketone* it is used in chewing gum and candy. Musk is also used in perfumery. No known toxicity.

MUSTARD. *Black, Brown, and Red.* Pulverized dried, ripe seeds of the mustard plant (nigra) grown in Europe and Asia and naturalized in the U.S. Used in mustard and spice flavorings for condiments (5,200 ppm) and meats (2,300 ppm). Used as an emetic. Has been used as a counterirritant on the skin. May cause sensitivity to light. On the FDA list of products to be studied for possible mutagenic, teratogenic, subacute, and reproductive effects. GRAS

MUSTARD. *Yellow and White.* The pulverized dried, ripe seeds of the mustard plant (alba) grown in Europe and Asia and naturalized in the U.S. Used in sausage and spice flavorings for beverages, baked goods, condiments (8,200 ppm), meats, and pickles (3,800 ppm). Used as an emetic. See Mustard, Black, for toxicity.

MUTAGENIC. Having the power to cause mutations. A mutation is a sudden change in the character of a gene that is perpetuated in subsequent divisions of the cells in which it occurs. It can be induced by the application of such stimuli as radiation, certain food chemicals, or pesticides. Certain food additives such as caffeine have been found to "break" chromosomes.

MYRCENE. A synthetic flavoring agent that occurs naturally in galbanum oil, pimenta oil, orange peel, palma rosa oil, and hop oil. Pleasant aroma. Used in fruit, root beer, and coriander flavorings for beverages, ice cream, ices, candy, and baked goods. No known toxicity.

MYRISTALDEHYDE. A synthetic citrus and fruit flavoring agent for beverages, ice cream, ices, candy, baked goods, and gelatin desserts. See Nutmeg for toxicity.

MYRISTIC ACID. A solid, organic acid which occurs naturally in butter acids (such as nutmeg butter to the extent of 80 percent), oil of lovage, coconut oil, mace oil, and cire d'abeille in palm seed fats (20 percent), and in most animal and vegetable fats; largely in sperm whale oil. Used in butter, butterscotch, chocolate, cocoa, and fruit flavorings for beverages, ice cream, ices, candy, baked goods, and gelatin desserts. Nontoxic.

MYRISTICA FRAGRANS HOUTT. See Mace, also Nutmeg.

MYROXYLON. See Balsam, Peru.

MYRRH. A yellow- to reddish-brown aromatic bitter gum resin from various trees. The gum is used in fruit, liquor, tobacco, and smoke flavorings for beverages, baked goods, ice cream, ices, candy, chewing gum, and soups. The oil is used in honey and liquor flavorings for beverages, ice cream, ices, candy, and baked goods. The gum resin has been used to break up intestinal gas and as a topical stimulant. Used for incense and perfume. It was one of the gifts of the Magi. No known toxicity.

N

β-NAPHTHYL ANTHRANILATE. Naphthyl Anthranilate. A synthetic fruit and grape flavoring agent for beverages, ice cream, ices, baked goods, and candy. No known toxicity.

β-NAPHTHYL METHYL ETHER. A synthetic berry, fruit, honey, and nut flavoring agent for beverages, ice cream, ices, chewing gum, candy, and baked goods. No known toxicity.

NARINGIN EXTRACT. Naringin is in the flowers, fruit, and rind of the grapefruit tree. Most abundant in immature fruit. Extracted from grapefruit peel. Used in bitters, grapefruit, and pineapple flavorings for beverages, ice cream, ices, and liquors. No known toxicity.

NEOFOLIONE. Occurs naturally in oil of lavender, orange leaf (absolute), palma rosa oil, rose, neroli, and oil of petitgrain. Used in citrus, honey, and neroli flavorings for beverages, ice cream, ices, candy, baked goods, gelatin desserts, puddings, and chewing gum. No known toxicity.

NEROL. A synthetic flavoring that occurs naturally in oil of lavender, orange leaf, palma rosa oil, rose, neroli, and oil of petitgrain. A mixture of terpene alcohol (see Terpene), it has a fresh, sweet rose odor. Used as a base in perfumes, and in citrus, neroli, and honey flavorings for beverages, ice cream, ices, candy, baked goods, gelatin desserts, puddings, and chewing gum. Similar to turpentine in toxicity.

NEROLI BIGARADE OIL. Named for the putative discoverer, Anne Maria de la Tremoille, princess of Nerole (1670). A fragrant, pale-yellow oil obtained from the flowers of the orange tree. Used chiefly as a cologne and in other perfumes but also in berry, orange, cola, cherry, spice, and ginger ale flavorings for beverages, ice cream, ices, candy, baked goods, and chewing gum. No known toxicity. GRAS

NEROSOL. See Nerol.

NERYL ACETATE. A synthetic citrus, fruit, and neroli flavoring agent for beverages, ice cream, ices, candy, and baked goods. No known toxicity.

NERYL BUTYRATE. A synthetic berry, chocolate, cocoa, citrus, and fruit flavoring agent for beverages, ice cream, ices, candy, and baked goods. No known toxicity.

NERYL FORMATE. Formic Acid. A synthetic berry, citrus, apple, peach, and pineapple flavoring agent for beverages, ice cream, ices, candy, and baked goods. See Formic Acid for toxicity.

NERYL ISOBUTYRATE. A synthetic citrus and fruit flavoring agent for beverages, ice cream, ices, candy, and baked goods. No known toxicity.

NERYL ISOVALERATE. A synthetic berry, rose, and nut flavoring agent for beverages, ice cream, ices, candy, and baked goods. No known toxicity.

NERYL PROPIONATE. A synthetic berry and fruit flavoring agent for beverages, ice cream, ices, candy, and baked goods. No known toxicity.

NIACIN. Nicotinic Acid. Nicotinamide. White or yellow, crystalline, odorless powder. An essential nutrient necessary for the conversion of food into energy. Participates in many energy-yielding reactions and aids in the maintenance of a normal nervous system. Added to prepared breakfast cereals, peanut butter, baby cereals, enriched flours, macaroni, noodles, breads, rolls, cornmeal, corn grits, and farina. Niacin is distributed in significant amounts in livers, yeast, meat, legumes, and whole cereals. Recommended daily intake is 6.6 mg per 1,000 kilocalories. In pregnancy, the requirements are 6 mg per 1,000 kilocalories. Nicotinic acid is a component of the Vitamin B complex.

NIACINAMIDE. Nicotinamide. Vitamin B_3. See Niacin.

NIACINAMIDE ASCORBATE. A complex of ascorbic acid (*see*)

and niacinamide (*see*). Occurs as a yellow powder which is practically odorless but which may gradually darken on exposure to air. Used as a dietary supplement. See Niacin.

NICKEL. Occurs in the earth's crust. Lustrous, white, hard metal which is used as a catalyst for the hydrogenation (*see*) of fat. Nickel may cause dermatitis in sensitive individuals and ingestion of large amounts of the soluble salts may cause nausea, vomiting, diarrhea.

NICKEL SULFATE. Emerald-green transparent crystals with a sweet antiseptic taste used as a mineral supplement up to 1 milligram per day. An emetic when swallowed in sufficient amounts. The lethal dose varies widely. The lethal dose in guinea pigs is 62 mg/kg.

NICOTINAMIDE. See Niacin.

NICOTINIC ACID. See Niacin.

NITER. See Nitrate.

NITRATE. *Potassium and Sodium.* Potassium nitrate, well known for gunpowder and fireworks, is also known as saltpeter and niter. It is used as a color fixative in cured meat products up to .02 percent, in pickling brine (7 pounds per 100 gallons), and in chopped meat (2¾ ounces per 100 pounds). Sodium nitrate, also called Chile saltpeter, is used as a color fixative in cured meats, frankfurters, bacon, uncooked smoked ham, bologna, meat spreads, potted meats, Vienna sausages, spiced ham, poultry, and wild game. Also used in baby food. Both nitrates are used in matches and improve burning properties of tobacco. They combine with natural stomach and food substances—secondary amines—to cause powerful cancer-causing agents—nitrosamines. Nitrosamines have been found in fish treated with nitrates. Nitrates have caused deaths from methemoglobinemia (its cuts off oxygen from the brain). The FDA has ordered priority testing for nitrates for possible cancer-causing effects and for mutagenic, teratogenic, subacute, and reproductive effects.

NITRITE, *Potassium and Sodium.* Potasium nitrite is used as a color fixative in cured meats up to .02 percent. Sodium nitrite has the peculiar ability to react chemically with the myoglobin molecule and impart red-bloodedness to processed meat, convey tanginess to the palate, and resist the growth of *Clostridium botulinum* spores, which put Bon Vivant out of the soup business. It is used as a color fixative in cured meats, bacon, bologna, frankfurter, deviled ham, meat spreads, potted meats, spiced ham, Vienna sausage (up to .02 percent), smoked cured tuna fish products (up to .001 percent) and in smoked cured shad and salmon (.02 percent). It is also used in baby food meats (its use here is purely cosmetic). Both nitrites are used in analytical chemistry; sodium nitrite is used in bleaching and dyeing. Nitrite combines with natural stomach and food chemicals—secondary amines—to cause a powerful cancer-causing agent—nitrosamines and nitrosamides. The law limits the nitrite residue on ready-to-eat meat to 200 ppm, though the USDA says that for years it has informally held the industry to that limit *going into the meat* (much is lost en route to the table). Deaths have been reported from sodium nitrite residue in food, the latest from meat tenderizer, containing almost pure sodium nitrite. The FDA has given top priority to the testing of sodium and potassium nitrite and dimethylnitrosamines (derived from nitrites) for cancer-causing effects, and for mutagenic, teratogenic, subacute, and reproductive effects.

NITROGEN. A gas which is 78 percent by volume of the atmosphere and essential to all living things. Odorless. Used for gas-packed foods and dressings for foods. In high concentrations it can asphyxiate. GRAS

NITROGEN OXIDES. Nitrous Oxide (see below), Nitric Oxide, Nitrogen Dioxide, Nitrogen Trioxide, Nitrogen Pentoxide. Bleaching agent for cereal flour. Nitrogen dioxide is a deadly poison gas. Short exposure may cause little pain or discomfort but several days later, fluid retention and inflammation of the lungs can cause death. About 200 ppm can be fatal.

NITROSYL CHLORIDE. Nonexplosive, very corrosive reddish-yellow gas, intensely irritating to eyes, skin, and mucosa. Used as a bleaching agent for cereal flour. Inhalation may cause pulmonary edema and hemorrhage.

NITROUS OXIDE. Laughing gas. A whipping agent for whipped cream and a propellant in pressurized containers for certain dairy and vegetable-fat toppings, slightly sweetish odor and taste. Colorless. An asphyxiant. Used in rocket fuel. Less irritating than other nitrogen oxides (*see*) but narcotic in high concentrations. GRAS

g-NONALACTONE. Aldehyde C-18. Prunolide. Coconut Aldehyde. A synthetic berry, coconut, fruit, and nut flavoring agent for beverages, ice cream, ices, candy, baked goods, gelatin desserts, chewing gum, and icings. No known toxicity.

NONALOL. See Nonyl Alcohol.

NONANAL. Pelargonic Aldehyde. A synthetic flavoring that occurs naturally in lemon oil, rose, sweet orange oil, mandarin, lime, orris, and ginger. Used in lemon and fruit flavorings for beverages, ice cream, ices, candy, baked goods, gelatin desserts, and chewing gum. No known toxicity.

1, 3-NONANEDIOL ACETATE. A synthetic berry, and fruit flavoring agent for beverages, ice cream, ices, candy, and baked goods. No known toxicity.

NONANOIC ACID. Pelargonic Acid. Nonoic Acid. Nonglic Acid. A synthetic flavoring agent that occurs naturally in cocoa and oil of lavender. Used in berry, fruit, nut, and spice flavorings for beverages, ice cream, ices, candy, baked goods, and shortenings. A strong irritant.

1-NONANOL. See Nonyl Alcohol.

NONANOL ISOVALERATE. See Nonyl Isovalerate.

3-NONANON-1-YL-ACETATE. A synthetic berry, rose, fruit, and cheese flavoring agent for beverages, ice cream, ices, candy, and baked goods. No known toxicity.

NONANOYL 4-HYDROXY-3-METHOXYBENZYLAMIDE. Perlargonyl Vanillylamide. A synthetic spice flavoring agent for candy, baked goods, and condiments. No known toxicity.

NONATE. See Isoamyl Nonanoate.

NONFAT DRY MILK. Milk from which the water and much of the fat have been removed. Comparisons between whole and dry milk: 100 grams fluid whole milk contains 68 calories; 87 grams of water, 3.5 grams of protein, 3.9 grams of fat; .7 gram of ash; 4.9 grams of carbohydrates; 118 milligrams of calcium; 93 milligrams of phosphorus; .1 milligram of iron; 50 milligrams of sodium; 140 milligrams of potassium; 160 international units of Vitamin A; .04 milligrams of Vitamin B_1; .17 milligram of B_2; .1 milligram of nicotinic acid; and 1 milligram of Vitamin C. Total calories for one cup of milk is 166. Nonfat, dry milk has 362 calories per 100 grams; 3.5 grams of water; 35.6 grams of protein; 1 gram of fat; 7.9 grams of ash; total carbohydrates of 52 grams; 1,300 milligrams of calcium; 1,030 milligrams of phosphorus; .6 milligram of iron; 77 milligrams of sodium; 1,130 milligrams of potassium; 40 international units of Vitamin A; .35 milligram of Vitamin B_1; 196 milligrams of Vitamin B_2; 1.1 milligrams of nicotinic acid; and 7 milligrams of Vitamin C. The total calories for a tablespoon of dry nonfat milk is 28.

NONYCARBINOL. See 1-Decanol.

NONYL ACETATE. A synthetic, pungent, citrus and fruit flavoring agent mushroomlike in odor. Used for beverages, ice cream, ices, candy, and baked goods. See Acetic Acid for toxicity.

NONYL ALCOHOL. Nonalol. A synthetic flavoring, colorless to yellow with a citronella oil odor. Occurs in oil of orange. Used in butter, citrus, peach, and pineapple flavorings for beverages, ice cream, ices, candy, baked goods, and chewing gum. Also used in the manufacture of artificial lemon oil. In experimental animals it has caused central nervous system and liver damage.

NONYL ISOVALERATE. A synthetic fruit and hazel nut flavoring agent for beverages, ice cream, ices, candy, and baked goods. No known toxicity.

NOPINENE. See β-Pinene.

NORDIHYDROGUAIARETIC ACID (NDGA). Occurs in resinous exudates of many plants. White or grayish white crystals, an antioxidant used in prepared piecrust mix, candy, lard, butter, ice cream, and pressure-dispensed whipped cream. In general food use, the percentage of fat or oil content including essential oil content should be no more than .02 percent NDGA. Lard containing 0.01 percent NDGA stored at room temperature for 19 months in diffused daylight showed no appreciable rancidity or color change. Canada banned the additive in 1967 after it was shown to cause cysts and kidney damage in a large percentage of tested rats. The FDA removed it from the GRAS list in 1968 and prohibited its use in products over which it has control. However, the U.S. Department of Agriculture, which controls antioxidants in lard and animal shortenings, still permits its use.

NOVATONE. See Acetanisole.

NUTMEG. A natural flavoring extracted from the dried ripe seed. Used in cola, vermouth, sausage, eggnog, and nutmeg flavorings for beverages, ice cream, ices, baked goods (2,000 ppm), condiments, meats, and pickles. Nutmeg *oil* is used in loganberry, chocolate, lemon, cola, apple, grape, muscatel, rum, sausage, eggnog, pistachio, root beer, cinnamon, dill, ginger, mace, nutmeg, and vanilla flavorings for beverages, ice cream, ices, candy, baked goods, chewing gum, condiments, meats, syrups, and icings. In common household use since the Middle Ages, nutmeg is still a potentially toxic substance. Ingestion of as little as 3 whole seeds or 5 to 15 grams of grated spice can cause flushing of the skin, irregular heart rhythm, absence of salivation, and central nervous system excitation, including euphoria and hallucinations. On the FDA list for study of short-term mutagenic, subacute, teratogenic, and reproductive effects. GRAS

O

OAK CHIP EXTRACT. Extract from the white oak used in bitters and whiskey flavorings for beverages, ice cream, ices, candy, baked goods, and whiskey (1,000 ppm). No known toxicity.

OAK MOSS, ABSOLUTE. Extracted from the lichen that grows on a variety of oak tress. Used in fruit, honey, and spice flavorings for beverages, ice cream, ices, candy, baked goods, gelatin desserts, condiments, and soups. No known toxicity.

OAT GUM. A plant extract used as an antioxidant in butter, cream, and candy up to 1.5 percent. Also a thickener and stabilizer in pasteurized cheese spread and cream cheese (with other foods) up to .8 percent. Causes occasional allergic reactions, diarrhea, and intestinal gas. No known toxicity.

OCIMUM BASILICUM. See Basil.

OCTADECANOIC ACID. See Stearic Acid.

9-OCTADECENOIC ACID. See Oleic Acid.

OCTAFLUOROCYCLOBUTANE. A nonflammable gas. A refrigerant and propellant and aerating agent in foamed or sprayed food products. Used alone or in combination with carbon dioxide or nitrous oxide (*see both*). Nontoxic when used alone.

2-OCTANONE. A synthetic fruit and cheese flavoring agent for beverages, ice cream, ices, candy, and baked goods. No known toxicity.

3-OCTANONE. A synthetic flavoring that occurs naturally in oil of lavender. Used in citrus, coffee, peach, cheese, and spice flavorings for beverages, ice cream, ices, candy, and baked goods. No known toxicity.

1-OCTEN-3-OL. A synthetic fruit and spice flavoring agent for

163

beverages, ice cream, ices, candy, baked goods, condiments, and soups. No known toxicity.

1-OCTENYL SUCCINIC ANHYDRIDE. A starch modifier incorporating up to 3 percent of the weight of the product. Limited to 2 percent in combination with aluminum sulfate (*see*). No known toxicity.

OCTYL BUTYRATE. *Butyric Acid.* A synthetic strawberry, butter, citrus, fruit, cherry, melon, peach, pineapple, pumpkin, and liquor flavoring agent for beverages, ice cream, ices, candy, and baked goods. No known toxicity.

OCTYL FORMATE. *Formic Acid.* A synthetic flavoring, colorless, with a fruity odor. Used in citrus and fruit flavorings for beverages, ice cream, ices, candy, and baked goods. See Formic Acid for toxicity.

OCTYL HEPTANOATE. A synthetic citrus, coconut, and fruit flavoring agent for beverages, ice cream, ices, candy, and baked goods. No known toxicity.

OCTYL ISOBUTYRATE. *Isobutyric Acid.* A synthetic citrus, fruit, melon, peach, liquor, and wine flavoring agent for beverages, ice cream, ices, candy, and baked goods. No known toxicity.

OCTYL ISOVALERATE. *Isovaleric Acid.* A synthetic berry, butter, citrus, apple, cherry, grape, honey, and nut flavoring agent for beverages, ice cream, ices, candy, and baked goods. No known toxicity.

OCTYL OCTANOATE. *Octanoic Acid.* A synthetic citrus, grape, and pineapple flavoring agent for beverages, ice cream, ices, candy, and baked goods. No known toxicity.

OCTYL PHENYLACETATE. *Phenylacetic Acid.* A synthetic berry, apple, banana, grape, peach, pear, and honey flavoring agent for beverages, ice cream, ices, candy, and baked goods. No known toxicity.

OCTYL PROPIONATE. *Propionic Acid.* A synthetic berry, citrus, and melon flavoring agent for beverages, ice cream, ices, candy, and baked goods. No known toxicity.

OIL OF NIOBE. See Methyl Benzoate.

OLEIC ACID. Obtained from various animal and vegetable fats and oils. Colorless. On exposure to air turns yellow to brown, with a rancid odor. Used as a defoaming agent; as a synthetic butter, cheese, and spice flavoring agent for beverages, ice cream, ices, candy, baked goods, and condiments; as a lubricant and binder in various foods; and as a component in the manufacture of food additives. Low oral toxicity and mildly irritating to the skin.

OLEINIC ACID.   See Oleic Acid.

OLEORESIN.   A natural plant product consisting of essential oil and resin extracted from a substance, such as ginger, by means of alcohol, ether, or acetone. The solvent, alcohol, for example, is percolated through the ginger. Although the oleoresin is very similar to the spice from which it is derived, it is not identical because not all the substances in the spice are extracted. Oleoresins are usually more uniform and more potent than the original product. The normal use range of an oleoresin is from one-fifth to one-twentieth the corresponding amount for the crude spice. Certain spices are extracted as oleoresins for color rather than for flavor. Examples of color-intensifying oleoresins are those from paprika and tumeric (*see both*).

OLIBANUM OIL. *Frankincense.*   The volatile distilled oil from the gum resin of a plant species found in Ethiopia, Egypt, Arabia, and Somaliland. One of the gifts of the Magi. Used in cola, fruit, and spice flavorings for beverages, ice cream, ices, candy, and baked goods. No known toxicity.

ONION OIL.   From crushed onion seeds of the widely cultivated plant first discovered in Asia. Used in meat, onion, and spice flavorings for beverages, ice cream, ices, baked goods, condiments, meats, and pickles. No known toxicity. GRAS

ORANGE B. *Coal-tar dye.*   Coloring for casings of frankfurters and sausages. The color additive is limited to not more than 150 ppm by weight of finished food. Permanently listed by the FDA.

ORANGE BLOSSOMS.   *Orange blossoms, absolute,* is a natural flavoring derived from the fruit of the bitter plant species. Used in citrus and fruit flavorings for beverages, ice cream, ices, candy, baked goods, and chewing gum. The *flowers* provide a natural flavoring extract for citrus and cola flavorings for beverages (2,000 ppm). The orange *leaf extract* is used as a natural fruit flavoring for beverages, ice cream, ices, and baked goods. *Orange peel bitter oil* is expressed from the fresh fruit and is used in orange and fruit flavorings for beverages, ice cream, ices, candy, gelatin desserts, chewing gum, and liquors. No known toxicity. GRAS

ORANGE FLOWERS, BITTER OIL.   See Orange Blossoms.

ORANGE LEAF. See Orange Blossoms.

ORANGE OIL. Terpeneless. The volatile oil expresed from the fresh peel of the ripe fruit of the sweet plant species. Intensely yellow or orange liquid. Used in grapefruit, orange, cola, pineapple, liquor, root beer, and ginger ale flavorings for beverages, ice cream, ices, baked goods, candy, gelatin desserts, puddings, chewing gum, and condiments. Used also in perfume and formerly as an expectorant. No known toxicity. GRAS

ORANGE OIL, DISTILLED. The volatile oil distilled from the fresh fruit of the sweet plant species. Yellowish, very intense, pleasant odor. Used in orange and fruit flavorings for beverages, ice cream, ices, candy, baked goods, gelatin desserts, and chewing gum. No known toxicity.

ORANGE PEEL, BITTER OIL. See Orange Blossoms.

ORANGE PEEL, SWEET EXTRACT. From the fresh rind of the fruit. Sweetish, fragrant odor; slightly bitter taste. Used in orange and ginger ale flavorings for beverages, ice cream, ices, candy, and baked goods. No known toxicity.

ORANGE PEEL, SWEET OIL. From the fresh rind of the fruit. Sweetish, fragrant odor; slightly bitter taste. Used in blueberry, orange, cola, banana, pear, root beer, and ginger ale flavorings for beverages, ice cream, ices, candy, baked goods, condiments, meats, gelatin desserts, puddings (1,300 ppm), chewing gum (4,200 ppm), syrups, icings, liquors, and cereals. No known toxicity.

ORANGE PEEL, SWEET OIL. Terpeneless. From the fresh rind of the fruit. Sweetish, fragrant odor; slightly bitter taste. Used in orange and fruit flavoring for beverages, ice cream, ices, candy, baked goods, gelatin desserts, and puddings. No known toxicity.

ORANGER CRYSTALS. See Methyl β-Naphthyl Ketone.

ORCHIDEE. See Isoamyl Salicylate.

OREGANO. Mexican Oregano. Mexican Sage. Origanum. The wild marjoram (*see*) plant, but spicier, originally found in Eurasia. Used in loganberry, cherry, sausage, root beer, and spice flavorings for beverages, baked goods, condiments (2,800 ppm), and meats. See Origanum Oil for toxicity. GRAS

ORIGAN. See Oregano.

ORIGANOL. See 4-Carvomenthenol.

ORIGANUM OIL. The volatile oil is obtained by steam distillation from a flowering herb. Yellowish red to dark brown, with a pungent odor. Used in vermouth, sausage, root beer, and spice flavorings for beverages, ice cream, ices, candy, baked goods, condiments, and meats. A teaspoonful can cause illness and less than an ounce has killed adults. GRAS

ORRIS. Concrete, Liquid, and Oil. White Flag. The volatile oil obtained by steam distillation from the peeled, dried root of orris, a European plant. Used in raspberry, blackberry, strawberry, violet, cherry, nut, and spice flavorings for beverages, ice cream, ices, candy, baked goods, gelatin desserts, chewing gum, and icings. Also used in cosmetics, perfumes, and in toothpaste and powder. Causes frequent allergic reactions and is no longer used in American dusting powders for the bath. See Orris Root Extract.

ORRIS ROOT EXTRACT. Obtained from dried orris root. Has an intense odor. Used in chocolate, fruit, nut, vanilla, and cream soda flavorings for beverages, ice cream, ices, candy, baked goods, gelatin desserts, and chewing gum. Causes frequent allergic reactions.

OX BILE. Oxygall. Emulsifier from the fresh bile of male castrated bovines. Brownish green or dark green; viscous. Characteristic odor. Bitter, disagreeable taste. Used in dried egg whites up to .1 percent. No known toxicity. GRAS

OXIDES OF IRON: ochre, sienna, ferrous oxide, and other natural and synthetic oxides of iron varying in color from red, brown black to orange or yellow. Used for dyeing eggshells and in bottled soft drinks. See Iron for toxicity.

OXIDIZED TALLOW. A defoaming component used in yeast and beet sugar production in reasonable amounts required to inhibit foaming. See Tallow Flakes.

2-OXOPROPANAL. See Pyruvaldehyde.

2-OXOPROPANOIC ACID. See Pyruvic Acid.

OXYSTEARIN. A mixture of the glycerides (*see*) of partially oxidized stearic acids (*see*) and other fatty acids (*see*). Occurs in animal fat and used chiefly in manufacture of soaps, candles, cosmetics, suppositories, pill coatings. Tan, waxy. Used as a crystallization inhibitor in cottonseed and soybean cooking. In salad oils up to .125 percent. Also used as a defoamer in the production of beet sugar and yeast. No known toxicity.

OXYTETRACYCLINE. An antibiotic substance used in feed to increase growth and found in edible tissue of chickens and turkeys. The carcasses are dipped in the solution to retard rancidity. Residues in the birds are permitted up to .0007 percent. Because it is an antimicrobial, it may cause sensitivity to light, nausea, inflammation of the mucous membrances of the mouth, and diarrhea.

P

PALATONE. See Maltol.

PALE CATECHU. See Catechu, Extract.

PALMA ROSA OIL. Geranium Oil. The volatile oil obtained by steam distillation from a variety of partially dried grass grown in East India and Java. Used in rose, fruit, and spice flavorings for beverages, ice cream, ices, candy, and baked goods. Believed as toxic as other essential oils, causing illness after ingestion of a teaspoonful and death after ingestion of an ounce.

PALMITIC ACID. A mixture of solid organic acids obtained from fats consisting chiefly of palmitic acid with varying amounts of stearic acid (see). It is white or faintly yellow and has a fatty odor and taste. Palmitic acid occurs naturally in allspice, anise, calamus oil, cascarilla bark, celery seed, butter acids, coffee, tea, and many animal fats and plant oils. Obtained from palm oil, Japan wax, or Chinese vegetable tallow. Used in butter and cheese flavorings for seasoning preparations. No known toxicity.

d-PANTOTHENAMIDE. B Complex Vitamin. Vitamin B_5. Made synthetically from royal jelly of the queen bee, yeast, and molasses. Cleared for use as a source of pantothenic acid activity in foods for special dietary use. Pantothenic acid (common sources are liver, rice bran, molasses) is essential for metabolism of carbohydrates, fats, and other important substances. Nerve damage has been observed in patients with low pantothenic acid. It is involved with the release of energy from carbohydrates in the breakdown of fats. Children and adults need from 5 to 10 mg per day. See Calcium Pantothenate.

d-PANTOTHENYL ALCOHOL. See Calcium Pantothenate.

PAPAIN. A proteinase enzyme for meat tenderizing. Prepared from papaya, a fruit grown in tropical countries. Used for clearing beverages. Added to enriched farina to reduce cooking time. Used medically to prevent adhesions. It is deactivated by cooking, however, but because of its protein-digesting ability it can dissolve necrotic material with disastrous results. The usual grade used in food digests about 35 times its weight of lean meat. It may cause allergic manifestations.

PAPRIKA. The finely ground pods of dried, ripe, sweet pepper. The strong, reddish orange powder is used in sausage and spice flavorings for baked goods (1,900 ppm), condiments, meats (7,400 ppm), and soups (7,500 ppm). The *oleoresin* (*see*) is used in fruit, meat, and spice flavorings for beverages, ice cream, ices, candy, baked goods, condiments, and meats. Both paprika and paprika oleoresins are used as a red coloring. No known toxicity.

PARAFFIN WAX. A colorless, somewhat translucent, odorless mass; greasy feel. Used as a defoaming component in yeast and beet sugar production. Not digested or absorbed in the intestines. Used to cover food products. Cleared for use as a synthetic masticatory substance in chewing gum. Raises melting point in ointments, used in wax paper and candles, and in many industrial products. Used for wound dressing. When used in cosmetic surgery, paraffin has caused sloughing of the skin.

PARSLEY. The aromatic leaves of the annual herb cultivated everywhere. Used in spice flavorings for beverages, meats, soups, baked goods, and condiments. Parsley *oil* is obtained by steam distillation of the ripe seeds of the herb. Yellow to light brown, with a harsh odor, it is used in fruit and spice flavorings for beverages, ice cream, ices, candy, baked goods, and condiments. Parsley *oleoresin* (*see*) is used in spice flavorings for condiments. Parsley may cause sensitivity to light. GRAS

PATCHOULY OIL. The natural extract from the leaves of an East Indian herb mint. Yields a fragrant essential oil used in cola, fruit, nut, and spice flavorings for beverages, ice cream, ices, candy, baked goods, and chewing gum. No known toxicity.

PEACH ALDEHYDE. See γ-Undecalactone.

PEACH KERNEL. Persic Oil. Fixed oil from a seed. Smells like almonds. Used as a natural flavoring in conjunction with other natural flavorings. Also used as an emollient. No known toxicity.

PEANUT OIL. Expressed from seeds of a low branch annual herb. A solvent, in salad oil, shortening, mayonnaise, and confections. Also used in conjunction with natural flavorings. Used in the manufacture of soaps and paints. Peanut butter is about 50 percent peanut oil suspended in peanut fibers. The oil acts as a mild cathartic and as a protective for the gastroinestinal tract when corrosive poisons have been swallowed. It is also an emollient for the skin and mucous membranes. GRAS

PEANUT STEARINE. See Peanut Oil.

PECTIN. *Includes low methoxyl pectin and sodium pectinate.* Pectin is found in the roots, stems, and fruits of plants, and seems to function as a cementing agent. It is a coarse or fine powder, practically odorless, with a gluey taste. Richest source of pectin is lemon or orange rind, which contains about 30 percent of this polysaccharide. Used as a stabilizer, thickener, bodying agent for artificially sweetened beverages, syrups for frozen products, ice cream, ice milk, confections, fruit sherberts, water ices, French dressing, fruit jelly, preserves, and jams to compensate for a deficiency in natural pectin. Also used as an antidiarrheal agent. No known toxicity.

PEGU CATECHU EXTRACT. See Catechu Extract.

PELARGONALDEHYDE. See Nonanal.

PELARGONIC ACID. See Nonanoic Acid.

PELARGONIC ALDEHYDE. See Nonanal.

PELARGONYL VANILLYLAMIDE. See Nonanoyl 4-Hydroxy-3-Methoxybenzylamide.

PENNYROYAL OIL. *Squaw Mint. Hedeoma.* From the dried leaves and flowering tops of plants raised from Canada to Florida and as far west as Nebraska. Used in mint flavorings for beverages, ice cream, ices, candy, and baked goods. Formerly used as an aromatic perspirant; to stimulate menstrual flow; for flatulence; an abortion inducer; and a counteractant for painful menstruation. Brain damage has been reported following doses of less than 1 teaspoon. Nausea, vomiting, bleeding, circulatory collapse, confusion, restlessness, and delirium have been reported.

ω-PENTADECALACTONE. *Thibetolide®. Angelica Lactone. Exaltolide.* A synthetic berry, fruit, liquor, wine, nut, and vanilla flavoring agent for beverages, ice cream, ices, candy, baked goods, gelatin desserts, and alcoholic beverages. No known toxicity.

PENTADECANOLIDE. See ω-Pentadecalactone.

PENTANAL. See Valeraldehyde.

2, 3-PENTANEDIONE. A synthetic flavoring agent that occurs naturally in coffee. Used in strawberry, butter, caramel, fruit, rum, and cheese flavorings for beverages, ice cream, ices, candy, baked goods, gelatin desserts, and puddings. No known toxicity.

PENTANOIC ACID. See Valeric Acid.

1-PENTANOL. See Amyl Alcohol.

2-PENTANONE. A synthetic flavoring that occurs naturally in pineapple. Used in fruit flavorings for beverages, ice cream, ices, candy, and baked goods. No known toxicity.

4-PENTENOIC ACID. A synthetic butter and fruit flavoring agent for beverages, ice cream, ices, candy, baked goods, and margarine. No known toxicity.

PENTYL ALCOHOL. See Amyl Alcohol.

PENTYL BUTYRATE. See Amyl Butyrate.

PEPPER, BLACK. A pungent product obtained from the dried, unripe berries of the East Indian pepper plant. Used in sausage and spice flavorings for beverages, baked goods, condiments, meats, soups, and pickles. Black pepper *oil* is used in meat and spice flavorings for beverages, ice cream, ices, candy, baked goods, condiments, and meats. Black pepper *oleoresin* (*see*) is used in sausage and pepper flavorings for beverages, ice cream, ices, candy, baked goods, condiments, and meats. Pepper was formerly used as a carminative to break up intestinal gas, to cause sweating, and as a gastric agent to promote gastric secretion. No known toxicity.

PEPPER, RED. See Cayenne Pepper.

PEPPER, WHITE. The pungent product obtained from the undecorticated (with the outercovering intact) ripe berries of the pepper plant. Used in sausage and spice flavorings for beverages, baked goods, condiments, meats, and soups. White pepper *oil* is used in spice flavorings for baked goods. White pepper *oleoresin* (*see*) is used in spice flavorings for meats. See Pepper, black for toxicity.

PEPPER TREE OIL. See Schinus Molle Oil.

PEPPERMINT LEAVES. See Peppermint Oil.

PEPPERMINT OIL. From the dried leaves and tops of a plant common to Asian, European, and American gardens. Used in chocolate, fruit, cordial, creme de menthe, peppermint, nut, and spice flavorings for beverages, ice cream, ices, candy (1,200 ppm), baked goods, gelatin desserts, chewing gum (8,300 ppm), meats, liquors, icings, and toppings. Peppermint has been used as a carminative to break up intestinal gas and as an antiseptic. Two patients who consumed large quantities of peppermint candy over a long period of time developed an irregular heart rhythm. GRAS

PEPSIN. A digestive enzyme found in gastric juice that helps break down protein. The product used to aid digestion is obtained from the glandular layer of the fresh stomach of a hog. Slightly acid taste and a mild odor. No known toxicity.

PEPTONES. Secondary protein derivatives formed during the process of digestion—the result of the action of the gastric and pancreatic juices upon protein. Peptones are used as a foam stabilizer for beer. No known toxicity.

PERACETIC ACID. *Peroxyacitic Acid.* A starch modifier prepared from acetaldehyde (*see*). It is 40 percent acetic acid and highly corrosive. Acrid odor; explodes violently on heating to 110°.

PEROXIDE. *Benzoyl, Calcium, and Hydrogen.* *Benzoyl peroxide* is a compound used as a bleaching agent for flours, oils, and cheese. Has been used as a paste for treating poison ivy and for burns. May explode when heated. *Calcium peroxide* or *dioxide* is odorless, almost tasteless. Used as a dough conditioner and oxidizing agent for bread, rolls, and buns. Formerly an antiseptic. *Hydrogen peroxide* or *dioxide* is a compound used as a bleaching and oxidizing agent, a modifier for food starch, and a preservative and bactericide for milk and cheese. Bitter taste. May decompose violently if traces of impurities are present. A strong oxidant that can injure skin and eyes. Chemists are cautioned to wear rubber gloves and goggles when handling it. On the FDA list of additives to be studied for mutagenic, teratogenic, subacute, and reproductive effects.

PERSIC OIL. See Apricot Kernel; also Peach Kernel.

PERUVIAN BALSAM. See Balsam, Peru.

PETITGRAIN OIL. The volatile oil obtained by steam distillation from the leaves and small twigs of the bitter orange tree, a variety of citrus. Brownish to yellow, with a bittersweet odor. Used in loganberry, violet, apple, banana, cherry, grape, peach, pear, honey, muscatel, nut, ginger, and ginger ale flavorings for beverages, ice cream, ices, candy, baked goods, gelatin desserts, chewing gum, and condiments. No known toxicity.

PETITGRAIN OIL (LEMON). A fragrant, essential oil from a variety of citrus tree. Used in citrus and fruit flavorings for beverages,

ice cream, ices, candy, and baked goods. No known toxicity. GRAS
PETITGRAIN OIL (MANDARIN). The fragrant essential oil from
a variety of citrus tree. Used in orange, tangerine, and grape flavorings for beverages, ice cream, ices, candy, baked goods, and gelatin
desserts. No known toxicity. GRAS
PETROLATUM. Petroleum or paraffin jelly. Vaseline. Practically
odorless and tasteless. A releasing agent and sealant for confections.
A coating for fruits, vegetables, and cheese. A defoaming agent in
yeast and beet sugar production. Used in baking products, a lubricant
in meat-packing plants and used in dried-egg albumin. A protective
dressing in medicine and used in cosmetics. When ingested, it produces a mild laxative effect. Not absorbed but may inhibit digestion.
PETROLEUM. Crude or mineral oil. A defoaming agent in food
processing, a detergent agent in a fruit rinse, and for cleaning vegetables. See Mineral Oil for toxicity.
PETROLEUM. Waxes. A defoaming agent in processing beet sugar
and yeast. Formerly used for bronchitis, tapeworms, and externally
for arthritis and skin problems. No known toxicity.
pH. Chemical symbol representing a scale to measure acidity versus
alkalinity. The pH of a solution is measured on a scale of 14. A truly
neutral solution, neither acidic nor alkaline, such as water, would
be 7. The desired pH for most crops is from 6 to 8. The pH of blood
is 7.3; vinegar is 2.3; lemon juice is 8.2; and lye is 13. pH actually
represents the hydrogen (H) ion concentration of a solution. "p"
stands for the *power* of the hydrogen ion.
α-PHELLANDRENE. A synthetic flavoring agent that occurs naturally in allspice, star anise, angelica root, bay, dill, sweet fennel, black
pepper, peppermint oil, and pimenta. Isolated from the essential oils
of the eucalyptus plant. Used in citrus and spice flavorings for beverages, ice cream, ices, candy, and baked goods. Can be irritating to
and absorbed through the skin. Ingestion can cause vomiting and
diarrhea.
PHENETHYL ALCOHOL. A synthetic flavoring that occurs naturally in oranges, raspberries, and tea. Floral odor. Used in strawberry,
butter, caramel, floral, fruit, and honey flavorings for beverages, ice
cream, ices, candy, baked goods, gelatin desserts, and chewing gum.
Practically all rose perfumes contain it. It is a strong local anesthetic
and has caused central nervous system injury in mice.
PHENETHYL ANTHRANILATE. A synthetic butter, caramel,

fruit, honey, and grape flavoring agent for beverages, ice cream, ices, candy, and baked goods. No known toxicity.

PHENETHYL BENZOATE. A synthetic fruit and honey flavoring agent for beverages, ice cream, ices, candy, baked goods, and chewing gum. No known toxicity.

PHENETHYL BUTYRATE. A synthetic strawberry, butter, caramel, floral, apple, peach, pineapple, and honey flavoring agent for beverages, ice cream, ices, candy, and baked goods. No known toxicity.

PHENETHYL CINNAMATE. A synthetic fruit flavoring for beverages, ice cream, ices, candy, baked goods, and puddings. No known toxicity.

PHENETHYL FORMATE. Formic Acid. A synthetic berry, apple, apricot, banana, cherry, peach, pear, plum, and honey flavoring agent for beverages, ice cream, ices, candy, and baked goods. See Formic Acid for toxicity.

PHENETHYL ISOBUTYRATE. A synthetic flavoring, slightly yellow, with a rose odor. Used in strawberry, floral, rose, apple, peach, pineapple, honey, and cheese flavorings for beverages, ice cream, ices, candy, and baked goods. No known toxicity.

PHENETHYL ISOVALERATE. A synthetic apple, apricot, peach pear, and pineapple flavoring agent for beverages, ice cream, ices, candy, baked goods, and chewing gum. No known toxicity.

PHENETHYL PHENYLACETATE. A synthetic fruit and honey flavoring agent for beverages, ice cream, ices, candy, baked goods, and Maraschino cherries. No known toxicity.

PHENETHYL PROPIONATE. A synthetic fruit and honey flavoring agent for beverages, ice cream, ices, candy, and baked goods. No known toxicity.

PHENETHYL SALICYLATE. A synthetic apricot and peach flavoring agent for beverages, ice cream, ices, candy, and baked goods. See Salicylic Acid for toxicity.

PHENETHYL SENECIOATE. A synthetic liquor and wine flavoring agent for ice cream, ices, candy, and alcoholic beverages.

PHENETHYL TIGLATE. A synthetic fruit and nut flavoring agent for beverages, ice cream, ices, candy, and baked goods. No known toxicity.

PHENOXYACETIC ACID. A synthetic fruit and honey flavoring

agent for beverages, ice cream, ices, candy, and baked goods. Used as a fungicide to soften calluses and corns and other hard surfaces. A mild irritant.

2-PHENOXYETHYL ISOBUTYRATE. A synthetic fruit flavoring, colorless, with a roselike odor. Used in beverages, ice cream, ices, candy, and baked goods. No known toxicity.

PHENYL ACETATE. A synthetic flavoring agent prepared from phenol and acetic chloride. Used in berry, butter, caramel, floral, rose, fruit, honey, and vanilla flavorings for beverages, ice cream, ices, candy, and baked goods. Phenol is highly toxic. Death from 1.5 grams has been reported.

4-PHENYL-2-BUTANOL. A synthetic fruit flavoring for beverages, ice cream, ices, candy, and baked goods. No known toxicity.

4-PHENYL-3-BUTEN-2-OL. A synthetic fruit flavoring for beverages, ice cream, ices, candy, and baked goods. No known toxicity.

4-PHENYL-3-BUTEN-2-ONE. A synthetic chocolate, cocoa, fruit, cherry, nut, and vanilla flavoring agent for beverages, ice cream, ices, candy, baked goods, gelatin desserts, and shortening. No known toxicity.

4-PHENYL-2-BUTYL ACETATE. A synthetic fruit and peach flavoring agent for beverages, ice cream, ices, candy, and baked goods. See Acetic Acid for toxicity.

PHENYL DIMETHYL CARBINYL ISOBUTYRATE. See a-a-Dimethylbenzyl Isobutyrate.

PHENYL 2-FUROATE. A synthetic chocolate and mushroom flavoring agent for beverages, candy, and baked goods. No known toxicity.

1-PHENYL-3-METHYL-3-PENTANOL. A synthetic fruit flavoring agent for beverages, candy, and gelatin desserts. No known toxicity.

1-PHENYL-1-PROPANOL. A synthetic fruit and honey flavoring agent for beverages, ice cream, ices, candy, and baked goods. No known toxicity.

3-PHENYL-1-PROPANOL. A synthetic flavoring that occurs naturally in tea. Used in strawberry, apricot, peach, plum, hazelnut, pistachio, cinnamon, and walnut flavorings for beverages, ice cream, ices, candy, baked goods, liqueurs, and chewing gum. No known toxicity.

3-PHENYL PROPYL ISOBUTYRATE. A synthetic apple, apricot,

175

peach, pear, pineapple, and plum flavoring agent for beverages, ice cream, ices, candy, and baked goods. No known toxicity.

PHENYLACETIC ACID. A synthetic flavoring agent that occurs naturally in Japanese mint, oil of neroli, and black pepper. A glistening, white solid with a persistent, unpleasant odor. Used in butter, chocolate, rose, honey, and vanilla flavorings for beverages, ice cream, ices, candy, baked goods, gelatin desserts, chewing gum, liquors, and syrups. No known toxicity.

PHENYLACETALDEHYDE. An oily, colorless flavoring agent with the odor of lilacs and hyacinths, derived from phenylethyl alcohol. Used in raspberry, strawberry, apricot, cherry, peach, honey, and spice flavorings for beverages, ice cream, ices, candy, baked goods, and chewing gum. The acetaldehyde of this compound is less irritating than formaldehyde (*see*) but is a stronger central nervous system depressant. In addition, it sometimes produces fluid in the lungs upon ingestion.

PHENYLACETALDEHYDE 2,3-BUTYLENE GLYCOL ACETAL. A synthetic floral and fruit flavoring agent for candy. See Phenylacetaldehyde for toxicity.

PHENYLACETALDEHYDE DIMETHYL ACETAL. A synthetic fruit, apricot, cherry, honey, and spice flavoring agent for beverages, ice cream, ices, candy, baked goods, and chewing gum. See Phenylacetaldehyde and Acetic Acid for toxicity.

PHENYLACETALDEHYDE GLYCERYL ACETAL. A synthetic floral and fruit flavoring agent for beverages, candy, ice cream, and ices. See Phenylacetaldehyde and Acetic Acid for toxicity.

PHENYLALANINE. An essential amino acid (*see*) considered essential for growth in normal human beings and not synthesized in the human body. Phenylalanine is involved in phenlyketonuria (PHK), an affliction that, if not detected soon after birth, leads to mental deterioration in children. Restricting phenylalanine in diets results in improvement. Whole egg contains 5.4 percent and skim milk 5.1 percent. It can also be isolated commercially. For a dietary supplement, recommended intake for normal adults is 2.2 milligrams per day. The FDA has asked for further short-term study of this additive.

2-PHENYLETHYL ISOVALERATE. See Phenethyl Isovalerate.

2-PHENYLPROPIONALDEHYDE. A synthetic berry, rose, apricot, cherry, peach, plum, and almond flavoring agent for beverages, ice cream, ices, candy, and baked goods. No known toxicity.

3-PHENYLPROPIONALDEHYDE. A synthetic flavoring agent, slightly yellow, with a strong, floral odor. Used in berry, rose, apricot, cherry, peach, plum, and almond flavorings for beverages, ice cream, ices, candy, and baked goods. No known toxicity.

2-PHENYLPROPIONALDEHYDE DIMETHYL ACETAL. A synthetic berry, floral, rose, fruit, honey, mushroom, nut, and spice flavoring agent for beverages, ice cream, ices, candy, baked goods, chewing gum, and condiments. See Acetic Acid for toxicity.

3-PHENYLPROPIONIC ACID. A synthetic flavoring agent that occurs naturally in raspberries. Used in fruit and cheese flavorings for beverages, ice cream, ices, candy, baked goods, gelatin desserts, and dairy products. No known toxicity.

3-PHENYLPROPYL ACETATE. A synthetic flavoring, colorless, with a spicy floral odor. Used in berry, fruit, and spice flavorings for beverages, ice cream, ices, candy, baked goods, chewing gum, and condiments. Propyl acetate may be irritating to skin and mucous membranes and narcotic in high concentrations.

2-PHENYLPROPYL BUTYRATE. A synthetic flavoring used in beverages, ice cream, ices, candy and baked goods. No specific flavorings listed. No known toxicity.

3-PHENYLPROPYL CINNAMATE. A synthetic butter, caramel, chocolate, cocoa, coconut, grape, and spice flavoring agent for beverages, ice cream, ices, candy, and baked goods. No known toxicity.

3-PHENYLPROPYL FORMATE. Formic Acid. A synthetic currant, raspberry, butter, caramel, apricot, peach, and honey flavoring agent for beverages, ice cream, ices, candy, and baked goods. See Formic Acid for toxicity.

3-PHENYLPROPYL HEXANOATE. A synthetic fruit flavoring for beverages, ice cream, ices, candy, and baked goods. No known toxicity.

2-PHENYLPROPYL ISOBUTYRATE. A synthetic fruit flavoring for beverages, ice cream, ices, and candy. No known toxicity.

3-PHENYLPROPYL ISOVALERATE. A synthetic butter, caramel, apple, pear, and nut flavoring agent for beverages, ice cream, ices, candy, and baked goods. No known toxicity.

3-PHENYLPROPYL PROPIONATE. A synthetic apricot flavoring for beverages, ice cream, ices, candy, and baked goods. No known toxicity.

2-3 (3-PHENYLPROPYL) TETRAHYDROFURAN. A synthetic

fruit, honey and maple flavoring agent for beverages, ice cream, ices, candy, gelatin, puddings, and chewing gum. No known toxicity.

PHOSPHATE. A salt or ester of phosphoric acid (*see*). An emulsifier salt, texturizer, and sequestrant in foods. Sodium phosphate is used in evaporated milk up to .1 percent of weight. A carbonated beverage contains phosphoric acid. Without sufficient phosphate there is abnormal parathyroid (gland) function, bone metabolism, intestinal absorption, malnutrition, and kidney malfunction. Chemicals that interfere with phosphate action include detergents, mannitol (an alcohol used as a dietary supplement, the basis of dietetic sweets), Vitamin D, and aluminum hydroxide (*see*), a leavening agent.

PHOSPHATE, AMMONIUM. *Dibasic and monobasic.* See Ammonium Phosphate.

PHOSPHATE, CALCIUM HEXAMETA-. See Calcium Hexametaphosphate.

PHOSPHATE, CALCIUM. *Mono and tri basic.* See Calcium Phosphate.

PHOSPHATE, POTASSIUM. *Mono and di basic.* See Potassium Phosphate.

PHOSPHORIC ACID. A colorless, odorless solution obtained commercially from phosphate rock. Used as a sequestering agent for rendered animal fat or a combination of such fat with vegetable fat. Also used as an acidulant and flavoring in soft drink beverages, jellies, frozen dairy products, bakery products, candy, cheese products, and in the brewing industry. In concentrated solutions, it is irritating to the skin and mucous membranes.

PHOSPHOROUS SOURCES: *Calcium Phosphate, Magnesium Phosphate, Potassium Glycerophosphate, and Sodium Phosphate.* Mineral supplements for cereal products, particularly breakfast foods such as farina. They are also used in incendiary bombs and tracer bullets. Phosphorus was formerly used to treat rickets and degenerative disorders. See Phosphate.

PHOSPHORUS CHLORIDE. Phosphate derivative used as a starch modifier and a chlorinating agent. Intensely irritating to the skin, eyes, mucous membranes. Inhalation may cause fluid in the lungs.

PIMENTA LEAF OIL. *Jamaica Pepper. Allspice.* Derived from the dried ripe fruit of the evergreen shrub grown in the Indies and Central and South America. Used in raspberry, fruit, nut, and spice flavorings for beverages, ice cream, ices, candy, baked goods, gelatin desserts, chewing gum, condiments, and meat products. No known toxicity. GRAS

PINE MOUNTAIN OIL. See Pine Needle Oil and Pine Needle Dwarf Oil.

PINE NEEDLE DWARF OIL. Pine Mountain Oil. The volatile oil obtained by steam distillation from a variety of pine tree. Colorless, with a pleasant pine smell. Used in citrus, pineapple, and liquor flavorings for beverages, ice cream, ices, candy, and baked goods.

PINE NEEDLE OIL. Pine Mountain Oil. A natural flavoring extracted from a variety of pine tree. Used in pineapple, citrus, liquor, and spice flavorings for beverages, ice cream, ices, candy, and baked goods. Ingestion can cause intestinal hemorrhages.

PINE SCOTCH OIL. Volatile oil obtained by steam distillation from the needles of a pine tree. Colorless or yellowish, with an odor of turpentine. Used in various flavorings for beverages, candy, and baked goods. See Turpentine for toxicity.

PINE TAR OIL. A synthetic flavoring obtained from a species of pine wood. Used in licorice flavorings for ice cream, ices, and candy. Also used as a solvent, disinfectant, and deodorant. Irritating to the skin and mucous membranes. Large doses can cause central nervous system depression.

α-PINENE. A synthetic flavoring agent that occurs naturally in angelica root oil, anise, star anise, asafoetida oil, coriander, cumin, fennel, grapefruit, juniper berries, oils of lavender and lime, mandarin, orange leaf, black pepper, peppermint, pimenta, and yarrow. It is the principal ingredient of turpentine (*see*). Used chiefly in the manufacture of camphor. Used in lemon and nutmeg flavorings for beverages, ice cream, candy, baked goods, and condiments. Also used in chewing gum base. Readily absorbed from the gastrointestinal tract, the skin, and respiratory tract. It is a local irritant, central nervous system depressant, and an irritant to the bladder and kidney. Has caused benign skin tumors from chronic contact. The fatal dose is estimated at 180 grams orally as turpentine.

2-PINENE. See α-Pinene.

β-PINENE. A synthetic flavoring that occurs naturally in black currant buds, coriander, cumin, black pepper, and yarrow herb. Used in citrus flavorings for beverages, ice cream, ices, candy (600 ppm), and baked goods (600 ppm). Also cleared for use in chewing gum base. See *a*-Pinene for toxicity.

PINUS PUMILIO OIL. See Pine Needle Dwarf Oil.

PIPERIDINE. A synthetic flavoring that occurs naturally in black pepper. Used in beverages, candy, baked goods, meats, soups, and condiments. Soapy texture. Has been proposed for use as a tranquilizer and muscle relaxant. No known toxicity.

PIPERINE. *Celery Soda.* A synthetic flavoring agent that occurs naturally in black pepper, it is used as a pungent brandy flavoring. It is also used as a nontoxic insecticide. Believed to be more toxic than the commercial pyrethrins.

d-PIPERITONE. A synthetic flavoring agent that occurs naturally in Japanese mint. Used in beverages, ice cream, ices, candy, and baked goods. Also used to give dentifrices a minty flavor. No known toxicity.

PIPERONAL. A synthetic flavoring agent that occurs naturally in vanilla and black pepper. White, crystalline powder, with a sweet floral odor. Used in strawberry, cola, cherry, rum, maple, nut, and vanilla flavorings in beverages, ice cream, ices, baked goods, gelatin puddings, and chewing gum. Used chiefly in perfumery. Ingestion of large amounts may cause central nervous system depression.

PIPERONYL ACETATE. A synthetic fruit flavoring agent for beverages, ice cream, ices, candy, and baked goods. See Piperonal for toxicity.

PIPERONYL ALDEHYDE. See Piperonal.

PIPERONYL ISOBUTYRATE. A synthetic fruit and cheese flavoring agent for beverages, ice cream, ices, candy, and baked goods. See Piperonal for toxicity.

PIPEROYLPIPERIDENE. See Piperine.

PIPSISSEWA LEAVES EXTRACT. *Love-in Winter. Prince's Pine.* Extracted from the leaves of an evergreen shrub. Used in root beer, sarsaparilla, wintergreen, and birch beer flavorings for beverages and candy. Its leaves have been used as an astringent, diuretic, and tonic. The Cree title means "to break up"— bladder stones, that is.

PLANTAROME. See Yucca.

POLYACRYLAMIDE. A compound used as a film former in the

imprinting of soft-shell gelatin capsules. Used in washing fruits and vegetables. No known toxicity.

POLYACRYLIC ACID. A polymer of acrylic acid used in clarification of sugar juice. Used as sizing in manufacture of nylon. A strong irritant.

POLYETHOXYLATED ALKYLPHENOL. Dodecyl, nonyl, and octyl. Components of a commercial detergent for raw foods, followed by water rinsing. The only symptoms shown in animals poisoned with this substance is gastrointestinal irritation.

POLYETHYLENE. Chewing-gum base component. Used especially in form of films and sheets for packaging. No known toxicity.

POLYETHYLENE GLYCOL. 400–2,000 molecular weight. Defoaming agent in processed beet sugar and yeast. No known toxicity.

POLYETHYLENE GLYCOL (600) DIOLEATE. Polyethylene glycol esters of mixed fatty acids from tall oil; Polyethylene glycol (400 through 6,000). An agent in nonnutritive artificial sweeteners; a component of coatings and binders in tablet food; improves resistance to oxidation and moisture. No known toxicity.

POLYGLYCEROL ESTERS. Prepared from edible fats, oils, and fatty acids, hydrogenated or nonhydrogenated (see Hydrogenation). Derived from corn, cottonseed, palm, peanut, safflower, sesame, and soybean oils; lard, and tallow. Used as emulsifiers. No known toxicity.

POLYISOBUTYLENE. See Resin, Isobutylene.

POLYLIMONENE. A general fixative derived from citrus oils. It is used in candy (4,500 ppm), chewing gum, and baked goods (1,000 ppm). It can be a skin irritant and sensitizer. See d-Limonene.

POLYMYXIN B$_4$. A generic term for antibiotics obtained from fermentations of various media by strains of Bacillus polymyxa. Used as a bactericide in yeast culture for beer. May cause symptoms of renal irritation and damage.

POLYOXYALKALENE GLYCOL. Defoaming agent in beet sugar production. No known toxicity.

POLYOXYETHYLENE GLYCOL. Ester of edible cottonseed oil and fatty acids. Solubilizing agent in pickles. No known toxicity.

POLYOXYETHYLENE GLYCOL (600) MONORICINOLEATE. Defoaming component used in processing beet sugar and yeast. No known toxicity.

POLYOXYETHYLENE (20) SORBITAN MONOSTEARATE.

Polysorbate 60. An emulsifier and flavor-dispersing agent in shortening and edible oils. Used in whipped vegetable oil topping, cake, and cake mixes; cake icing or filling; sugar-type confection coatings; coconut spread; beverage mixes; confectionery; chicken bases; gelatin desserts; dressings made without egg yolks; solid-state, edible vegetable fat-water emulsions used as substitutes for milk or cream; dietary vitamin supplement; foaming agent in nonalcoholic beverage mix to be added to alcoholic beverages; and a wetting and dispersing agent for powdered processed foods. The FDA has asked for further study of this additive.

POLYOXYETHYLENE (140) MONOSTEARATE. Defoaming agent in processed food; emulsifier for frozen desserts. On the FDA list for further study for long- and short-term effects.

POLYOXYETHYLENE (20) SORBITAN MONOOLEATE. Emulsifier and defoamer in the production of beet sugar; a dietary vitamin and mineral supplement. Used in dill oil in spiced green beans, icing, frozen custard, iced milk, fruit, and sherbet. The FDA has asked for short-term mutagenic, teratogenic, subacute, and reproductive effects. No known toxicity.

POLYOXYETHYLENE (20) SORBITAN MONOPALMITATE. An emulsifier, flavor-dispersing agent, and defoaming agent. Used in whipped cream, beverages, confectionery, and soup. The FDA has asked for further study of the safety of this additive.

POLYOXYETHYLENE (20) SORBITAN TRISTEARATE. An emulsifier, defoaming agent, and flavor-dispersing agent. Used in cakes and cake mixes, including doughnuts, whipped mixes, whipped vegetable oil toppings, cake icings and fillings, ice cream, frozen custard, ice milk, fruit sherbet, and nonstandardized frozen desserts; solid-state edible vegetable fat-water emulsions used as substitutes for milk or cream in coffee; and as a wetting and dispersing agent in processed powdered food. No known toxicity.

POLYOXYPROPYLENE GLYCOL. Defoaming agent for yeast and beet sugar. No known toxicity.

POLYPROPYLENE GLYCOL. Defoaming agent in processed beet sugar and yeast. No known toxicity.

POLYSORBATE 80. See Sorbitan Monooleate.

POLYSORBATE 60. See Polyoxyethylene (20) Sorbitan Monostearate.

POLYVINYL ACETATE.   Used as a chewing-gum base. No known toxicity.

POLYVINYL CHLORIDE (PVC).   Used in plastic wrap for a variety of products, including meats. Human blood can extract potentially harmful chemicals from the plastic used in blood-storage bags. The chemicals are added to polyvinyl chloride to make it flexible and they migrate from the plastic to the blood in amounts directly proportional to the length of time of storage. The result of the contamination of the blood is lung shock, which is characterized by an impeded circulation of the blood in the lungs. Three graduate students who had never received blood transfusions were found to have the substances in their body.

POLYVINYLPOLYPYRROLIDONE.   Used in dietary products up to 40 mg per day. Also a clarifying agent in vinegar. See Polyvinylpyrrolidone for toxicity.

POLYVINYLPYRROLIDONE.   Clarifying agent in vinegar and used as a plasma expander in medicine. In vinegar, up to .004 mg. It is not absorbed from the intestinal tract and may produce bulk evacuation, gas, and fecal impaction. It has damaged liver and kindeys when given intravenously. It is slowly excreted and may last in the system several months to a year. Found to cause cancer in experimental animals.

POMEGRANATE BARK EXTRACT.   A flavoring from dried bark, stem, or root of trees grown in the Mediterranean region and elsewhere. Contains about 20 percent tannic acid (*see*); rind of fruit contains 30 percent. Formerly used as a teniafuge (to expel tapeworms). Overdose can cause nausea, vomiting, and diarrhea. GRAS

POPPY SEED.   The seed of the poppy. Used as a natural spice flavoring for baked goods (8,600 ppm). Also used in the manufacture of paints, varnishes, and soaps. No known toxicity. GRAS

POT MARIGOLD.   See Marigold, Pot.

POT MARJORAM.   See Marjoram, Pot.

POTASSIUM ACID TARTRATE.   The salt of tartaric acid. Colorless, with a pleasant odor. An acid and buffer, it is the acid constituent of some baking powders. Used in effervescent beverages. It is also used in some confectionery products. Formerly a cathartic. No known toxicity.

POTASSIUM BISULFITE.   Same uses as for sodium sulfite (*see*)

in ale, beer, fruit-pie mix. The FDA has asked for a further study to determine short-term reproductive teratogenic, mutagenic, and subacute effects of this additive. GRAS

POTASSIUM BROMATE. See Calcium Bromate.

POTASSIUM BROMIDE. A preservative used in washing fruits and vegetables. Used medically as a sedative and antiepileptic. In large doses it can cause central nervous system depression. Prolonged intake may cause bromism. Bromism's main symptoms are headache, mental inertia, slow heartbeat, gastric distress, skin rash, acne, muscular weakness, and occasionally violent delirium. Bromides can cross the placental barrier, and have caused skin rashes in the fetus.

POTASSIUM CARBONATE. *Salt of Tartar. Pearl Ash.* Odorless, with a strong alkaline taste. Used as an alkali in combination with potassium hydroxide (*see*) for extracting color from annatto seed (*see*). Also used in confections and cocoa products. Formerly employed as a diuretic to reduce body water and as an alkalizer. It is an irritant with caustic action.

POTASSIUM CASEINATE. A texturizer used in ice cream, frozen custard, ice milk, and fruit sherbets. See Casein.

POTASSIUM CHLORIDE. A colorless, crystalline, odorless powder with a salty taste. A yeast food used in the brewing industry to improve brewing and fermentation and in the jelling industry. Small intestinal ulcers may occur with oral administration. Large doses ingested can cause gastrointestinal irritation, purging, weakness, and circulatory collapse. Used as a substitute for sodium chloride (*see*) in low-sodium dietary foods. GRAS

POTASSIUM CITRATE. A transparent or white powder, odorless, with a cool, salty taste. Used as a buffer in confections and in artificially sweetened jellies and preserves. It is a urinary alkalizer and gastric antacid. No known toxicity. GRAS

POTASSIUM GLYCEROPHOSPHATE. See Phosphorous Sources.

POTASSIUM HYDROXIDE. An alkali used to extract color from annatto seed, a peeling agent for tubers and fruits, also in cacao products. Extremely corrosive. Ingestion may produce violent pain in the throat, bleeding, and collapse. Stricture of the esophagus may follow. Occasionally used to prevent the growth of horns in calves. The FDA banned household products containing more than 10 percent potassium hydroxide. GRAS

POTASSIUM IODATE. See Iodine Sources.

POTASSIUM IODIDE. In table salt as a source of dietary iodine restricted to .01 percent. It is also used in some drinking water. See Iodine Sources for use and toxicity. GRAS

POTASSIUM METABISULFITE. White or colorless, with an odor of sulfur dioxide (*see*), it is an antioxidant, preservative and antifermentative in breweries and wineries. Also used for bleaching straw. The FDA has asked for further study of this additive for short-term mutagenic, teratogenic, subacute, and reproductive effects. GRAS

POTASSIUM-n-METHYLDITHIO-CARBAMATE. A bacteria-killing component in controlling microorganisms in cane sugar mills. Carbamates are used to prevent sprouting in potatoes and other products by stopping cell division, something we call mutations. Carbamate mutations may lead to defective children and to cancer.

POTASSIUM NITRATE. See Nitrate, Potassium.

POTASSIUM NITRITE. See Nitrite, Potassium.

POTASSIUM PERMANGANATE. Dark purple or bronzelike odorless crystals with a sweet, antiseptic taste, used as a starch modifier. Dilute solutions are mildly irritating. Highly concentrated solutions are caustic.

POTASSIUM PHOSPHATE. Mono and dibasic. Colorless to white powder used as yeast food in brewing industry in the production of champagne and other sparkling wines. Has been used as a urinary acidifier. No known toxicity.

POTASSIUM SORBATE. White crystalline powder used as a preservative; a mold and yeast inhibitor; and a fungistat in beverages, baked goods, chocolate, and soda fountain syrups, fresh fruit cocktail, tangerine puree (sherbet base), salads (potato, macaroni, cole slaw, gelatin), cheesecake, pie fillings, cake, cheeses in consumer-size packages, and artificially sweetened jellies and preserves. Low oral toxicity but may cause mild irritation of the skin. GRAS

POTASSIUM STEARATE. A defoaming agent, with the slight odor of fat, in brewing. A strong alkali. No known toxicity.

POTASSIUM SULFATE. Colorless or white crystalline powder, bitter taste. A water corrective used in the brewing industry. Also used as a fertilizer and as a cathartic. Large doses can cause severe gastrointestinal bleeding.

POTASSIUM SULFITE. See Sulfites.

POTATO STARCH. A flour prepared from potatoes, ground to a pulp and washed free of fiber. GRAS for packaging. A potential sensitizer.

PRICKLY ASH BARK. A natural cola, maple, and root beer flavor extract from a prickly aromatic shrub or small tree bearing yellow flowers. Used in beverages, candy, and baked goods. No known toxicity. GRAS

PROLINE. L and DL forms. An amino acid (*see*), used as a supplement but classified as nonessential. Usually isolated from wheat or gelatin. L-Proline is the naturally occurring form and DL-Proline is the synthetic. GRAS

PROPANE. A gas, heavier than air, odorless when pure. It is used as fuel, and as a refrigerant. Cleared for use in combination with octafluorocyclobutane as a spray propellant and aerating agent for foamed and sprayed foods. May be narcotic in high concentrations. GRAS

PROPANOIC ACID. See Propionic Acid.

PROPENYLGLUAETHOL. A synthetic chocolate, maple, nut, and vanilla flavoring agent for beverages, ice cream, ices, candy, baked goods, puddings, and chocolate. No known toxicity.

PROPIONALDEHYDE. Propanal. A synthetic flavoring agent that occurs naturally in apples and onions. Used in fruit flavorings for beverages, ice cream, ices, candy, and baked goods. Suffocating odor. May cause respiratory irritation.

PROPIONIC ACID. Propanoic Acid. A synthetic flavoring agent that occurs naturally in dairy products in small amounts and apples, strawberries, tea, and violet leaves. Can be obtained from wood pulp waste liquor. Oily, with a slightly pungent, rancid odor. Used in butter and fruit flavorings for beverages, ice cream, ices, candy, baked goods, and cheese (600 ppm). Also an inhibitor and preservative. A perfume base. Salts have been used as antifungal agents to treat skin infections. GRAS

PROPYL ACETATE. A synthetic currant, raspberry, strawberry, apple, cherry, peach, pienapple, and rum flavoring agent for beverages, ice cream, ices, candy, and baked goods. It may be irritating to skin and mucous membranes and narcotic in high concentrations.

PROPYL ALCOHOL. Obtained from crude fusel oil. Alcoholic and slightly overpowering odor. Occurs naturally in cognac green oil, cognac white oil, and onion oil. A synthetic fruit flavoring for beverages, ice cream, ices, candy, and baked goods. Mildly irritating to the eyes and mucous membranes. Ingestion causes symptoms similar to that of ethyl alcohol (*see*), also known as grain alcohol.

p-*PROPYL ANISOLE.* A synthetic flavoring agent, colorless to pale yellow, with an anise odor. Used in licorice, root beer, spice, vanilla, wintergreen, and birch beer flavorings for beverages, ice cream, candy, and baked goods. No known toxicity.

PROPYL BENZOATE. A synthetic fruit flavoring agent for beverages, ice cream, ices, candy, and baked goods. No known toxicity.

PROPYL BUTYRATE. Contains propyl alcohol (*see*) and butyric acid (*see*). A synthetic strawberry, banana, pineapple, plum, tutti-frutti, liquor, and rum flavoring agent for beverages, ice cream, ices, candy, and baked goods. See Propyl Alcohol and Butyric Acid for toxicity.

PROPYL CINNAMATE. Cinnamic Acid. A synthetic berry, floral, rose, apple, grape, and honey flavoring agent for beverages, ice cream, ices, candy, baked goods, and gelatins. No know toxicity.

PROPYL FORMATE. Formic Acid. A synthetic berry, apple, and rum flavoring agent for beverages, ice cream, ices, candy, and baked goods. See Formic Acid for toxicity.

PROPYL 2-FURANACRYLATE. A synthetic coffee and honey flavoring agent for beverages and candy. No known toxicity.

PROPYL 2-FUROATE. A synthetic chocolate and mushroom flavoring agent for candy, baked goods, and condiments. No known toxicity.

PROPYL GALLATE. A fine, white, odorless powder with a bitter taste used as an antioxidant for foods, fats, and oils. Also used in lemon, lime, fruit, and spice flavorings for beverages, ice cream, ices, candy, baked goods, and gelatin desserts. On the FDA list for further study for short-term mutagenic, teratogenic, subacute, and reproductive effects. GRAS

PROPYL HEPTANOATE. A synthetic berry, coffee, fruit, cognac, and rum flavoring agent for beverages, ice cream, ices, candy, liqueurs, and baked goods. No known toxicity.

PROPYL HEXANOATE. A synthetic pineapple flavoring agent for beverages, ice cream, ices, and candy. No known toxicity.

PROPYL-p-HYDROXYBENZOATE. Propylparaben. A preservative used in beverages, candy, baked goods, artificially sweetened jellies and preserves. Also used in fruit flavorings for beverages, ice cream, ices, candy, and baked goods. Less toxic than benzoic (*see*) or salicylic (*see*) acid. Experimental animals showed no kidney or liver damage. On the FDA list for further study for short-term mutagenic, subacute, teratogenic, and reproductive effects. GRAS

PROPYL ISOVALERATE. A synthetic strawberry, apple, banana, and peach flavoring agent for beverages, ice cream, ices, candy, and baked goods. No known toxicity.

PROPYL MERCAPTAN. A synthetic berry and onion flavoring agent for baked goods and pickles. No known toxicity.

PROPYL METHOXYBENZENE. See *p*-Propyl Anisole.

PROPYL PHENYLACETATE. A synthetic butter, caramel, rose, fruit, and honey flavoring agent for beverages, ice cream, ices, candy, and baked goods. See Acetic Acid for toxicity.

PROPYL PROPIONATE. Propyl alcohol and propionic acid. A synthetic banana, cherry, melon, peach, pineapple, plum, and rum flavoring agent for beverages, ice cream, ices, candy, and baked goods. See Propyl Alcohol and Propionic Acid for toxicity.

PROPYLENE GLYCOL. Viscous, slightly bitter-tasting solvent, wetting agent, and humectant. Used in confectionery, chocolate products, ice cream emulsifiers, shredded coconut, beverages, baked goods, toppings, icings, and meat products to prevent discoloration during storage. Used in antifreeze in breweries and dairy establishments. Practically nontoxic. No adverse reactions reported but large oral doses in animals can produce central nervous system depression and slight kidney changes. GRAS

***PROPYLENE GLYCOL ALGINATE. Kelcolid.*®** The propylene glycol ester of alginic acid (*see*) derived from seaweed. Used as a stablizer and defoaming agent. Cleared for use in French dressing and salad dressing under the food standard regulations. Use as a stablizer in ice cream, frozen custard, ice milk, fruit sherbet, and water ices is permitted up to .5 percent of the weight of the finished product. The FDA has asked for further study of this widely used additive concerning long-term and short-term effects.

PROPYLENE OXIDE. Propene Oxide. Colorless, liquid starch modifier. No known toxicity.

PROPYLIC ALCOHOL. See Propyl Alcohol.

3-PROPYLIDENEPHTHALIDE. A synthetic fruit and spice flavoring agent for beverages, ice cream, ices, candy, and baked goods. No known toxicity.

PROPYLPARASEPT. See Propyl p-Hydroxybenzoate.

α-PROPYLPHENETHYL ALCOHOL. A synthetic fruit flavoring agent for beverages, ice cream, ices, candy, and puddings. Toxicity similar to ethanol (see).

PROTEIN. Proteins are the chief nitrogen-containing constituents of plants and animals—essential constituents of every living cell. They contain (by weight) about 50 percent carbon, about 20 percent oxygen, about 15 percent nitrogen, about 7 percent hydrogen, and some sulfur; some proteins also contain iron and phosphorous. Proteins are colorless, odorless, and generally tasteless. They vary in solubility and readily undergo putrification, hydrolysis, and dilution with acids or alkalies. They are considered combinations of amino acids (see).

PROVITAMIN A. See Carotene.

PSYLLIUM SEED HUSK. A stablizer from the seed of the fleaseed plant used in frozen desserts up to .5 percent of the weight of the finished product. No known toxicity.

PULEGONE. Found in oils of plants, principally the pennyroyal. Pleasant odor, midway between camphor and peppermint. Used in peppermint flavorings for beverages, ice cream, ices, candy, and baked goods. See Pennyroyal Oil for toxicity.

PULP. From wood, straw, bagasse, or other natural sources. A source of cellulose in food. The wood is treated either with a mixture containing mainly sodium hydroxide (see). Treatment removes the fibrous lignin—the resinous substance that binds the fiber that lines the cells of wood. See Sodium Hydroxide for toxicity. GRAS

PYRIDINE. Occurs naturally in coffee and coal tar. Disagreeable odor. Sharp taste. Used in chocolate flavorings for beverages, ice cream, ices, candy, and baked goods. Also used as a solvent for organic liquids and compounds. Once used to treat asthma but may cause central nervous system depression and irritation of the skin and respiratory tract. Large doses can produce gastrointestinal disturbances and kidney and liver damage. Pyridine is absorbed from the respiratory and gastrointestinal tract. Small oral doses in man have produced loss of appetite, nausea, fatigue, and mental depression. After prolonged daily administration, kidney and liver damage resulted.

PYRIDOXINE HYDROCHLORIDE. *Vitamin B₆.* A colorless or white crystalline powder, added to evaporated milk base in infant foods. Present in many foodstuffs. Especially good sources are yeast, liver, and cereals. A coenzyme which helps in the metabolism of amino acids (*see*) and fat. Permits normal red blood cell formation. GRAS

PYROLIGNEOUS ACID AND EXTRACT. A yellowish acid. Consists of 6 percent acetic acid (*see*), and small concentrations of creosote, methyl alcohol, and acetone (*see*). It is obtained by the destructive distillation of wood. Used as a synthetic flavoring in butter, butterscotch, caramel, rum, tobacco, smoke, and vanilla flavorings for beverages, ice cream, ices, candy, baked goods, puddings, and meats (300 ppm). The *extract* is used largely for smoking meats (300 ppm) and in smoke flavorings for baked goods (200 ppm) and alcoholic beverages. It is corrosive and may cause epigastric pain, vomiting, circulatory collapse, and death.

PYROMUCIC ALDEHYDE. See Furfural.

PYRORACEMIC ACID. See Pyruvic Acid.

PYRUVALDEHYDE. A synthetic flavoring, yellowish, with a pungent odor. Formed as an intermediate in the metabolism or fermentation of carbohydrates and lactic acid (*see*). Used in coffee, honey, and maple flavorings for beverages, ice cream, ices, candy, and baked goods. No known toxicity.

PYRUVIC ACID. An important intermediate in fermentation and metabolism, it occurs naturally in coffee and when sugar is metabolized in muscle. It is reduced to lactic acid (*see*) during exertion. Pyruvic acid is isolated from cane sugar. It is a synthetic flavoring used in coffee and rum flavorings for beverages, ice cream, ices, candy, baked goods, and chewing gum. Has been used as a paste in the treatment of deep burns. No known toxicity.

Q

QUACK GRASS. A cough grass, a pernicious weed in cultivated fields. See Dog Grass Extract.

QUASSIA EXTRACT. *Bitter Ash. Bitterwood.* From the wood and bark of a tree bearing bright scarlet flowers grown in Jamaica, the Caribbean Islands, and South America. So named for a Negro slave who discovered the medicinal value in the mid-eighteenth century. Slight odor, very bitter taste. Used in bitters, citrus, cherry, grape, liquor, root beer, sarsaparilla, and vanilla flavorings for beverages, baked goods, and liquors. Also used for fly poison on flypaper; to imitate hops; and as a bitter tonic and remedy for roundworms in children. No known toxicity.

QUEBRACHO BARK EXTRACT. Extract of a native Argentine tree, used in fruit, rum, and vanilla flavorings for beverages, ice cream, candy, ices, and baked goods. Closely related to the tranquilizer reserpine. Once promoted as an aphrodisiac, it can cause low blood pressure, nausea, abdominal distress, weakness, and fatigue.

QUERCETIN-3-RUTINOSIDE. See Rutin.

QUERCUS ALBA. See Oak Chip Extract.

QUICK GRASS. Triticum. See Dog Grass Extract.

QUILLAIA. China Bark Extract. See Quillaja.

QUILLAJA. Soap Bark. Quillay Bark. Panama Bark. China Bark. The inner dried bark of a tree grown in South America. Used in fruit, root beer, and spice flavorings for beverages, ice cream, candy, and syrups. Formerly used internally to treat bronchitis, and externally as a detergent and local irritant. No known toxicity.

QUINCE SEED EXTRACT. From the seed of a plant known for its acid fruit, grown in Southeastern Asia and Europe. Used in fruit flavorings for beverages, ice cream, ices, and baked goods. No known toxicity.

QUININE BISULFATE. Most important alkaloid of cinchona bark (*see*), from trees that grow wild in South America and are cultivated in Java. Very bitter. Used in bitters flavoring for beverages and not to exceed 83 ppm in soda. Used to treat fever and as a local anesthetic and analgesic. No known toxicity.

QUININE EXTRACT. See Cinchona Bark, Extract.

QUININE HYDROCHLORIDE. A synthetic flavoring agent derived from cinchona bark (*see*) and used in bitters, citrus, and fruit flavorings for beverages. Some medical use as quinine sulfate (*see*). No known toxicity.

QUININE SULFATE. A synthetic flavoring agent derived from cinchona bark (*see*) and used in bitters flavoring for beverages.

Also used medicinally to treat malaria; as an analgesic; and as a local anesthetic.

R

RACEMIC ACID. See Tartaric Acid.

RENNET. Rennin. Enzyme from the lining membrance of the stomach of suckling calves. Used for curdling milk in cheese-making and in junket. Sometimes used as a digestant. No known toxicity. GRAS

RESIN. The brittle substance, usually translucent or transparent, formed from the hardened secretion of plants. See Gum.

RESIN, ACRYLAMIDE—ACRYLIC ACID. A clarifying agent in beet sugar and cane sugar juice. The acid is used in the synthesis of this acrylic resin. No known toxicity.

RESIN, COUMARONE—INDENE. A chewing-gum base and protective coating for citrus fruit. Coumarone is derived from coal tar and is used with a mixture of indene chiefly in the synthesis of coumarone resins. No known toxicity.

RESIN, ISOBUTYLENE. Polyisobutylene. A chewing-gun base made from the chemical used chiefly in manufacturing synthetic rubber. No known toxicity.

RESIN, METHACRYLIC AND DIVINYL BENZENE. A compound of fine particle size, weakly acidic. Used as an absorbent for Vitamin B_{12} in nutritional supplement-type products. No known toxicity.

RESIN, PETROLEUM HYDROCARBON. A chewing-gum base synthesized from fuel oil. No known toxicity.

RESIN, TERPENE. Alpha and Beta Pinene. A chewing-gum base and coating for fresh fruits and vegetables. Pinene has the same toxicity as turpentine (*see*).

RHATANY EXTRACT. Krameria. A synthetic flavoring derived from the dried root of either of two American shrubs. Used in raspberry, bitters, fruit, and rum flavorings for beverages, ice cream, ices, candy, chewing gum, and liquor. Also used as an astringent. Low oral toxicity. Large doses may produce gastric distress. Can cause tumors and death after injection, but not after ingestion.

RHODENAL. See Citronellal.

RHODINOL. 3,7-Dimethyl 6 Octen-1-ol. Citronellol. A synthetic flavoring agent isolated from geranium rose oil (*see*). Odor of roses. Used in strawberry, chocolate, rose, grape, honey, spice, and ginger ale flavorings for beverages, ice cream, ices, candy, baked goods, gelatin desserts, chewing gum, and jelly. No known toxicity.

RHODINYL ACETATE. Acetic Acid. An acidulant and synthetic flavoring, colorless to slightly yellow, with a light, fresh, roselike odor. Used in berry, coconut, apricot, floral, rose, and honey flavorings for beverages, ice cream, ices, candy, and baked goods. No known toxicity.

RHODINYL BUTYRATE. Butyric Acid. A synthetic raspberry, strawberry, and fruit flavoring agent for beverages, ice cream, ices, candy, baked goods, and chewing gum. No know toxicity.

RHODINYL FORMATE. Formic Acid. A synthetic flavoring, colorless to slight yellow, with a roselike odor. Used in raspberry, rose, apple, cherry, plum, pear, and pineapple flavorings for beverages, ice cream, ices, candy, baked goods, and gelatin desserts. See Formic Acid for toxicity.

RHODINYL ISOBUTYRATE. Isobutyric Acid. A synthetic raspberry, floral, rose, apple, pear, pineapple, and honey flavoring agent for beverages, ice cream, ices, candy, baked goods, and gelatin desserts. No known toxicity.

RHODINYL ISOVALERATE. Isovaleric Acid. A synthetic berry, rose, and fruit flavoring agent for beverages, ice cream, ices, candy, and baked goods. No known toxicity.

RHODINYL PHENYLACETATE. Phenylacetic Acid. A synthetic flavoring used in beverages, ice cream, ices, candy, and baked goods. No known toxicity.

RHODINYL PROPIONATE. Propionic Acid. A synthetic berry, rose, plum, and honey flavoring agent for beverages, ice cream, ices, candy, and baked goods. No known toxicity.

RHODYMENIA PALMATA. See Dulse.

RIBOFLAVIN. Vitamin B$_2$. Lactoflavin. Vitamin G. B-Complex. Formerly called B$_2$ or G. Riboflavin is a factor in the vitamin B-complex. Every plant and animal cell contains a minute amount. Good sources are milk, eggs, malted barley, yeast, liver, kidney, heart. It is necessary for healthy skin and respiration, protects the eyes from sensitivity to light, and is used for building and maintaining many body tissues. Deficiency leads to lesions at the corner of the mouth and to changes in the cornea. Recommended daily requirements for infants is 4000 micrograms per day and for adults 1,300 micrograms. Its yellow to orange-yellow color is used to dye eggshells. Riboflavin and its more soluble form, riboflavin-5-phosphate, are added as enrichment to dry baby cereals, poultry stuffing, peanut butter, prepared breakfast cereals, enriched flour, enriched cornmeal, enriched corn grits, enriched macaroni, and enriched breads and rolls. GRAS

RIBOFLAVIN-5-PHOSPHATE.   A more soluble form of riboflavin (*see*).

ROCHELLE SALT. Sodium Potassium Tartate.   Used in manufacture of Seidlitz powders (a laxative), in baking powder, and in the silvering of mirrors. No known toxicity.

ROSA ALBA.   See Rose, Absolute.

ROSA CANINA.   See Rose Hips Extract.

ROSA CENTIFOLIA.   See Rose, Absolute.

ROSE, ABSOLUTE.   Same origin as for Rose Bulgarian (*see*). Used as a berry, rose, fruit, and nut flavoring agent for beverages, ice cream, ices, candy, and baked goods. No known toxicity except for allergic reactions. GRAS

ROSE BULGARIAN. True Otto Oil. Attar of Roses.   Derived from dried petals of a variety of roses collected just before expanding. Grown in both Western Asia, Europe, and the United States. Rose extracts are used for a variety of flavors including loganberry, raspberry, strawberry, orange, rose, violet, cherry, grape, peach, honey, muscatel, maple, almond, pecan, and ginger ale flavorings for beverages, ice cream, ices, candy, baked goods, gelatin desserts, chewing gum, and jellies. Also used in mucilage, coloring matter, and as a flavoring in pills. No known toxicity except for allergic reactions. GRAS

ROSE GERANIUM OIL.   See Geranium Rose Oil.

ROSE HIPS EXTRACT. Hipberries.   The fruits or berries from wild rose bushes. Rich in ascorbic acid (*see*). Widely used by organic food enthusiasts. Used as a natural flavoring in a number of foods. No known toxicity.

ROSE LEAVES EXTRACT.   Derived from the leaves of the species Rosa. Used in raspberry and cola beverages. No known toxicity except for allergic reactions. GRAS

ROSEMARY. Garden Rosemary. A meat and spice flavoring from the fresh aromatic flowering tops of the evergreen shrub grown in the Mediterranean. Light blue flowers and gray green leaves. Used for beverages, condiments, and meats. The oil is obtained by steam distillation. Colorless or pale yellow with the odor of rosemary. Used in citrus, peach, meat, and ginger flavorings for beverages, ice cream, ices, candy, baked goods, condiments, and meats. Also used in perfumery. A teaspoonful may cause illness in an adult, and an ounce may cause death. GRAS

ROSMARINUS OFFICINALIS. See Rosemary.

RUBBER, BUTADIENE STYRENE. Latex. A chewing gum base. No known toxicity.

RUBBER, SMOKED SHEET. A chewing gum base. No known toxicity.

RUE. A spice agent obtained from fresh aromatic blossoming plants grown in Southern Europe and the Orient. Fatty odor. Used in baked goods. The *oil*, obtained by steam distillation, is used in blueberry, raspberry, coconut, grape, peach, rum, cheese, nut, and spice flavorings for beverages, ice cream, ices, candy, baked goods, and condiments. Formerly used medically to treat menstrual disorders and hysteria. On the FDA list for further study for mutagenic, teratogenic, subacute, and reproductive effects. GRAS

RUM ETHER. A synthetic flavoring, consisting of water, ethanol, ethyl acetate, methanol, ethyl formate, acetone, acetaldehyde, and formaldehyde (*see all*). Used in butter, liquor, and rum flavorings for beverages, ice cream, ices, candy, baked goods, gelatin, chewing gum, and alcoholic beverages (1,600 ppm). No known toxicity.

RUTIN. Pale yellow crystals found in many plants, particularly buckwheat. Used as a dietary supplement for capillary fragility. No known toxicity.

S

SACCHARIN. An artificial sweetener in use since 1879. Pound for pound it is 300 times as sweet as natural sugar but leaves a bitter aftertaste. It was used along with cyclamates in the experiments which led to the ban on cyclamates in 1969. The FDA has proposed restricting saccharin to 15 milligrams per day for each kilogram of body weight or 1 gram a day for a 150-pound person. On the FDA top priority list to retest for mutagenic, teratogenic, subacute, and reproductive effects.

SAFFLOWER OIL. The edible oil expressed or extracted from safflower seeds. Safflower is an Old World yellow herb with large, orange-red flower heads. The oil thickens and becomes rancid on prolonged exposure to air. It is used in salad oils and shortenings, and as a vehicle for medicines. As a dietary supplement it is alleged to be a preventative in the development of atherosclerosis—fat-clogged arteries. A drug consisting of the dried flowers of safflower is used in medicines in place of saffron (*see*). No known toxicity.

SAFFRON. Crocus. Vegetable Gold. Spanish or French Saffron. The dried stigmas of the crocus grown in Western Asia and Southern Europe. Orange-brown; strong, peculiar aromatic odor; bitterish, aromatic taste. Almost entirely employed for coloring and flavoring. Used in bitters, liquor, and spice flavorings for beverages, baked goods, meats, and liquors. Cleared by the USDA Meat Inspection Department for coloring sausage casings, oleomargarine, shortening, and for marking ink. The *extract* is used in honey and rum flavorings for beverages, ice cream, ices, candy, baked goods, and condiments, and it goes into yellow coloring. Saffron was formerly used to treat skin diseases. No known toxicity. GRAS

SAGE. The flowering tops and leaves of the shrubby mints. Spices include Greek sage and Spanish sage. The genus is *salvia*, so named for the plant's supposed healing powers. Greek sage is used in fruit and spice flavorings for beverages, baked goods, and meats (1,500 ppm). Greek sage *oil*, obtained by steam distillation, is used in berry, grape, liquor, meat, creme de menthe, nutmeg, and sage flavorings for beverages, ice cream, ices, candy, baked goods, chewing gum, condiments, meats, and pickles. Greek sage *oleoresin* (*see*) is used in sausage and spice flavorings for condiments and meats. Spanish sage oil is used in fruit and spice flavorings for beverages, ice cream, ices, candy, baked goods, condiments, and meats. Greek sage is used in medicine. No known toxicity. GRAS

SAIGON CINNAMON. See Cinnamon.

SAIGON CINNAMON LEAF OIL. See Cinnamon.

SAINT-JOHN'S-BREAD. See Carob Bean.

SALICYLALDEHYDE. Salicylic Aldehyde. A synthetic flavoring made by heating phenol (very toxic) and chloroform. Occurs naturally in cassia bark. Clear, bitter almondlike odor, burning taste. Used in butter, caramel, violet, fruit, muscatel, nut, spice, cinnamon, cassia, and vanilla flavorings for beverages, ice cream, ices, candy, baked goods, chewing gum, condiments, and liqueurs. Used chiefly in perfumery. Lethal dose in rats is 1 gram per kilogram of body weight.

SALICYLIC ACID. A synthetically prepared powder obtained by heating phenol (very toxic) with carbon dioxide, which is used as a preservative in food products. It occurs naturally in the form of esters in several plants, notably wintergreen leaves and the bark of sweet birch. Also used in manufacture of aspirin; in medicine it is used as a remedy for rheumatic and gout conditions. The dose for external antimicrobial use is topically 2–20 percent concentration in lotions, ointments, powders, and plasters. Absorption of large amounts may cause vomiting, abdominal pain, increased respiration, acidosis, mental disturbances, and skin rash in sensitive individuals.

SALICYLIC ETHER. See Ethyl Salicylate.

SALTPETER. *Potassium Nitrate. Niter.* See Nitrate, Potassium. Acute intoxication is unlikely because large doses cause vomiting and because it is rapidly excreted. Potassium poisoning disturbs the rhythm of the heart and orally poisoned animals die from respiratory failure. Prolonged exposure to even small amounts may produce anemia, methemoglobinemia (lack of oxygen in the blood) and kidney damage.

SALVIA. See Sage.

SAMBUCUS. See Elder Flowers.

SANDALWOOD OIL. *East Indian.* The volatile oil obtained by steam distillation from the dried, ground roots and heartwood of trees grown in the East Indies. Yellow, somewhat viscous, with a strong odor. Used in floral, fruit, honey, and ginger ale flavorings for beverages, ice cream, ices, candy, baked goods, and chewing gum. Also used for incense and as a fumigant. No known toxicity.

SANDALWOOD OIL. *West Indian.* Less soluble than the East Indian variety above. See Amyris Oil.

SANDALWOOD OIL, YELLOW. *Arheol.* Same origin as East Indian sandalwood oil (*see*). A floral, fruit, honey, and ginger ale flavoring agent for beverages, ice cream, ices, candy, baked goods, and chewing gum. No known toxicity.

SANTALOL. See Arheol.

SANTALUM ALBUM. See Sandalwood Oil.

SANTALYL ACETATE. Acetic Acid. A synthetic flavoring agent obtained from sandalwood oils (*see*). Used in floral, pear, and pineapple flavorings for beverages, ice cream, ices, candy, baked goods, and chewing gum. No known toxicity.

SANTALYL PHENYLACETATE. Phenylacetic Acid. A synthetic flavoring obtained from sandalwood oils (*see*). Used in butter, caramel, fruit, and honey flavorings for beverages, ice cream, ices, candy, and baked goods. No known toxicity.

SAP. See Sodium Acid Pyrophosphate.

SARSAPARILLA EXTRACT. The dried root from tropical American plants. Used in cola, mint, root beer, sarsaparilla, wintergreen, and birch beer flavorings for beverages, ice cream, ices, candy, and baked goods. Still used for psoriasis; formerly used for the treatment of syphilis. No known toxicity.

SASSAFRAS BARK EXTRACT. Safrol-free. Extracted with dilute alcohol from the bark of the tree. Used in rum and root beer flavorings for beverages, ice cream, ices, candy, and baked goods. Safrol is a constituent of several essential oils, notably of sassafras of which it constitutes 80 percent. The lethal dose of safrol in rabbits is 1 gram per kilogram of body weight. Sassafras by itself has no known toxicity. It is used as a topical antiseptic, to mask the odor of medicines, and to break up intestinal gas.

SASSAFRAS LEAVES. Safrol-free. Same origin as above. Used in soups (30,000 ppm). See above for toxicity.

SAUNDERS WHITE OIL. See Sandalwood Oil.

SAVORY. A flavoring from the aromatic mints, known as summer savory and winter savory. The dried leaves of summer savory is a spice used in baked goods, condiments, and meats. Summer savory oil is obtained from the dried whole plant. It is used as a spice in condiments, candy, and baked goods. Summer savory oil oleoresin (*see*) is a spice used in candy, baked goods, and condiments. Winter savory oil and oleoresin spices are used in candy, baked goods, and condiments. No known toxicity. GRAS

SCHINUS MOLLE OIL. A natural flavoring extract from the tropical pepper tree, *Schinus molle*. Used in candy, baked goods, and condiments. No known toxicity. GRAS

SEBACIC ACID. See Dibutyl Sebacate.

SEQUESTERING. To render ions, usually from metal, inactive by absorbing them. This is how water is softened. Sequestrants are added to food to attract the trace metals to remove them.

SERINE. L and DL forms. An amino acid (see), nonessential, taken as a supplement. On the FDA list requiring further information.

SESAME. Seeds and Oils. The edible seeds of an East Indian herb, which has a rosy or white flower. The seeds, which flavor bread, crackers, cakes, confectionery, etc., yield a pale yellow, bland tasting, almost odorless oil used in the manufacture of margarine. The oil has been used as a laxative and skin softener, and contains elements active against lice. Bland taste flavoring. No known toxicity except for allergies. GRAS

SHELLAC. A resinous excretion of certain insects feeding on appropriate host trees, usually in India. As processed for marketing, the lacca, which is formed by the insects, may be mixed with small amounts of arsenic trisulfide (for color) and with rosin. White shellac is free of arsenic. Shellac is used as a candy glaze and polish up to .4 percent. May cause skin irritation.

SHORTENING. A fat such as a butter, lard, or vegetable oil used to make cake, pastry, bread, etc., light and flaky.

SIBERIAN FIR OIL. See Pine Needle Oil.

SILICA AEROGEL. Silicon Dioxide. A finely powdered, microcellular silica foam having a minimum silica content of 89.5 percent. Chemically and biologically inert, it is used as an antifoaming agent in beverages and as a surface active agent. Used chiefly in manufacture of glass. See Silicon Dioxide for toxicity. GRAS

SILICON DIOXIDE. Silica. Transparent, tasteless crystals or powder, practically insoluble in water. Occurs in nature as agate, amethyst, chalcedony, cristobalite, flint, quartz, sand, and tridymite. Used as a defoaming agent in beer production. Cleared for use as a food additive and as an anticaking agent at a level not to exceed 2 percent in salt and salt substitutes, in BHT (see butylated hydroxytoluene), in vitamins up to 3 percent, in urea up to 1 percent, in sodium propionate (see all) up to 1 percent. Also used in ceramics and in scouring and grinding compounds. Prolonged inhalation of the dust can injure lungs. GRAS for packaging.

SLOE BERRIES. Blackthorn Berries. The fruit of the common juniper. The extract is a natural flavoring used in berry, plum, and liquor flavorings for beverages, ice cream, ices, candy, baked goods, and cordials (up to 43,000 ppm). Sloe gin is flavored with sloe berries. No known toxicity. GRAS

SMALLAGE. See Lovage.

SMELLAGE. See Lovage.

SMOKED SHEET RUBBER. A chewing gum base. No known toxicity.

SNAKEROOT OIL. Canadian Oil. Derived from the roots of the plant, which had a reputation for curing snakebites. Grown from Canada to North Carolina and Kansas. Used in ginger, ginger ale, wintergreen, and birch beer flavorings for beverages, ice cream, ices, candy, baked goods, and condiments. No known toxicity.

SOAP. Sodium Oleate and Sodium Palmitate. Any salt of a fatty acid, usually made by saponification of a vegetable oil with caustic soda. Hard soap consists largely of sodium oleate or sodium palmitate. Used medically as an antiseptic, detergent, or suppository; as a laxative and antacid. GRAS for food packaging.

SOAP BARK. See Quillaja.

SODIUM ACETATE. Transparent crystals highly soluble in water. Used as a preservative in licorice candy. In industrial forms it is used in photography and dyeing processes, and in foot and bottle warmers because of its heat retention. Medically it is used as an alkalizer. It was also used as a diuretic to reduce retention of fluids and as an expectorant. No known toxicity. GRAS in packaging.

SODIUM ACID PYROPHOSPHATE (SAP). A white mass or free-flowing powder used as a buffer. It is a slow-acting acid constituent of a leavening mixture for self-rising and prepared cakes, doughnuts, waffles, muffins, cupcakes, and other types of flours and mixes. Also used in canned tuna fish. The U.S. Department of Agriculture has proposed that SAP be added to hot dogs and other sausages to accelerate the development of a rose-red color, thus cutting production time by some 25 to 40 percent. It is related to phosphoric acid, which is sometimes used as a gastric acidifier. No known toxicity. GRAS

SODIUM ACID SULFITE. See Sodium Bisulfite.

SODIUM ALGINATE. See Alginates.

SODIUM ALUMINATE. A strong alkaline employed in the manufacture of lake colors used in foods (see FD and C Lakes). Also used in water softening and printing. GRAS for packaging.

SODIUM ALUMINOSILICATE. A chemical substance used in dental compounds, colored lakes (*see* FD and C Lakes) for foods, and in washing compounds. On the FDA list for further study for mutagenic, teratogenic, subacute, and reproductive effects.

SODIUM ALUMINUM PHOSPHATE. A white, odorless powder, insoluble in water, used as a buffer in self-rising flour. Used with sodium bicarbonate (*see*). Used also in various cheeses. No known toxicity. GRAS

SODIUM ALUMINUM SULFATE. A bleaching agent for flour at no more than 6 parts by weight, alone, or in combination with potassium aluminum, calcium sulfate, and other compounds. No known toxicity.

SODIUM ASCORBATE. Vitamin C Sodium. Aside from its use in Vitamin C preparations, it can serve as an antioxidant in chopped meat and other foods to retard spoiling; also used in curing meat. No known toxicity. GRAS

SODIUM BENZOATE. Benzoate of Soda. White, odorless powder or crystals; sweet, antiseptic taste. Works best in slightly acid media. Used in liver function tests and as a preservative in margarine, codfish, bottled soft drinks, Maraschino cherries, mincemeat, fruit juices, pickles, confectionery, fruit jelly, preserves, and jams. Also used in the ice for cooling fish. Once used medicinally for rheumatism and tonsillitis. The lethal dose in dogs and cats is 2 grams but an adult human male has taken as much as 50 grams without ill effect. It can cause intestinal upset. GRAS

SODIUM BICARBONATE. Bicarbonate of Soda. Baking Soda. Sodium Acid Carbonate. An alkali prepared by the reaction of soda ash with carbon dioxide and used in prepared pancakes, biscuit, and muffin mixes; a leavening agent in baking powders; in various crackers and cookies; to adjust acidity in tomato soup, ices, and sherbets; in pastes and beverages; in syrups for frozen products; confections; and self-rising flours. Also used in cornmeals and canned peas. Also as a fire extinguisher. Used medicinally as an antacid and to take the sting out of insect bites. It may alter the urinary excretion of other drugs thus making those drugs either more toxic or less effective. GRAS

201

SODIUM BISULFITE. Sodium Acid Sulfite. Sodium Hydrogen Sulfite. A white powder with a disagreeable taste used as a bleaching agent in ale, wine, beer, and other food products. Commercial bisulfite consists chiefly of sodium metabisulfite (*see*). Used externally for parasitic skin diseases. Concentrated solutions are highly irritating to the skin and mucous membranes. Sodium bisulfite can change the genetic material of bacteria which can change cytosine— a compound of nucleic acid (the heart of the cell)—into uracil, also a nucleic acid compound. Nucleic acids are the fundamental substances of heredity, and changes in them are considered mutations. On the FDA list for further study. GRAS

SODIUM BORATE. See Boron Sources.

SODIUM CARBONATE. Soda Ash. Colorless or white odorless crystals occurring naturally as thermonatrite, natron, or natrite. Usually obtained commercially. Used as a neutralizer for butter, cream, fluid milk, and ice cream; in the processing of olives before canning; and in cocoa products. A strong alkali used as lye. Used to treat skin rashes, and as a water softener. Has been used as mouthwash and vaginal douche. Ingestion of large quantities may produce corrosion of the gastrointestinal tract, vomiting, diarrhea, circulatory collapse, and death.

SODIUM CARBOXYMETHYL CELLULOSE. Made from a cotton by-product, it occurs as a white powder or granules. Used as a stabilizer in ice cream, beverages, confections, baked goods, icings, toppings, chocolate milk, chocolate-flavored beverages, gassed cream (pressure-dispensed whipped cream), syrup for frozen products, variegated mixtures, cheese spreads, and in certain cheeses. Also used in French dressing, artifically sweetened jellies and preserves, gelling ingredients, mix-it-yourself powdered drinks, and baby foods. Used to extend and stabilize baked pies. Medicinally used as a laxative (1.5 grams orally), antacid (15–30 milligrams of 5 percent solution), and in pharmacy for preparing suspensions. It has been shown to cause cancer in animals.

SODIUM CASEINATE. Casein. A white odorless powder from cow's milk. Used as a texturizer in ice cream, frozen custard, ice milk, and sherbet. Cleared by the USDA Meat Inspection Department for use in imitation sausage, nonspecific loaves, soups, and stews. No known toxicity. GRAS

SODIUM CHLORIDE. Common table salt. In addition to seasoning it is used as a pickling agent, a preservative for meats, vegetables, butter. Prevents browning in cut fruit. Not generally considered toxic, but can adversely affect persons with high blood pressure and kidney disease. Accidental substitution of salt for lactose in baby formulas has caused poisonings. GRAS

SODIUM CHLORITE. A powerful oxidizer prepared commercially and used to modify food starch (see modified starch) up to .5 percent. Used as a bleaching agent for textiles and paper pulp and in water purification. Toxicity depends upon concentration.

SODIUM CITRATE. White odorless granules, crystals, or powder, with a salty taste. Prevents "cream plug" in cream and "feathering" when cream is used in coffee, an emulsifier in ice cream, processed cheese, evaporated milk; a buffer to control acidity and retain carbonation in beverages, in frozen fruit drinks, confections, fruit jellies, preserves, and jams. It attaches itself to trace metals present in water and inhibits their entering the living cell. Proposed as a replacement for phosphates in detergents but also causes algal growth and removes the necessary trace metals from water as well as the toxic ones. Can alter urinary excretion of other drugs, thus making those drugs either less effective or more toxic. GRAS

SODIUM DEHYDROACETATE. Dehydroacetic Acid. A preservative, white, odorless, powered, with an acrid taste. Used in cut or peeled squash and as a plasticizer, fungicide, and bacteriacide in antienzyme toothpaste. It is a kidney tube blocking agent, and can cause impaired kidney function. Large doses can cause vomiting, ataxia, and convulsions. There are no apparent allergic skin reactions.

SODIUM DIACETATE. A compound of sodium acetate and acetic acid (see); a white crystalline solid. Smells like vinegar. Used as a preservative. Inhibits molds and rope-forming bacteria in baked goods. No known toxicity.

SODIUM DODECYL BENZENESULFONATE. Used in commercial detergents to treat raw food products, which is followed by a water rinsing. It may cause skin irritations, and if swallowed, will cause vomiting.

SODIUM ERYTHORBATE. Sodium Isoascorbate. A white odorless powder, it is an antioxidant used in pickling brine up to 7.5 ounces per 100 gallons and in meat products up to ¾ of an ounce per

100 pounds. Also used in beverages and baked goods; in cured cuts and cured, pulverized products to accelerate color fixing in curing. No known toxicity.

SODIUM 2-ETHYL 1-HEXYLSULFATE. A component of a commercial detergent for washing raw foods, followed by water rinsing. No known toxicity.

SODIUM HEXAMETAPHOSPHATE. An emulsifier, sequestering agent, and texturizer. Used in breakfast cereals, angel food cake, flaked fish, ice cream, ice milk, bottled beverages, reconstituted lemon juice, puddings, processed cheeses, artificially sweetened jellies, potable water supplies to prevent scale formation and corrosion, and in pumping pickle for curing hams and shoulders, etc. Because it keeps calcium, magnesium, and iron salts in solution, it is an excellent water softener and detergent; used in Calgon, Giltex, and other such products. Lethal dose in dogs is 140 milligrams per kilogram of body weight. GRAS for packaging.

SODIUM HYDROSULFITE. A bacterial inhibitor and antifermentative in the sugar and syrup industries. Slight odor. No known toxicity. GRAS for packaging.

SODIUM HYDROXIDE. Caustic Soda. Soda Lye. A alkali used as a modifier for food starch; as a glazing agent for pretzels; as a peeling agent for tubers and fruits; in the refining process for vegetable oils and animal fats to neutralize free fatty acids; in sour cream and butter; cocoa products; and canned peas as a neutralizer. The FDA banned use of more than 10 percent in household liquid drain cleaners. Its ingestion causes vomiting, prostration, and collapse. Inhalation causes lung damage. GRAS for use in packaging.

SODIUM HYPOCHLORITE. A preservative used in the washing of cottage cheese curd. Also used medically as an antiseptic for wounds. Ingestion may cause corrosion of mucous membranes, esophageal or gastric perforation. The aqueous solutions are Eau de Javelle, Clorox, Dazzle.

SODIUM ISOASCORBATE. See Erythorbic Acid.

SODIUM LAURYL SULFATE (SLS). Used in commercial detergents to treat raw foods, followed by a water rinsing. Also an ingredient of toothpaste and a whipping aid in cake mixes and dried egg products. On the FDA list of further studies on the safety of this widely used additive.

SODIUM METABISULFITE. A bacterial inhibitor in wine, ale, and beer; an antifermentative in sugar and syrups; preservative for fruit and vegetable juices; antibrowning agent in cut fruits, frozen apples, dried fruits, prepared fruit pie mix, peeled potatoes, and Maraschino cherries. No known toxicity. GRAS

SODIUM METASILICATE. An alkali usually prepared from sand and soda ash. Used as a peeling solution for peaches and as a denuder for tripe "in amounts sufficient for the purpose." The FDA has charged that sodium metasilicate in nonphosphate detergents "is a caustic substance, corrosive to skin, harmful if swallowed, and the cause of severe eye irritations."

SODIUM METHYL NAPHTHALENE SULFONATE. In solutions for peeling fruits and vegetables; water rinse. No known toxicity.

SODIUM METHYL SULFATE. Used in processing of pectin (*see*). No known toxicity.

SODIUM NITRATE. See Nitrate, Sodium.

SODIUM NITRITE. See Nitrite, Sodium.

SODIUM PECTINATE. A stablizer and thickener for syrups for frozen products, ice cream, ice milk, confections, fruit sherbets, French dressing, and other salad dressings, fruit jelly, preserves, jams. Used in "quantities which reasonably compensate for the deficiency, if any, of natural pectin content of the fruit ingredients." No known toxicity. GRAS

SODIUM PHOSPHATE. See Phosphorous Sources.

SODIUM PHOSPHOALUMINATE. The acid salt of phosphoric acid. An ingredient of baking powders and other leavening mixtures. GRAS for packaging. See Phosphoric Acid for toxicity.

SODIUM POTASSIUM TARTRATE. *Rochelle Salt.* A buffer for confections, fruit jelly, preserves, and jams. For each 100 pounds of saccharine in the above products 3 ounces of sodium potassium tartrate is used. Also used in cheese. Used medically as a cathartic. No known toxicity. GRAS

SODIUM PROPIONATE. Colorless or transparent odorless crystals which gather water in moist air. Used as a preservative, and to prevent mold and fungus in foodstuffs. It has been used to treat fungal infections of the skin but can cause allergic reactions. GRAS

SODIUM PYROPHOSPHATE. An emulsifier salt and texturizer. Used in cold water puddings and processed cheeses. No known toxicity.

SODIUM SACCHARIN. See Saccharin.

SODIUM SALT. See Sodium Benzoate.

SODIUM SESQUICARBONATE. Lye. Produced on a large scale from sodium carbonate and a slight excess of sodium bicarbonate (*see both*). Used as a neutralizer for butter, cream, fluid milk, ice cream, in the processing of olives before canning, cacao products, and canned peas. Chiefly used in laundering in conjunction with soap. Irritating to skin and mucous membrane. GRAS

SODIUM SILICATE. Water Glass. Soluble Glass. In the forms of crystallike pieces or lumps. Used in packaging. Strongly alkaline. Irritating to skin. If swallowed, causes vomiting and diarrhea. GRAS in packaging.

SODIUM SILICO ALUMINATE. Anticaking agent used in table salt up to 2 percent; dried egg yolks up to 2 percent; in sugar up to 1 percent; and in baking powder up to 5 percent. Slightly alkaline. No known toxicity.

SODIUM SORBATE. See Calcium Sorbate.

SODIUM STEARATE. Alkaline; white, powdery, soapy texture; slight tallowlike odor. Used as an emulsifier in foods. Also used in suppositories and toothpaste, and as a waterproofing agent. Has been used to treat skin diseases. No known toxicity.

SODIUM STEARYL FUMARATE. A fine white powder used as a dough conditioner in yeast and leavened bakery products in amounts not exceeding .5 percent by weight of flour used. Also used as a conditioning agent in dehydrated potatoes in an amount not exceeding 1 percent by weight. No known toxicity.

SODIUM STEAROYL-2-LACTYLATE. The sodium salt of a lactylic ester of fatty acid. Prepared from lactic acid and fatty acids. It is used as an emulsifier, plasticizer, or surface active agent in an amount not greater than required to produce the intended physical or technical effect, and where standards of identity do not preclude use, in the following: bakery mixes, baked products, cake icings, fillings and toppings, dehydrated fruits and vegetables, dehydrated fruit and vegetable juices; frozen desserts, liquid shortenings for household use; pancake mixes, precooked instant rice, pudding mixes, solid state edible vegetable water emulsions as a substitute for milk, cream in beverage coffee and with shortening and edible fats and oils when such are required in the foods listed above. See Lactic Acid for toxicity.

SODIUM SULFATE. Occurs in nature as the minerals mirabilite and thenardite. Used in chewing-gum base; medicinally to reduce body water. Used chiefly in manufacture of dyes, soaps, and detergents. Taken by mouth it stimulates gastric mucous production and sometimes inactivates a natural digestive juice—pepsin. Fatally poisoned animals show only diarrhea and intestinal bloating with no gross lesions outside the intestinal tract.

SODIUM SULFITE. Slightly pink, odorless powder, with a salty taste, used as a bacterial inhibitor in wine, brewing, and distilled-beverage industries. Also an antifermentative in the sugar and syrup industries and a preservative in fruit and vegetable juices, meats, and egg yolks. Prevents browning in cut fruits, and is used in frozen apples, dried fruit, prepared fruit pie mix, peeled potatoes, Maraschino cherries, dried fruits, and glacéed fruits. Used to bleach straw, silk, and wool; a developer in photography; treats upset stomachs and combats fungus infections. No known toxicity. GRAS for use in packaging.

SODIUM TAUROCHOLATE. *Taurocholic Acid.* The chief ingredient of the bile of carnivorous animals. Used as an emulsifier in dried egg white up to .1 percent. It is a lipase accelerator. Lipase is a fat-splitting enzyme in the blood, pancreatic secretion, and tissues. No known toxicity.

SODIUM THIOSULFATE. An antioxidant used to protect sliced potatoes and uncooked French fries from browning and as a stabilizer for potassium iodide in iodized salt. Also used to neutralize chlorine and to bleach bone. It is an antidote for cyanide poisoning and has been used in the past to combat blood clots; used to treat ring worms and mange in animals. Poorly absorbed by the bowel. On the FDA list to be studied for mutagenic, teratogenic, subacute, and reproductive effects.

SODIUM p-TOLUENE SULFOCHLORAMINE. *Chloramine T.* A water purifying agent and a deodorant used to remove weed odor in cheese. Suspected of causing rapid allergic reaction in the hypersensitive. Poisoning by Chloramine T is characterized by pain, vomiting, sudden loss of consciousness, circulatory and respiratory collapse, and death.

SODIUM TRIMETAPHOSPHATE. A starch modifier. No known toxicity.

SODIUM TRIPOLYPHOSPHATE (STPP). A texturizer and sequestrant cleared for use in food starch modifiers. A water softener. Also cleared by the USDA Meat Inspection Department to preserve meat by decreasing cooked-out juices in canned hams, pork shoulders, chopped ham, and bacon. Also used as a dilutant for Citrus Red No. 2 (*see*). Moderately irritating to the skin and mucous membranes. Ingestion of large amounts can cause violent purging. It may deplete the body of calcium if taken in sufficient amounts and such a case of low calcium was reported in a patient poisoned with water softener. GRAS for packaging only.

SORBATE, CALCIUM. See Calcium Sorbate.

SORBIC ACID. A white, free-flavoring powder obtained from the berries of the mountain ash. Also made from chemicals in the factory. A mold and yeast inhibitor. Used in beverages, baked goods, chocolate syrup, fresh fruit cocktail, soda-fountain syrups, tangerine puree (sherbet base), salads (potato, macaroni, cole slaw, gelatin), cheesecake, pie fillings, cake, cheese in consumer-size packages, and artificially sweetened jellies and preserves. Percentages range from .003 in beverages to .2 percent in cheeses. Practically nontoxic but may cause a slight skin irritation. GRAS

SORBITAN MONOOLEATE. Polysorbate 80. An emulsifying agent for special dietary products and pharmaceuticals, a defoamer in yeast production, and a chewing gum plasticizer. An unintentionally administered daily dose of 19.2 grams per kilogram of body weight for 2 days to a 4-month-old baby caused no harm except loose stools.

SORBITAN MONOPALMITATE. An emulsifier and flavor-dispersing agent used as an alternate for sorbitan monostearate (*see*) in cake mixes. No known toxicity.

SORBITAN MONOSTEARATE. An emulsifier, defoaming, and flavoring dispersing agent. Used in cakes and cake mixes, whipped vegetable oil toppings, cookie coatings, cake icings and fillings, solid-state edible vegetable fat-water emulsions used as substitutes for milk or cream in coffee, coconut spread, beverages, confectionery, baked goods. Percentages range from 1 to .0006 percent. No single dose is known to be lethal in animals and man has been fed a daily single dose of 20 grams without harm.

SORBITAN TRISTEARATE. An emulsifier and alternate for sorbitan monostearate (*see*) in candy coatings. No known toxicity.

SORBITOL. A white, crystalline, sweet, water-soluble powder, first found in ripe berries of the mountain ash. Also occurs in other berries (except grapes) and in cherries, plums, pears, apples, seaweed, and algae by the breakdown of dextrose. A sugar substitute for diabetics. Used in candy as a thickener, in vegetable oils as a sequestrant, as a stabilizer and sweetener in frozen desserts for special dietary purposes, as a humectant and texturizing agent in shredded coconut and dietetic fruits and soft drinks. Medically used to reduce body water, as a cathartic, for intravenous feeding, and to increase absorption of vitamins in pharmaceuticals. Industrially used in plasticizers and resins to control moisture on printing rolls, in leather and tobacco; used in writing inks to ensure a smooth flow from the point of the pen; and as an antifreeze. The FDA has asked for further study of sorbitol. Although it has a sweetening effect similar to sugar, its safety for diabetics has yet to be proved. It may alter the absorption of other drugs, making them less effective or more toxic. It can cause diarrhea and gastrointestinal disturbances when taken in excess.

SORBOSE. Derived from sorbitol (*see*) by fermentation. Used in the manufacture of Vitamin C (accounts for nearly 1,000 tons of ascorbic acid (*see*) produced yearly). No known toxicity. GRAS for packaging.

SOYBEAN. *Bean, Oil, and Flour.* Soybeans came originally from Eastern Asia but are now cultivated in the midwestern United States. The oil is made up of 40 percent protein, 17 percent carbohydrates, 18 percent oil, and 4.6 percent ash. It contains ascorbic acid, Vitamin A, and thiamine. Debittered soybean flour contains practically no starch and is widely used in dietetic foods. Soybean oil is used in defoamers in the production of beet sugar and yeast, in the manufacture of margarine, shortenings, candy, and soap. Soybean is used in many products including MSG, dough mixes, Lea and Perrins Sauce, Heinz's Worcester Sauce, La Choy Oriental Show You Sauce, soy sauce, salad dressings, pork link sausages, luncheon meats, hard candies, nut candies, milk and coffee substitutes. It is made into soybean milk, soybean curd, and soybean cheese. About 300 million bushels of soybeans are grown yearly in the U.S.A., one third more than in China. No known toxicity but it may cause allergic reactions.

SPANISH HOPS. See Ditanny of Crete.

SPANISH ORIGANUM. See Origanum Oil.

SPEARMINT FLAVORING. *Garden Mint. Green Mint.* Fresh
ground parts of an aromatic herb used in spearmint flavoring for
beverages, meats, and condiments (1,000 ppm). Widely cultivated
in the United States. The volatile, colorless oil (principal active
constituent contains at least 50 percent carvone; *see*) obtained by
steam distillation of the flowering plant, is used in butter, caramel,
citrus fruit, garlic, soy, and spice flavorings for beverages, ice cream,
ices, candy, baked goods, condiments (100,000 ppm), fats, oils, and
icings (50,000 ppm). Has been used to break up intestinal gas, but
has no known toxicity. GRAS

SPERM OIL. *Hydrogenated* (see Hydrogenation). Obtained from
the sperm whale. Yellow, thin liquid; slightly fishy odor if not of
good quality. Used as a release agent or lubricant in baking pans and
as an industrial lubricant. No known toxicity.

SPIKE LAVENDER. A pale yellow liquid obtained from flowers
in the Mediterranean region and used chiefly in perfume and for
fumigating against moths. Used in fruit, floral, mint, and spice flavorings for beverages, ice cream, ices, candy, and baked goods. No known
toxicity. GRAS

SPIRAL FLAG OIL. See Costus Root Oil.

SPIRIT OF NITROUS ETHER. See Ethyl Nitrite.

SPRUCE OIL. See Hemlock Oil.

STANNOUS CHLORIDE. *Tin Dichloride.* An antioxidant used for
canned asparagus, canned soda (11 ppm), and other foods. Soluble
in water and a powerful reducing agent, particularly in manufacture
of dyes, and tinning agent. Used to revive yeast. Low systemic toxicity
but may be highly irritating to the skin and mucous membranes.
On the FDA list for further study for mutagenic, teratogenic, subacute, and reproductive effects. GRAS

STAR ANISE. *Chinese Anis.* Fruit of *Illicium verum* from China,
called star because of the fruit's shape. The *extract* is used in fruit,
licorice, anise, liquor, sausage, root beer, sarsaparilla, vanilla, wintergreen, and birch beer flavorings for beverages, ice cream, ices, candy,
meats (1,000 ppm), and liqueurs. The oil is used in blackberry, peach,
licorice, anise, liquor, meat, root beer, spice, wintergreen, and birch
beer flavorings for beverages, ice cream, ices, candy, baked goods,
meats, syrups, and liqueurs. The fruit is a source of Anise Oil (*see*
Anise). Star anise has been used as an expectorant and carminative.

Japanese star anise is *Illicium anisatum* and contains a toxic lactone called anisatin, unknown to the Chinese variety. No known toxicity. GRAS

STARCH. *Acid Modified, Pregelatinized, and Unmodified.* Starch is stored by plants and is taken from grains of wheat, potatoes, rice, corn, beans, and many other vegetable foods. Insoluble in cold water or alcohol but soluble in boiling water. Comparatively resistant to naturally occurring enzymes and this is the reason processors "modify" starch (*see* Modified Starch) to make it more digestible. Starch is modified with propylene oxide, succinic anhydride, 1-octenyl succinic anhydride, aluminum sulfate, or sodium hydroxide (*see all*). Used internally as a gruel in diarrhea and externally to soothe skin rashes; used in dusting powder as a demulcent for irritated colon and an antidote for iodine poisoning. Modified starches are on the FDA list for further study for safety. GRAS for packaging.

STEARIC ACID. *Octadecanoic Acid.* Occurs naturally in some vegetable oils, cascarilla bark extract, and as a glyceride (*see*) in tallow and other animal fats and oils. Prepared synthetically by hydrogenation (*see*) of cottonseed and other vegetable oils. Slight tallowlike odor. Used in butter and vanilla flavorings for beverages, baked goods, and candy (4,000 ppm). Also a softener in chewing-gum base, used in suppositories, ointments, vanishing creams, and other cosmetics. A possible sensitizer for allergic types.

STEARYL CITRATE. A metal scavenger to prevent adverse effects of trace metals in foods and an antioxidant to prevent rancidity in oleomargarine. See Citrate Salts for toxicity.

STEARYL-2-LACTYLIC ACID. Occurs in tallow and other animal fats, as well as in animal and vegetable oils. Used to emulsify shortening in non-yeast-leavened bakery products and pancake mixes. Also used to emulsify cakes, icings, and fillings. No known toxicity.

STEARYL MONOGLYCERIDYL CITRATE. The soft, practically tasteless, off-white, waxy solid used as an emulsion stabilizer in shortening with emulsifiers. It is prepared by the chemical reaction of citric acid on monoglycerides of fatty acids (*see*). No known toxicity.

STERCULEN. *Sterculia.* See Karaya Gum.

STPP. See Sodium Tripolyphosphate.

STORAX. *Styrax. Sweet Oriental Gum.* A liquid balsam obtained from the trunk of a small tree. American storax is produced chiefly in Honduras. Used in strawberry, fruit, and spice flavorings for beverages, ice cream, ices, candy, baked goods, chewing gum, and toppings. Used in medicine as a weak antiseptic and in perfumery. Has been used as an expectorant. Moderately toxic.

STRAWBERRY ALDEHYDE. See Ethyl 3-Methyl-3-Phenylglycidate.

STYRACIN. See Cinnamyl Cinnamate.

STYRAX EXTRACT. *Storax.* Extract of large shrubs that yield commercially important resins such as storax and benzoin. Used in chocolate, fruit, and liquor flavorings for beverages, ice cream, ices, candy, baked goods, and gelatin desserts. See Storax and Benzoin for toxicity.

STYROLENE ACETATE. See α-Methylbenzyl Acetate.

STYRYL CARBINOL. See Cinnamyl Alcohol.

SUBACUTE. A zone between acute and chronic or the process of a disease that is not overt. Subacute endocarditis, for example, is an infection of the heart. It is usually due to a "strep" germ and and may follow a temporary infection after a tooth extraction.

SUCCINIC ACID. Occurs in fossils, fungi, lichens, etc. Prepared from acetic acid (*see*). Odorless, very acid taste. The acid is used as a plant-growth retardant. Also a buffer and neutralizing agent. Used in perfumes. Has been used as a laxative. Lethal dose in rats is 8.40 mg/kg. GRAS

SUCCINIC ANHYDRIDE. A starch modifier up to 4 percent. See Modified Starch.

SUCROSE. *Sugar. Saccharose. Cane Sugar (15–20 percent). Beet Sugar (10–17 percent).* A sweetening agent for food. Table sugar can stimulate the production of fat in the body, apart from its calorie content in the diet, and may be particularly fat-producing in women on the "pill." Sugar is used also as a starting agent in fermentation production, in pharmacy as a preservative, as an antioxidant (in form of invert sugar), as a demulcent, as substitute for glycerol (*see*), as coating for tablets. No known toxicity.

SUCROSE OCTAACETATE. Prepared from sucrose (*see*). A synthetic flavoring used in bitters, spice, and ginger ale flavorings for beverages. Used in adhesives; a denaturant for alcohol. No known toxicity.

SULFATED TALLOW. Fat from fatty tissues of sheep and cattle which becomes solid at 40 to 46 degrees F. It is a defoaming agent in yeast and beet sugar production in "amounts reasonably required to inhibit foaming." See Tallow Flakes for toxicity.

SULFITES. *Sodium, Potassium, and Ammonium.* Preservatives, antioxidants, and antibrowning agents used in foods. Should not be used in foods or meats recognized as sources of Vitamin B_1. In large doses it can cause gastric irritation, severe colic, and diarrhea, circulatory disturbances, and central nervous system depression. GRAS

SULFO-*p*-TOLUENE. *Sodium Chloramine.* A water-purifying agent and a deodorant used to remove onion and weed odors in cheese. Toulene may cause mild anemia and is narcotic in high concentrations.

SULFUR DIOXIDE. A gas formed when sulfur burns. Used to bleach vegetable colors and to preserve fruits and vegetables; a disinfectant in breweries and food factories; a bleaching agent in gelatin, glue, and beet sugars; an antioxidant, preservative, and antibrowning agent in wine, corn syrup, table syrup, jelly, dried fruits, brined fruit, Maraschino cherries, beverages, dehydrated potatoes, soups, and condiments. Should not be used on meats or on foods recognized as a source of Vitamin A because it destroys the vitamin. Very poisonous, highly irritating. Often cited as an air pollutant. Inhalation produces respiratory irritation and death when sufficiently concentrated. The FDA has asked for further studies of its safety. GRAS

SULFURIC ACID. *Oil of Vitriol.* A clear, colorless, odorless, oily acid used to modify starch (*see*) and to regulate acidity-alkalinity in the brewing industry. It is very corrosive and produces severe burns on contact with the skin and other body tissues. Inhalation of the vapors can cause serious lung damage. Dilute sulfuric acid has been used to stimulate appetite and to combat overalkaline stomach juices. Ingestion of undiluted sulfuric acid can be fatal. GRAS

SUNSET YELLOW. See FD and C Yellow No. 6.

SWEET FLAG. See Calamus.

SYNTHETIC. Made in the laboratory and not by nature. Vanillin, for example, made in the laboratory may be identical to vanilla extracted from the vanilla bean but vanillin cannot be called "natural."

T

TAGETES. Meal, Extract, and Oil. The *meal* is the dried, ground flower petals of the Aztec marigold, a strong-scented, tropical American herb, mixed with no more than .3 percent ethoxyquin, a herbicide and antioxidant. The *extract* is taken from tagetes petals. Both the meal and the extract are used to enhance the yellow color of chicken skin and eggs. They are incorporated in chicken feed, supplemented sufficiently with the yellow coloring, xanthophyll. The coloring is exempt for certification. The oil is extracted from the Aztec flower and used in fruit flavorings for beverages, ice cream, ices, candy, baked goods, gelatin, desserts, and condiments. No known toxicity.

TALC. Talcum. French Chalk. The lumps are known as Soapstone or Steatite. An anticaking agent added to vitamin supplements to render a free flow; also a chewing gum base. Talc is finely powdered native magnesium silicate, the same that is used in dusting powder and in paints. There is no acute toxicity but there can be lung damage after inhalation. The high incidence of stomach cancer among the Japanese is suspected to be due to the fact that the Japanese prefer their rice treated with talc, a mineral whose chemical composition is similar to the known cancer-causing agent asbestos. GRAS for packaging.

TALL OIL. Liquid Rosin. A by-product of the wood pulp industry. "Tall" is Swedish for "pine." It may be a mild irritant and sensitizer. GRAS for use in packaging.

TALLOW FLAKES. Suet. Dripping. Animal fat obtained in North America mainly from sheep and cattle. Used as a defoaming agent in yeast and beet sugar production. In miniature pigs in one year, feeding tallow caused moderate-to-severe atherosclerosis (clogging of the arteries) similar to that in humans in type and location of lesions. GRAS

TAMARIND. Partially dried ripe fruit of large tropical tree grown in the East Indies and Africa. Preserved in sugar or syrup. Used as a natural food flavoring. Pulp contains about 10 percent tartaric acid (*see*). Has been used as a cooling laxative drink. No known toxicity.

TANGERINE OIL. The oil obtained by expression from the peels of the ripe fruit from several related tangerine species. Reddish orange, with a pleasant orange aroma. Used in blueberry, mandarin orange, tangerine, and other fruit flavorings for beverages, ice cream, ices, candy, baked goods, gelatin desserts, and chewing gum. No known toxicity. GRAS

TANNIC ACID. Occurs in the bark and fruit of many plants, notably in the bark of the oak species, in sumac, cherry, wild bark, and in coffee and tea. It is used to clarify beer and wine, and as a refining agent for rendered fats. As a flavoring it is used in butter, caramel, fruit, brandy, maple, and nut flavorings for beverages, ice cream, ices, candy, baked goods, and liquor (1,000 ppm). Used medicinally as a mild astringent. When applied, it may turn the skin brown. Low toxicity orally, but large doses may cause gastric distress. Can cause tumors and death by injection, but not, evidently, by ingestion. However, scientists have asked for further study. GRAS

TANNIN. See Tannic Acid.

TAPIOCA STARCH. A preparation of cassava, the tapioca plant. Used for thickening liquid foods such as puddings, juicy pies, and soups. No known toxicity. GRAS for packaging.

TAR OIL. Distilled from wood tar, a black residue insoluble in water. The principal toxic ingredients are phenols (very toxic) and other aromatic hydrocarbons such as napthalenes. Toxicity estimates are hard to make because even the United States Pharmacopoeia does not specify the phenol content of official preparations. However, if ingested, it is estimated that one ounce would kill. See Pine Tar Oil, which is a rectified tar oil used as a licorice food flavoring.

TARAXACUM ERYTHROSPERMUM. See Dandelion Root Extract.

TARTARIC ACID. Described in ancient times as being a residual of grape fermentation, it occurs naturally in grapes and a few other fruits and is sold today as a by-product of wine making. It is the acidic constituent of some baking powders and is used to adjust acidity in frozen dairy products, jellies, bakery products, beverages, confections, dried egg whites, candies, artificially sweetened preserves up to 4 percent. It has been used medicinally as a laxative and is used in refrigerant drinks. Essentially nontoxic but in concentrated solutions it may be irritating. GRAS

TARTRATE, SODIUM POTASSIUM. See Sodium Potassium Tartrate.

TARTRAZINE. FD and C Yellow No. 5. Bright orange-yellow powder used in foods, drugs, and cosmetics and as dye for wool and silk. Those allergic to aspirin are also allergic to tartrazine. Allergies have been reported in persons eating sweet corn, soft drinks, and cheese crackers—all colored with Yellow No. 5. It is derived from coal tar.

TEA. The leaves, leaf buds, and internodes of plants having leaves and fragrant white flowers, prepared and cured to make an aromatic beverage. Cultivated principally in China, Japan, Ceylon, and other Asian countries. Tea is a mild stimulant and its tonic properties are due to the alkaloid caffeine; the tannin makes it astringent. See Caffeine and Tannic Acid for toxicity. GRAS

TERATOGENIC. From the Greek *terat* (monster) and Latin *genesis* (origin): The origin or cause for the introduction of a monster—or a defective fetus.

TERPENE. A class of unsaturated hydrocarbons. Its removal from products improves their flavor.

TERPINOLENE. A synthetic citrus and fruit flavoring agent for food, beverages, ice cream, ices, candy, and baked goods. See Turpentine for toxicity.

TERPINYL ACETATE. Acetic Acid. A synthetic flavoring agent that occurs naturally in cardamon. Clear, colorless, with a lavender odor. Used in berry, lime, orange, cherry, peach, plum, and meat flavorings for beverages, ice cream, ices, candy, baked goods, chewing gum, condiments, and meats. See Turpentine for toxicity.

TERPINYL ANTHRANILATE. A synthetic fruit flavoring agent for beverages, ice cream, ices, candy, and baked goods. See Turpentine for toxicity.

TERPINYL BUTYRATE. A synthetic fruit flavoring agent for beverages, ice cream, ices, candy, baked goods, and chewing gum. See Turpentine for toxicity.

TERPINYL CINNAMATE. A synthetic fruit flavoring agent for beverages, ice cream, ices, candy, and baked goods. See Turpentine for toxicity.

TERPINYL FORMATE. Formic Acid. A synthetic fruit flavoring agent for beverages, ice cream, ices, candy, baked goods, and liqueurs. See Turpentine for toxicity.

TERPINYL ISOBUTYRATE. A synthetic fruit flavoring agent for beverages, ice cream, ices, candy, and baked goods. See Turpentine for toxicity.

TERPINYL ISOVALERATE. A synthetic fruit fiavoring for beverages, ice cream, ices, candy, and baked goods. See Turpentine for toxicity.

TERPINYL PROPIONATE. A synthetic fruit flavoring agent, colorless, with a lavender odor. Used in beverages, ice cream, ices, candy, and baked goods. See Turpentine for toxicity.

TERRA JAPONICA. See Catechu Extract.

TETRADECANAL. See Myristaldehyde.

TETRADECANOIC ACID. See Ethyl Myristate.

TETRADECYL ALDEHYDE. See Myristaldehyde.

TETRAHYDROFURFURYL BUTYRATE. Butyric Acid. A synthetic fruit flavoring agent for beverages, ice cream, ices, candy, and baked goods. May be irritating to the skin and mucous membranes.

TETRAHYDROFURFURYL PROPIONATE. Propionic Acid. A synthetic chocolate, honey, and maple flavoring agent for beverages, ice cream, ices, candy, and baked goods. Also used as a solvent for intravenous drugs. Moderately irritating to skin and mucous membranes.

TETRASODIUM PYROPHOSPHATE (TSPP). Used in cheese emulsification, in cleansing compounds, oil well drilling, water treatment, and as a general sequestering agent to remove rust stains. It is alkaline and irritating and ingestion can cause nausea, diarrhea, and vomiting. GRAS for use in packaging.

TEXTURIZER. In food terminology, the chemicals used to improve the texture of various foods. For instance, canned tomatoes, canned potatoes, and canned apple slices tend to become soft and fall apart, unless the texturizer calcium chloride (*see*), for example, or its salts are added, which keep the product firm.

THEINE. See Caffeine.

THIAMINE HYDROCHLORIDE. Vitamin B_1. A white crystalline power used as a dietary supplement in prepared breakfast cereals, peanut butter, poultry, stuffing, baby cereals, skimmed milk, bottled soft drinks, enriched flours, enriched farina, cornmeal, enriched maraconi and noodle products, and enriched bread and rolls. Acts as a helper in important energy-yielding reactions in the body. Practically all B_1 sold is synthetic. The vitamin is destroyed by alkalies and alkaline drugs such as phenobarbital. No known toxicity. GRAS

THIAMINE MONONITRATE. Vitamin B_1. A white crystalline powder, used as a diet supplement in multivitamin capsules and enriched flour. It is a more stable form of thiamine in dry mixes. A potential allergen. No known toxicity. GRAS

THIBETOLIDE®. See ω-Pentadecalactone.

2-THIENYL MERCAPTAN. A synthetic flavoring agent that occurs naturally in coffee. Used in coffee flavoring for candy and baked goods. No known toxicity.

THIODIPROPIONIC ACID. An antioxidant employed in the manufacture of food packaging material. Based on a sulfur and propionic acid (see). No known toxicity.

THIODIPROPTONIC ACID. An antioxidant in general food use. Percent of fat or oil, including essential oil, content of food is up to .02. On the FDA list for further study for mutagenic, teratogenic, subacute, and reproductive effects. GRAS

THIOLLYL ETHER. See Allyl Sulfide.

THISTLE, BLESSED. Holy Thistle. Extract of the prickly plant. Cleared for use as a natural flavoring in alcoholic beverages. No known toxicity.

THREONINE. L and DL forms. An essential amino acid (see), the last to be discovered (1935). Prevents the buildup of fat in the liver. Occurs in whole eggs, skim milk, casein, and gelatin. On the FDA list for further study. GRAS

THYME. A seasoning from the dried leaves and flowering tops of the wild or creeping thyme grown in Eurasia and throughout the United States. Used in meat, tuna, and spice flavorings for beverages, candy, baked goods, meats, and soups (1,000 ppm). Has been used in cough medicines, and it is a muscle relaxant. No known toxicity. GRAS

THYME OIL. The volatile oil obtained by distillation from the flowering thyme (see). Colorless, yellow, or red, with a pleasant odor. Used in sausage, spice, and thyme flavorings for beverages, ice cream, ices, candy, baked goods, chewing gum, condiments, meats, and soups. A muscle relaxant. No known toxicity. GRAS

THYME WHITE OIL. Obtained from the plant and used in fruit, liquor, and thyme flavorings for beverages, ice cream, ices, candy, baked goods, condiments, meats, and wine. A muscle relaxant. No known toxicity.

THYMOL. Occurs naturally in Dittany of Crete, oil of lavender, origanum oil, and thyme (*see all*). Used in fruit, peppermint, and spice flavorings for beverages, ice cream, ices, candy, baked goods, and chewing gum. Oral dose as medicine is .067 grams. It can cause vomiting, diarrhea, dizziness, and cardiac depression when taken in sufficient amounts.

TIGLIC ACID. See Allyl Tiglate.

TITANIUM DIOXIDE. A white pigment that occurs naturally in minerals and is used for coloring candy, gums, and a marking ink for confectionary. As a natural color, it is not subject to FDA certification. High concentrates of the dust may cause lung damage. The amount of dioxide may not exceed 1 percent by weight of food. A pound has been ingested without apparent ill effects.

TOCOPHEROLS. *Vitamin E.* Obtained by the vacuum distillation of edible vegetable oils. Used as a dietary supplement and as an antioxidant for essential oils, rendered animal fats, or a combination of such fats with vegetable oils. Helps form normal red blood cells, muscle, and other tissues. Protects fat in the body's tissues from abnormal breakdown. Experimental evidence shows Vitamin E may protect the heart and blood vessels and retard aging.

TOLU BALSAM. *Extract and Gum.* Extract from the Peruvian or Indian plant. Contains cinnamic acid and benzoic acid (*see both*). Used in butter, butterscotch, cherry, and spice flavorings for beverages, ice cream, ices, candy, and baked goods, and chewing gum. The gum is used in fruit, maple, and vanilla flavorings for beverages, ice cream, ices, candy, baked goods, and syrups. Mildly antiseptic and may be mildly irritating to the skin.

*a-***TOLUALDEHYDE.** See Phenylacetaldehyde.

TOLUALDEHYDE GLYCERYL ACETAL. A synthetic chocolate, fruit, cherry, coconut, and vanilla flavoring agent for beverages, ice cream, ices, candy, and baked goods. No known toxicity.

TOLUALDEHYDES (MIXED O,M,P). Synthetic berry, loganberry, fruit, cherry, muscatel, peach, apricot, nut, almond, and vanilla flavoring agents for beverages, ice cream, ices, candy, baked goods, gelatin desserts, chewing gum, and Maraschino cherries. No known toxicity.

TOLYL ACETATE. Acetic Acid. A synthetic butter, caramel, fruit, honey, nut, and spice flavoring agent for beverages, ice cream, ices, candy, baked goods, chewing gum, and condiments. No known toxicity.

o-TOLYL ACETATE. Acetic Acid. A synthetic butter, caramel, fruit, cherry, and honey flavoring agent for beverages, ice cream, ices, candy, baked goods, gelatin desserts, and chewing gum. No known toxicity.

p-TOLYL ACETATE. Acetic Acid. A synthetic butter, caramel, fruit, honey, nut, and spice flavoring agent for beverages, ice cream, ices, candy, baked goods, chewing gum, and condiments. No known toxicity.

4-(p-TOLYL)-2-BUTANONE. A synthetic fruit flavoring agent for beverages, ice cream, ices, candy, and baked goods. No known toxicity.

p-TOLYL ISOBUTYRATE. A synthetic fruit flavoring agent for beverages, ice cream, ices, candy, and baked goods. No known toxicity.

p-TOLYL LAURATE. Dodecanoic Acid. A synthetic miscellaneous flavoring agent for beverages, ice cream, ices, candy, and baked goods. No known toxicity.

p-TOLYL PHENYLACETATE. A synthetic butter, caramel, fruit, honey, and nut flavoring agent for beverages, ice cream, ices, candy, and baked goods. No known toxicity.

2-(p-TOLYL) PROPIONALDEHYDE. A synthetic caraway flavoring agent for beverages, ice cream, ices, candy, baked goods, and liqueurs. No known toxicity.

TOLYLACETALDEHYDE. A synthetic berry, loganberry, fruit, cherry, muscatel, peach, apricot, nut almond, and vanilla flavoring agent for beverages, ice cream, ices, candy, baked goods, gelatin desserts, chewing gum, and Maraschino cherries. No known toxicity.

p-TOLYLACETALDEHYDE. A synthetic honey and nut flavoring agent for ice cream, ices, candy, and baked goods. No known toxicity.

TONKALIDE. See δ-Hexalactone.

TRAGACANTH. See Gum Tragacanth.

TRIACETIN. Glyceryl Triacetate. See (tri) Acetin.

TRIBUTYL ACETYLCITRATE. A synthetic fruit flavoring agent for beverages. No known toxicity.

TRICALCIUM PHOSPHATE. An anticaking agent in table salt;

used also in vanilla powder and vanilla-vanillin powder; as a bleaching agent in flour at not more than six parts by weight alone or in combination with potassium alum, calcium sulfate (*see*), and other compounds. Also a dietary supplement. No known toxicity.

TRICALCIUM SILICATE. Used in table salt and baking powder as an anticaking agent up to 2 percent. On the FDA list to be studied for subacute, mutagenic, teratogenic, and reproductive effects. No known toxicity. GRAS

TRICHLOROETHYLENE. Residue in decaffeinated coffee powder. Used in spice oleoresins as a solvent. Moderate exposure can cause symptoms similar to alcohol inebriation, and its analgesic and anesthetic properties make it useful for short operations. High concentrations have a narcotic effect. Deaths have been attributed to irregular heart rhythm.

2-TRIDECENAL. A synthetic citrus and fruit flavoring agent for beverages, ice cream, ices, candy, baked goods, and chewing gum. No known toxicity.

TRIETHANOLAMINE. A coating agent for fresh fruit and vegetables. Its principal toxic effect in animals has been attributed to overalkalinity. Gross pathology has been found in the gastrointestinal tract in fatally poisoned guinea pigs.

TRIETHYL CITRATE. *Citric Acid.* An odorless, practically colorless, bitter liquid. Used in dried eggs as a sequestrant and to prevent rancidity. See Citrate Salts for toxicity. GRAS

2-4-5 TRIHYDROXYBUTYROPHENONE (THBP). An antioxidant used alone or in combination with other antioxidants. Total antioxidant not to exceed .02 percent of the oil or fat content of any product. Also used in the manufacture of food packaging materials, with a limit of .005 percent in food. On the FDA list for further study of this widely used additive.

TRIISOPROPANOLAMINE. A component of a coating used for fresh fruits and vegetables. No known toxicity.

2-6-6-TRIMETHYL BICYCLO-(3.1.1)-2 HEPTENE. See α-Pinene.

1, 3, 7-TRIMETHYL-2-6-DIOXOPURINE. See Caffeine.

TRITICUM. See Dog Grass.

TRYPTOPHAN. An essential amino acid (*see*) which is a precursor of niacin and, like niacin, is capable of preventing and curing pellagra. It is a partial precursor of the brain hormone serotonin and is indispensable for the manufacture of certain cell proteins. The FDA has called for further study of this additive. GRAS

TUBEROSE EXTRACT. From a Mexican bulbous herb commonly cultivated for its white, spike flowers. Used in peach flavorings for beverages, ice cream, ices, candy, and baked goods. No known toxicity. GRAS

TUMERIC. *Turmeric.* Derived from an East Indian herb. An aromatic pepperlike but somewhat bitter taste. The cleaned, boiled, sun-dried, pulverized root is used in coconut, ginger ale, and curry flavorings for puddings, condiments, meats, soups, and pickles; also for yellow coloring used to color sausage casings, oleomargarine, shortening, and marking ink. The *extract* is used in fruit, meat, and cheese flavorings for beverages, condiments, meats, soup bases, and pickles. The *oleoresin* (*see*) is obtained by extraction with one or more of the solvents acetone, ethyl alcohol, ethylene dichloride (*see all*), and others. It is used in spice flavorings for condiments, meats, pickles, and brine. No known toxicity. GRAS

TUNU EXTRACT. *Tuno.* From a Central American tree closely related to the rubber tree. Cleared for use as a natural masticatory substance of vegetable origin in chewing gum base. No known toxicity.

TURMERIC. See Tumeric.

TURPENTINE. *Gum and Steam Distilled.* Any of the various resins obtained from coniferous trees. A yellowish, viscous exudate with a characteristic smell, both forms are used in spice flavorings for baked goods. Steam-distilled turpentine is used also in candy. Turpentine is irritating to skin and mucous membranes, and can cause severe kidney irritation. It is readily absorbed from the gastrointestinal tract, the lungs, and skin. In addition to being a local irritant, it is a central nervous system depressant. Death is usually due to respiratory failure. As little as 15 milliliters has killed children.

TYROSINE. *L and DL forms.* A widely distributed amino acid (*see*) termed nonessential because it does not seem to be necessary for growth. Used as a dietary supplement. The FDA has asked for further study of this additive. GRAS

U

2,3-UNDECADIONE. A synthetic butter flavoring agent for beverages, ice cream, ices, candy, and baked goods. No known toxicity.

γ-UNDECALACTONE. 4-Hydroxyundecanoic Acid. γ-Lactone. γ-Undecyl Lactone. γ-Heptyl Butyrolactone. Aldehyde C-14 Pure (so-called). Peach Aldehyde. A synthetic fruit flavoring, colorless or yellow, with a strong peach odor. Used for beverages, ice cream, ices, candy, baked goods, gelatin desserts, and chewing gum. No known toxicity.

UNDECANAL. A synthetic flavoring agent. Colorless to slightly yellow, with a sweet, fatty odor. Used in lemon, orange, rose, fruit, and honey flavorings for beverages, ice cream, ices, candy, baked goods, and chewing gum. No known toxicity.

9-UNDECANAL. A synthetic citrus and nut flavoring agent for beverages, ice cream, ices, candy, and baked goods. No known toxicity.

10-UNDECANAL. A synthetic citrus, floral, and fruit flavoring agent for beverages, ice cream, ices, and candy. No known toxicity.

2-UNDECANONE. A synthetic flavoring agent that occurs naturally in rue and hops oil. Used in citrus, coconut, peach, and cheese flavorings for beverages, ice cream, ices, candy, baked goods, and puddings. No known toxicity.

10-UNDECEN-1-YL ACETATE. A synthetic citrus and fruit flavoring agent for beverages, ice cream, ices, candy, and baked goods. No known toxicity.

UNDECYL ALCOHOL. A synthetic lemon, lime, orange, and rose flavoring agent for beverages, ice cream, ices, candy, and baked goods. No known toxicity.

UREA. Occurs in urine and other body fluids as a product of protein metabolism. Used in yeast food and wine production up to 2 pounds per gallon. Also in fertilizer, animal feeds, in the making of plastics, in ammoniated dentifrices, and to known baked goods such as pretzels. Used medicinally to reduce body water and intracranial and eye pressures. No known toxicity. GRAS for packaging.

V

VALERAL. See Valeraldehyde.

VALERALDEHYDE. Pentanal. A synthetic flavoring agent which occurs naturally in coffee extract. Used in fruit and nut flavorings for beverages, ice cream, ices, candy, and baked goods. Has narcotic properties and is a mild irritant.

VALERIAN ROOT. Extract and Oil. A flavoring extracted from the dried roots of a widely cultivated herb in the United States and Europe. Used in cheese, fruit, maple, black walnut, walnut, and vanilla flavorings for beverages, ice cream, ices, candy, baked goods, and condiments. The yellowish green to brown oil is used in raspberry, cheese, grape, peach, honey, maple, and black walnut flavorings for beverages, ice cream, ices, candy, baked goods, and gelatin desserts. Has been used as a sedative. No known toxicity.

VALERIC ACID. A synthetic flavoring agent that occurs naturally in apples, cocoa, coffee, oil of lavender, peaches, and strawberries. Colorless, with an unpleasant odor. Used in butter, butterscotch, fruit, rum, and cheese flavorings for beverages, ice cream, ices, candy, and baked goods. Also used in perfumery. No known toxicity.

VALERIC ALDEHYDE. See Valeraldehyde.

γ-*VALEROLACTONE.* A synthetic vanilla flavoring agent for beverages, ice cream, ices, candy, and baked goods. No known toxicity.

VALINE. L and DL forms. An essential amino acid (*see*) classified as essential. Occurs in the largest quantities in fibrous protein. It is indispensable for growth and nitrogen balance. The FDA has asked for further study of this nutrient. GRAS

VANAY®. See (*tri*) Acetin.

VANILLA. A natural flavoring from the cured, full-grown but unripe fruit of the genus Vanilla grown in Mexico and the West Indies. Used in butter, butterscotch, caramel, chocolate, fruit, and vanilla flavorings for beverages, ice cream, ices, candy, baked goods, puddings, syrups, icings, and toppings. No known toxicity. GRAS

VANILLA EXTRACT. Derived from the vanilla bean. Contains not less than 35 percent aqueous ethyl alcohol (*see*) and one or more of the following ingredients: glycerin, propylene glycol, sugar (including invert sugar) and corn syrup. Used in many foods and beverages as flavorings. No known toxicity.

VANILLAL. See Ethyl Vanillin.

VANILLIN. Occurs naturally in vanilla (*see*) and potato parings but is an artificial flavoring. Odor and taste of vanilla. Made synthetically from eugenol (*see*); also from waste of wood pulp industry. One part vanillin equals 400 parts vanilla pods. Used in butter, chocolate, fruit, root beer, and vanilla flavorings for beverages, ice cream, ices, candy, baked goods, gelatin desserts, puddings, syrups (30,000 ppm), toppings, margarine, chocolate products, and liqueurs. The lethal dose in mice is 3 grams per kilogram of body weight. GRAS

VANILLIN ACETATE. Vanillin. A synthetic spice and vanilla flavoring agent for beverages, ice cream, ices, candy, and baked goods.

VERATRALDEHYDE. A synthetic fruit, nut, and vanilla flavoring agent for beverages, ice cream, ices, candy, baked goods, and puddings. Derived from vanillin. May have narcotic and irritant effects but no specific data.

VERATRIC ALDEHYDE. See Veratraldehyde.

VIBURNUM PRUNIFOLIUM. See Haw Bark.

VINEGAR. See Acetic Acid.

VINEGAR NAPHTHA. See Ethyl Acetate.

VINYL ACETATE. A starch modifier not to exceed 2.5 percent in modified starch (*see*). Vapors in high concentration may be narcotic; animal experiments show low toxicity.

VIOLA ODORATA. See Violet Extract, leaves.

VIOLET EXTRACT. Flowers and Leaves. From the plant widely grown in the United States. Used in berry, violet, and fruit flavorings for beverages, ice cream, ices, candy, and baked goods. No known toxicity. GRAS

VIRIDINE. See Phenylacetaldehyde Dimethyl Acetal.

VITAMIN A. Acetate and Palmitate. An anti-infective, antixerophthalmic vitamin, essential to growth and development. Deficiency leads to retarded growth in the young, diminished visual acuity, night blindness, and skin problems. Insoluble in water. Toxic when children or adults receive more than 100,000 units daily over several months. Recommended daily dietary allowance is 1,500 units for infants and 4,500 units for adults and 2,000–3,500 units for children. It is used to fortify mellorine (vegetable fat imitation ice cream) skim milk, dietary infant formula, blue cheese, Gorgonzola cheese, milk, and oleomargarine (1 pound of margarine contains 15,000 USP units of Vitamin A.) The FDA has asked for further study of the safety and uses of Vitamin A enrichment of food. No known toxicity.

VITAMIN B₁ HYDROCHLORIDE. See Thiamine Hydrochloride.

VITAMIN B₂. See Riboflavin.

VITAMIN B₆. See Pyridoxine Hydrochloride.

VITAMIN B₁₂. Cyanocobalamin. An antipernicious anemia factor used as a growth factor in feed for hogs, chickens, and turkeys in the presence of antibiotics. It is a coenzyme in the synthesis of materials for the nucleus of all cells. It contributes to the health of the nervous system and normal red blood cell formation. Recommended daily allowance is 5 mg per day. It occurs predominantly in foods of animal origin. GRAS

VITAMIN C. See Ascorbic Acid.

VITAMIN D₂. Calciferol. Nutritional factor added to prepared breakfast cereals, Mellorine (vegetable-fat imitation ice cream), Vitamin D milk, evaporated and skim milks, margarine, infant dietary formulas, enriched flour, self-rising flour, enriched cornmeal and grits, enriched macaroni and noodle products (250–1,000 USP), enriched farina, and enriched bread, rolls, etc. Vitamin D speeds the body's production of calcium and has been found to cause calcium deposits and facial deformities and subnormal IQs in children of mothers given too much Vitamin D. Nutritionists recommend 400 units per day for pregnant women. Some pregnant women taking vitamin pills and vitamin enriched milk and foods consume as much as 2,000 to 3,000 units daily. The FDA has asked for studies of the safety of Vitamin D in present enriched foods. GRAS

VITAMIN D₃. Activated 7-Dehydrocholesterol. Approximately as effective as Vitamin D₂ (see).

VITAMIN E. See Tocopherols.

VITAMIN G. See Riboflavin.

VITAMIN H. See Biotin.

VIVERRA CIVETTA SCHREBER. See Civet, Absolute.

VIVERRA ZIBETHA SHREBER. See Civet, Absolute.

W

WALNUT HULL EXTRACT. The extract of the edible nut of the English walnut tree. Used in walnut flavorings for beverages, ice cream, ices, candy, and baked goods. No known toxicity.

WHEAT. A cereal grain that yields a fine white powder. Wheat is avoided by some allergic types. Breads, cakes, crackers, cookies, pretzels, pastries, and noodles are made of wheat, also, breakfast foods such as Cream of Wheat, Pablum, Grapenuts, Wheaties, Puffed Wheat, Shredded Wheat, and bran; and sauces, soups, gravies; Postum, Ovaltine, malted milk; sausages, hamburger, and meat loaf. Nontoxic.

WHEAT STARCH. A minor part of starch production in the U.S. See Wheat. GRAS for food packaging.

WHEY. Milk Serum. Serum Lactis. The water part of milk remaining after the separation of the casein (*see*). Cleared by the U.S. Department of Agriculture's Meat Inspection Department to bind and extend imitation sausage, and for use in soups and stews. Nontoxic.

WHITE FLAG EXTRACT. See Orris.

WILD CHERRY. Wild Black Cherry Bark. Dried stem bark collected in autumn in North America. Used in cherry flavorings for foods and medications and as a cough medicine. No known toxicity. GRAS

WILD GINGER. Canadian Oil. See Snakeroot Oil.

WINTERGREEN. Extract and Oil. Methyl Salicylate. Checkerberry Extract. Obtained naturally from betula, sweet birch, or teaberry oil. Present in certain leaves and bark but usually prepared by treating salicylic acid (*see*) with methanol. Wintergreen *extract* is used in root beer and wintergreen flavorings for beverages and candy (5,000 ppm). The *oil* is used for checkerberry, raspberry, teaberry, fruit, nut, root beer, sassafras, spice, and wintergreen flavorings for beverages, ice cream, ices, candy, baked goods (1,500 ppm), and chewing gum (3,900 ppm). Wintergreen is a strong irritant. Ingestion of relatively small amounts may cause severe poisoning and death (average lethal dose in children is 10 milliliters and in adults 30 milliliters). Symptoms of poisoning are nausea, vomiting, acidosis, pulmonary edema, pneumonia, and convulsions. Can be fatal. Very irritating to the mucous membranes and skin and can be absorbed rapidly through the skin. Like other salicylates, it has a wide range of interaction with other drugs, including alcohol, antidiabetic medications, Vitamin C, and tranquilizers.

WORMWOOD. Absinthium. A European woody herb with a bitter taste used in bitters and liquor flavoring for beverages and liquors. The *extract* is used in bitters, liquor, and vermouth flavorings for beverages, ice cream, candy, and liquors, and in making absinthe. The *oil* is a dark green to brown and a narcotic substance. Used in bitters, apple, vermouth, and wine flavorings for beverages, ice cream, ices, candy, baked goods, and liquors. In large doses or frequently repeated doses, it is a narcotic poison, causing headache, trembling, and convulsions. Ingestion of the volatile oil or of the liqueur, absinthe, may cause gastrointestinal symptoms, nervousness, stupor, coma, and death.

X

XANTHOPHYLL. *Vegetable Lutein.* A yellow coloring originally isolated from egg yolk, now isolated from petals of flowers. Occurs also in colored feathers of birds. One of the most widespread carotenoid alcohols (a groups of red and yellow pigments) in nature. Provisionally listed for use in food. Although carotenoids can usually be turned into Vitamin A, Xanthophyll has no Vitamin A activity.

XANTHOXYLUM AMERCANUM. See Ash Bark.

XYLITOL. Synthetic sweetener for special dietary uses. Used in marmalades and jams other than those for which standards of identity have been promulgated. No known toxicity.

Y

YARA YARA. See β-Naphthyl Methyl Ether.

YARROW. *Milfoil.* A strong scented Eurasian herb now widely grown in North America. Used in liquor, root beer, and spice flavorings for beverages and liquor. Can cause sensitivity to light.

YEAST. A dietary source of folic acid, it is used in enriched farina, enriched cornmeals and corn grits, and in bakery products. It is also used in hot dogs, hamburger and frankfurter buns and rolls, pretzels, milk fortified with vitamins, meat fried in cracker crumbs, mushrooms, truffles, cheeses of all kinds, vinegars, catsup, barbeque sauce, fermented brews, and all dried fruits. Any yeast is a type of one-celled fungus. Ordinary yeast produces the enzymes invertase and zymase which eventually convert cane sugar to alcohol and carbon dioxide in the fermentation process. Some of the living organisms pressed into a damp, starchy, or other absorbent material give a product known as "baker's yeast," which is not as potent as brewer's yeast. No known toxicity.

YELLOW WAX. See Beeswax.

YERBA SANTA FLUID EXTRACT. Holy Herb. Fruit flavoring derived from evergreen shrubs grown in California. Used in beverages, ice cream, ices, candy, and baked goods, and to mask the bitter taste of drugs. Also used as an expectorant. No known toxicity.

YLANG-YLANG OIL. Cananga Oil. A yellow essential oil with a fine floral odor from the flowers of a tree grown in the Philippines and Java. Light yellow, very fragrant. Used in raspberry, cola, violet, cherry, rum, and ginger ale flavorings for beverages, ice cream, ices, candy, baked goods, chewing gum, and icings. Used in perfumes, cosmetics, and soap. No known toxicity. GRAS

YUCCA. Joshua Tree. Mohave Extract. A root beer flavoring from a southwestern U.S. plant used for beverages, ice cream, and ices. No known toxicity.

Z

ZEODARY. A bark extract from the East Indies used as a bitters and ginger ale flavoring for beverages. No known toxicity. GRAS

ZINC SOURCES: Zinc Acetate, Zinc Carbonate, Zinc Chloride, Zinc Oxide, Zinc Sulfate, and Zinc Hydrosulfate. The blueish-white lustrous metal known since very early times. It is a mineral source and added as a nutrient to food. Ingestion of the salts may cause nausea, vomiting, and purging. The FDA has asked for further study of the dietary uses of zinc. GRAS

ZINGERONE. A synthetic flavoring occurring naturally in ginger. Used in fruit, root beer, sarsaparilla, spice, ginger ale, wintergreen, and birch beer flavorings for beverages, ice cream, ices, candy, baked goods, and chewing gum. No known toxicity.

ZINGIBER OFFICINALE ROSC. See Ginger.

ZINGIBERONE. See Zingerone.

NOTES

The majority of the notes in this Dictionary refer to *The Merck Index* (listed in the Notes as "Merck"), 8th ed., Rahway, N.J.: Merck, Sharp and Dohme Research Laboratories, 1966; *Clinical Toxicology of Commercial Products* (listed in the Notes by the author "Gleason") by Marion N. Gleason, et al.: Baltimore: The Williams & Wilkins Co., 1969; and *Hazards of Medication* (listed under its full title) by Eric W. Martin, et al.: Philadelphia: J. B. Lippincott Co., 1971. All other references in the Notes are listed in full. The first note refers to page 17 of the Dictionary, the tenth line down, and the original source for the material can be found on page 7 in "Gleason."

p. 17 (line 10: Gleason, p. 7); p. 17 (line 11: Merck, p. 1) p. 17 (line 28: Gleason, p. 7); p. 18 (line 2: K. B. Lehman and F. Flurry, *Toxicology and Hygiene of Industrial Solvents* (Baltimore: Williams and Wilkins Co., 1943); p. 19 (line 8: Gleason, p. 7); p. 19 (line 19: Gleason, p. 66); p. 19 (line 26: Gleason, p. 145); p. 20 (line 5: Merck, p. 7); p. 20 (line 11: *Food Chemical Codex,* p. 14); p. 20 (line 20: Merck, p. 8); p. 25 (line 18: Merck, p. 38); p. 26 (line 29: Gleason, p. 13); p. 27 (line 6: Gleason, p. 13); p. 27 (line 16: Merck, p. 42); p. 27 (line 29: Merck, p. 45); p. 28 (line 8: Merck, p. 823); p. 28 (line 16: Gleason, p. 13); p. 29 (line 27: Merck, p. 66); p. 30 (line 3: Lawrence Mackenzie Miall and D. W. A. Sharp, *A New Dictionary of Chemistry* (New York: John Wiley & Sons, Inc., 1968); p. 30 (line 12: Gleason, p. 16); p. 30 (line 21: Gleason, p. 6); p. 32 (line 16: A. Loveman, "Stomatitus Vemenata," *Archives of Dermatology and Syphilology,* 37:70–81, 1938); p. 32 (line 31: *Hazards of Medication,* p. 350); p. 35 (line 17: Merck, p. 105); p. 35 (line 27: *Hazards of Medication,* p. 413); p. 37 (line 21: Merck, p. 118); p. 38 (line 31: Merck, p. 126); p. 38 (line 31: Gleason, p. 22); p. 39 (line 21: Merck, p. 133); p. 40 (line 5: Gleason, p. 22); p. 40 (line 6: Merck, p. 136); p. 40 (line 12: Merck, p. 137); p. 40 (line 23: Gleason, p. 23); p. 41 (line 19: Merck, p. 137); p. 41 (line 23: Merck, p. 139); p. 42 (line 22: *Hazards of Medication,* p. 767); p. 43 (line 1: *Hazards of Medication,* p. 350); p. 44 (line 23: Merck, p. 160); p. 44 (line 34: Merck, p. 161); p. 45 (line 9: Gleason, p. 46); p. 45 (line 23: Gleason, p. 48); p. 45 (line 27: U.S. Department of Agriculture's Meat Inspection Division Regulations); p. 46 (line 5: Merck, p. 172); p. 46 (line 15: Merck, p. 174); p. 46 (line 17: Merck, p. 990); p. 47 (line 7: Merck, p. 177); p. 47 (line 16: Merck, p. 178); p. 47 (line 26: Merck, p. 180); p. 49 (line 7: Merck, p. 183); p. 49 (line 32: *Handbook of Food Additives,* Chemical Rubber Co., Cleveland, Ohio, p. 585); p. 49 (line 35: *Beware of the Food You Eat,* Crown Publishers, Inc., New York, 1971, p. 40); p. 50 (line 14: *Federal Register* July 9, 1965); p. 50 (line 25: Merck, p. 435); p. 50 (line 34: Merck, p. 184); p. 51 (line 3: Merck, p. 184); p. 51 (line 21: Merck, p. 185); p. 51 (line 35: *Medical Tribune,* August 11, 1969, p. 22); p. 51 (line 36: *Hazards of Medicine,*

p. 277); p. 52 (line 6: Merck, p. 191); p. 53 (line 23: Merck, p. 192); p. 53 (line 30: L. Mackenzie Miall, p. 106); p. 54 (line 20: Gleason, p. 30); p. 54 (line 33: Merck, p. 192); p. 55 (line 3: Merck, p. 194); p. 55 (line 13; *Recommended Daily Allowances,* Seventh Edition, 1968, National Academy of Sciences); p. 56 (line 6: Gleason, p. 31); p. 56 (line 14: Merck, p. 196); p. 56 (line 36: Merck, pp. 190, 194); p. 57 (line 15: Gleason, p. 115); p. 58 (line 4: Merck, p. 199); p. 58 (line 9: Gleason, p. 56); p. 58 (line 39: Gleason, p. 30); p. 59 (line 33: Merck, p. 208); p. 60 (line 17: *Poisons in Your Food,* Crown Publishers, Inc., New York, 1968, p. 123); p. 60 (line 30: Merck, p. 212); p. 61 (line 4: *Merck Manual,* 1966, p. 294); p. 61 (line 35: Gleason, p. 31); p. 63 (line 3: L. Mackenzie Miall, p. 121); p. 64 (line 37: Wajkin Nopanitaya, report from University of North Carolina, June 1971); p. 65 (line 5: Gleason, p. 105); p. 65 (line 6: *Hazards of Medication,* p. 350); p. 65 (line 20: *Hazards of Medication,* p. 350); p. 66 (line 4: Merck, p. 228); p. 67 (line 3: Merck, p. 237); p. 67 (line 7: Merck, p. 237); p. 67 (line 24: *Poisons in Your Food,* pp. 41–46 and *Physicians Desk References, Medical Economics,* Oradell, N.J., 1970, p. 1135); p. 67 (line 37: *Recommended Dietary Allowances,* Seventh Edition, 1968, National Academy of Sciences, Washington, D.C.); p. 68 (line 11: Merck, p. 263); p. 68 (line 23: Gleason, p. 38); p. 69 (line 3: Merck, p. 265); p. 71 (line 32: Gleason, p. 105); p. 73 (line 26: Merck, p. 715); p. 74 (line 16: Merck, p. 271); p. 75 (line 7: *Hazards of Medication,* p. 350); p. 75 (line 11: *Merck Manual,* 1966, p. 363); p. 75 (line 20: Merck, p. 272 and Gleason, p. 39); p. 75 (line 23: *Poisons in Your Food,* p. 56); p. 76 (line 13: Merck, p. 946); p. 76 (line 13: Gleason, p. 127); p. 76 (line 23: *Recommended Dietary Allowances,* Seventh Edition, 1968, National Academy of Sciences, Washington, D.C.); p. 77 (line 13: Howard Rappaport, M.D., and Shirley Mutterlinde, *The Complete Allergy Guide,* Simon & Schuster, New York, 1970, p. 246); p. 77 (line 17: ibid, p. 244); p. 79 (line 23: Gleason, p. 43); p. 79 (line 32: Merck, p. 310); p. 80 (line 1: Gleason, p. 44); p. 80 (line 29: Gleason, p. 227); p. 82 (line 36: W. C. Heuper and W. D. Conway, *Chemical Carcinogenesis and Cancers,* Charles Thomas, Springfield, Ill., 1964); p. 83 (line 30: Merck, p. 566); p. 84 (line 9: G. LöFroth and T. Gejvall, "Diethyl Pyrocarbonate: Formation of Urethan in Treated Beverages," *Science,* Vol. 174, December 17, 1971, pp. 248–49); p. 84 (line 17: *Food Chemical Codex,* National Academy of Sciences, p. 224); p. 85 (line 1: *New England Journal of Medicine,* Spring 1971); p. 85 (line 2: "U.S. moving to sue farmers," UPI, Washington, D.C., Feb. 8, 1971); p. 85 (line 21: Gleason, p. 41); p. 85 (line 31: *Hazards of Medication,* p. 350); p. 86 (line 7: Gleason, p. 124); p. 87 (line 35: Merck, p. 380); p. 88 (line 16: Gleason, p. 74); p. 88 (line 34: Merck, p. 964); p. 90 (line 34: Merck, p. 410); p. 90 (line 36: E. Freuder and C. D. Leake, "The Toxicity of Epichlorhydrin," University of California publication: *Pharmacology,* 2:69–78, 1941); p. 91 (line 15: Merck, p. 580); p. 91 (line 27; Gleason, p. 65); p. 92 (line 20: C. R. Spealman, et al., "Monomeric methyl methyacrylate"; Studies on Toxicity, *Indiana Medicine,* 14:292–98, 1945); p. 92 (line 25: Merck, p. 430); p. 92 (line 38: Merck, p. 430); p. 93 (line 7: Gleason,

NOTES

p. 97); p. 95 (line 1: Merck, p. 436); p. 96 (line 27: Merck, p. 438); p. 98 (line 3: *Hazards of Medication,* p. 419); p. 99 (line 3: Merck, p. 434); p. 99 (line 5: Gleason, p. 67); p. 99 (line 10: Merck, p. 434); p. 99 (line 12: Merck, p. 686); p. 99 (line 19: Merck, p. 434); p. 99 (line 25: *Hazards of Medication*); p. 100 (line 2: Gleason, p. 69); p. 100 (line 12: J. O. Cray, "Poisoning by Volatile Oils in Childhood," *Archives of Diseases of Childhood,* 28:475–83, 1953); p. 100 (line 27: Gleason, p. 70); p. 103 (line 6: World Health Organization Technical Report Series 309, 445); p. 103 (line 11: Charles Cameron, *Truth About Cancer,* Collier, New York, 1968); p. 103 (line 27: World Health Organization Technical Report Series 445); p. 104 (line 12: Charles Cameron, op. cit.); p. 104 (line 18: Charles Cameron, op. cit.); p. 104 (line 34: Press Reports, September 17, 1941); p. 106 (line 30: Merck, p. 450); p. 107 (line 4: *Hazards of Medication,* p. 350); p. 107 (line 38: Merkc, p. 458); p. 108 (line 29: *Hazards of Medication,* p. 277); p. 108 (line 30: Michael J. Cousins M.D., Stanford University, paper presented October 20, 1971); p. 109 (line 7: Merck, p. 469); p. 109 (line 9: Gleason, p. 71); p. 109 (line 16: Gleason, p. 71); p. 109 (line 16: Merck, p. 469); p. 110 (line 16: Merck, p. 476); p. 110 (line 24: Merck, p. 476); p. 111 (line 11: Merck, p. 477); p. 112 (line 18: Merck, p. 484); p. 113 (line 9: Gleason, p. 105); p. 114 (line 19: Gleason, p. 74); p. 114 (line 23: Merck, p. 488); p. 116 (line 29: Gleason, p. 73); p. 116 (line 32: Merck, p. 499); p. 118 (line 9: Merck, p. 31, under Algaroba); p. 119 (line 30: Gleason, p. 144); p. 121 (line 3: Merck, p. 524); p. 125 (line 15: Merck, p. 541); p. 128 (line 2: Merck, p. 574); p. 130 (line 15: Merck, p. 579); p. 130 (line 29: Gleason, p. 7); p. 132 (line 18: Merck, p. 580); p. 133 (line 16: Merck, p. 580); p. 136 (line 17: Merck, p. 602); p. 138 (line 7: *Hazards of Medication,* p. 350); p. 138 (line 31; Heuper and Conway, *Chemical Carcinogenesis and Cancers,* Charles Thomas, Springfield, Ill., 1964); p. 138 (line 38: Gleason, p. 105); p. 139 (line 22: E. G. Gross, J. D. Dexter, R. G. Roth, "Hypokalemic Myopathy," *New England Journal of Medicine,* 274:602–6, May 17, 1966); p. 139 (line 34: *Hazards of Medication,* p. 350); p. 140 (line 5: Merck, p. 619); p. 141 (line 31: P. Gyorgy, et al., "Unsaturated Fatty Acids," *Journal of Experimental Medicine,* 76:413–20, 1942); p. 141 (line 36: Merck, p. 624); p. 142 (line 29: Merck, p. 628); p. 143 (line 37: Merck, p. 640); p. 143 (line 38: Rachel Carson, *Silent Spring,* 1962); p. 144 (line 38: Therese Mondeika, *Journal of the American Medical Association,* September 29, 1971, Vol. 217, No. 112); p. 145 (line 1: *Hazardous Drug Reactions,* p. 357); p. 146 (line 2: Gleason, p. 89); p. 146 (line 3: Merck, p. 653); p. 146 (line 11: Merck, p. 1019); p. 146 (line: 21: Merck, p. 671); p. 146 (line 35: Gleason, p. 42); p. 147 (line 24: Merck, p. 680); p. 147 (line 28: Merck, p. 680); p. 149 (line 5: Merck, p. 689); p. 149 (line 11: Gleason, p. 95); p. 150 (line 29: Merck, p. 691); p. 150 (line 31: *Hazards of Medication,* p. 419); p. 150 (line 36: Press releases, H. E. W., September 27, 1971); p. 151 (line 34: Gleason, p. 155); p. 154 (line 19: Gleason, p. 87); p. 155 (line 13: H. H. Shaumberg, et al., "Monosodium Glutamate," *Science,* 163:829, 1969); p. 155 (line 15: John Olney, "Brain Lesions," *Science,* 164:719, October 17, 1969); p. 155 (line 30: Merck, p. 703 and Gleason,

p. 99); p. 156 (line 12: *Hazards of Medication*, p. 350); p. 157 (line 2: Gleason, p. 99); p. 159 (line 7: Merck, p. 727); p. 159 (line 11: Gleason, p. 101); p. 159 (line 28: "Common Compounds Linked to Cancer," *Journal of the American Medical Association*, May 17, 1971, Vol. 216, No. 7, p. 1106, and Barry Commoner, speech before AAAS, New York, December 27, 1967); p. 159 (line 37: *Medical World News*, February 25, 1972, Vol. 13, No. 8); p. 160 (line 8: "Common Compounds Linked to Cancer," ibid.); p. 160 (line 11: *Medical World News*, ibid.); p. 160 (line 13: Subcommittee of Commerce Committee hearings, March 29, 1971); p. 160 (line 27: Merck, p. 739); p. 160 (line 30: Merck, p. 743); p. 160 (line 36: Merck, p. 744); p. 162 (line 15: Merck, p. 745); p. 163 (line 8: Gleason, p. 104); p. 165 (line 3: Merck, p. 763); p. 167 (line 4: Gleason, p. 65); p. 168 (line 4: Merck, p. 777); p. 168 (line 16: Gleason, p. 73); p. 169 (line 1: Dr. James W. Holsinger, Jr., et al., *Journal of the American Medical Association*, May 20, 1968); p. 169 (line 3: Merck, p. 781); p. 169 (line 14: Gleason, p. 109); p. 169 (line 19: Merck, p. 782); p. 169 (line 27: *Hazards of Medication*, p. 350); p. 170 (line 4: *The Pharmacologic Basis of Therapeutics*, 2d ed., Good and Gilman, Macmillan, New York, p. 1019); p. 170 (line 30: C. O. Jonrd, "A Case of Poisoning by Pennyroyal," *British Medical Journal*, 2:746, 1913; D. F. Early, "Pennyroyal, a Rare Case of Epilepsy," *Lancet*, 2:580–81, 1961); p. 171 (line 23: Merck, p. 797); p. 172 (line 4: T. H. Eickholt, et al., "Toxicities of Peppermint," *Journal of Pharmacological Sciences*, 54:1071–72, 1965); p. 172 (line 14: Gleason, p. 110); p. 172 (line 15: Merck, p. 797); p. 172 (line 27: Merck, pp. 136, 194, 545); p. 173 (line 12: Gleason, p. 87); p. 173 (line 32: Merck, p. 802); p. 173 (line 38: Merck, p. 807); p. 175 (line 3: Merck, p. 812); p. 175 (line 10: Merck, p. 810); p. 176 (line 15: Gleason, p. 7); p. 176 (line 34: Merck, p. 814); p. 177 (line 17: Merck, p. 875); p. 178 (line 30: Merck, p. 825); p. 179 (line 11: Gleason, p. 115); p. 179 (line 25: Gleason, p. 115); p. 179 (line 37: Merck, p. 835 and Gleason, p. 114); p. 180 (line 24: Merck, p. 839); p. 181 (line 4: Merck, p. 17, under Acrylic Acid); p. 181 (line 9: Gleason, p. 11); p. 181 (line 27: Merck, p. 619); p. 181 (line 31: Merck, p. 848); p. 183 (line 12: Dr. Robert J. Rubin, *Chemical and Engineering News*, The Johns Hopkins School of Public Health, February 17, 1971); p. 183 (lint 20: Gleason, p. 117); p. 183 (line 21: W. C. Hueper and W. D. Conway, *Chemical Carcinogenesis and Cancers*, Charles Thomas, Springfield, Ill., 1964); p. 184 (line 10: Gleason, p. 48); p. 184 (line 11: *Hazards of Medication*, p. 275); p. 184 (line 17: Merck, p. 853); p. 185 (line 14: Rachel Carson, *Silent Spring*, 1962); p. 184 (line 24: Merck, p. 853); p. 184 (line 35: Merck, p. 855); p. 185 (line 20: Merck, p. 856); p. 185 (line 31: Merck, p. 857); p. 185 (line 37: Merck, p. 858); p. 186 (line 3: Stephen Lockey, "Adulteration of Drugs, Food, and Cosmetics," AMA, June 20, 1971, Atlantic City); p. 186 (line 15: Merck, p. 871); p. 186 (line 24: Merck, p. 873); p. 186 (line 32: Merck, p. 874); p. 186 (line 36: Merck, p. 875); p. 187 (line 4: Merck, p. 875); p. 188 (line 4: A. Osol and G. Farrar, Jr.: *The Dispensary of USA*, 25th ed., J. B. Lippincott, Philadelphia, 1955); p. 188 (line 27: Gleason, p. 121); p. 189 (line 35: Merck, p. 890); p. 190 (line 2: American Petroleum Institute, "Pyridine," *API Toxicological Review*, 1953); p. 190 (line 17: Gleason, p. 3); p. 191 (line 13; Gleason, p. 153); p. 191 (line 22: Merck, p. 900); p. 191 (line 30: Merck, p. 905); p. 192 (line 1: Merck, p. 905); p. 192 (line 30: Gleason, p. 114); p. 192 (line 35: Weisburger, "Colon Carginogens," *Cancer*, July, 1971, Vol. 28, No. 1, pp. 60–66); p. 192 (line 36: Gleason, p. 139); p. 195 (line 8: Gleason, p. 65); p. 196 (line 22: Merck, p. 928); p. 197 (line 5: Merck, p. 928); p. 197 (line 16: Merck, p. 930); p. 197 (line 21: Gleason, p. 118); p. 197 (line 22: Merck, p. 856); p. 198 (line 22: Merck, p. 761); p. 199 (line 19: Merck, p. 944); p. 199 (line 37: Merck, p. 946); p. 200 (line 18: Merck, p. 952); p. 201 (line 27: Gleason. p. 22); p. 201 (line 38: *Hazards of Medication*, p. 404); p. 202 (line 6: Merck, p. 955); p. 202 (line 21: Merck, p. 956); p. 202 (line 33: W. C. Heuper and W. D. Conway, *Chemical Carcinogenesis and Cancers*, p. 654, op. cit.); p. 203 (line 6: Merck, p. 956); p. 203 (line 19: Dr. Walter A. Glooschenko, paper presented to American Chemical Society, September 15, 1971); p. 203 line 20: *Hazards of Medication*, p. 404); p. 203 (line 27: Gleason, p. 46); p. 203 (line 35: Merck, p. 958); p. 204 (line 27: Merck, p. 960); p. 204 (line 30: Merck, p. 960); p. 205 (line 10: FDA papers, June, 1971); p. 205 (line 35: Merck, p. 965); p. 206 (line 7: Merck, p. 965); p. 206 (line 10: Merck, p. 965); p. 207 (line 7: H. F. Smyth, Jr., et al., "Some Pharmacologic Properties," *Journal of Industrial Hygiene and Toxicology*, 23:478–83, 1941); p. 207 (line 16: Merck, p. 966); p. 207 (line 20: Merck, p. 1015); p. 207 (line 28: Merck, p. 967); p. 207 (line 36: Gleason, p. 33); p. 208 (line 7: Merck, p. 968); p. 208 (line 10: H. M. Camn, et al., "Esophageal stricture following ingestion of detergent," National Clearing House for Poison Control Center, Washington, D.C., January, 1958); p. 208 (line 20: Merck, p. 971); p. 208 (line 26: Gleason, p. 117); p. 208 (line 37: Gleason, p. 133); p. 209 (line 14: Therese Mondeika, op. cit.); p. 209 (line 16: *Hazards of Medication*, p. 393); p. 209 (line 17: Therese Mondeika, op. cit.); p. 210 (line 27: Merck, p. 979); p. 212 (line 5: Gleason, p. 134); p. 212 (line 31: "Table Sugar Promotes Blood Fat Promotion," Brookhaven National Laboratory report, Upton, N.J., July 29, 1971); p. 213 (line 9: O. G. Fitzhugh, et al., "Chronic Toxicity of Sulfites," *Journal of Pharmacy and Experimental Therapy*, 86:37, 1941, and M. F. Lockett and I. L. Natoff, "A Study of the Toxicity of Sulfite," *Journal of Pharmacy and Pharmaceuticals*, 12:488, 1960); p. 213 (line 12: Merck, p. 1058); p. 213 (line 32: Merck, p. 1005); p. 214 (line 22: *Medical World News*, October 8, 1971, p. 76A); p. 214 (line 25: Merck, p. 1011); p. 214 (line 32: Eldon G. Hill, et al., "Experimental Atherosclerosis in Swine," Mayo Clinic Proceedings, September, 1971, Vol. 46, pp. 621–25); p. 215 (line 12: Merck, p. 1012); p. 215 (line 14: John H. Weisburger, "Color Carcinogens," *Cancer*, July 1971, Vol. 28, No. 1, pp. 60–66); p. 215 (line 25: Gleason, p. 138); p. 215 (line 37: Merck, p. 1014); p. 216 (line 5: Max Samter, M.D., Ray Beers, M.D., "Intolerance to Aspirin," *Annals of Internal Medicine*, May, 1968); p. 217 (line 20: Merck, p. 1027); p. 217 (line 25: Gleason, p. 141); p. 218 (line 30: Gleason, p. 143); p. 218 (line 36: Gleason, p. 143); p. 219 (line 1: Gleason, p. 143); p. 219 (line 7: Merck, p. 1050); p. 219 (line 15: Gleason, p. 144);

p. 219 (line 29: Gleason, p. 20); p. 221 (line 14: Merck, p. 1069); p. 221 (line 21: Gleason, p. 147); p. 222 (line 26: Merck, p. 1089); p. 222 (line 30: Gleason, p. 223); p. 224 (line 15: Merck, p. 1100); p. 225 (line 15: Merck, p. 1103); p. 225 (line 23; Merck, p. 1109); p. 226 (line 25: National Institutes of Health, December 15, 1967); p. 227 (line 34: Merck, p. 691); p. 227 (line 35: Gleason, p. 152); p. 227 (line 38: *Hazards of Medication*, pp. 768–70); p. 228 (line 10: *Steadman's Medical Dictionary*, Williams and Wilkins, Baltimore, p. 7); p. 228 (line 30: *Hazards of Medication*, p. 350); p. 229 (line 28: Merck, p. 1127).